Magickal Faerytales

Published by Blue Angel Publishing®
80 Glen Tower Drive, Glen Waverley, Victoria, Australia 3150
Email: info@blueangelonline.com
Website: www.blueangelonline.com

Illustrated by Jasmine Becket-Griffith

Edited by Jamie Morris

Blue Angel is a registered trademark of Blue Angel Gallery Pty. Ltd.

ISBN: 978-1-925538-72-4

Magickal Faerytales

An Enchanted Collection of Retold Tales

Lucy Cavendish

WITH ILLUSTRATIONS BY
JASMINE BECKET-GRIFFITH

BLUE ANGEL® PUBLISHING

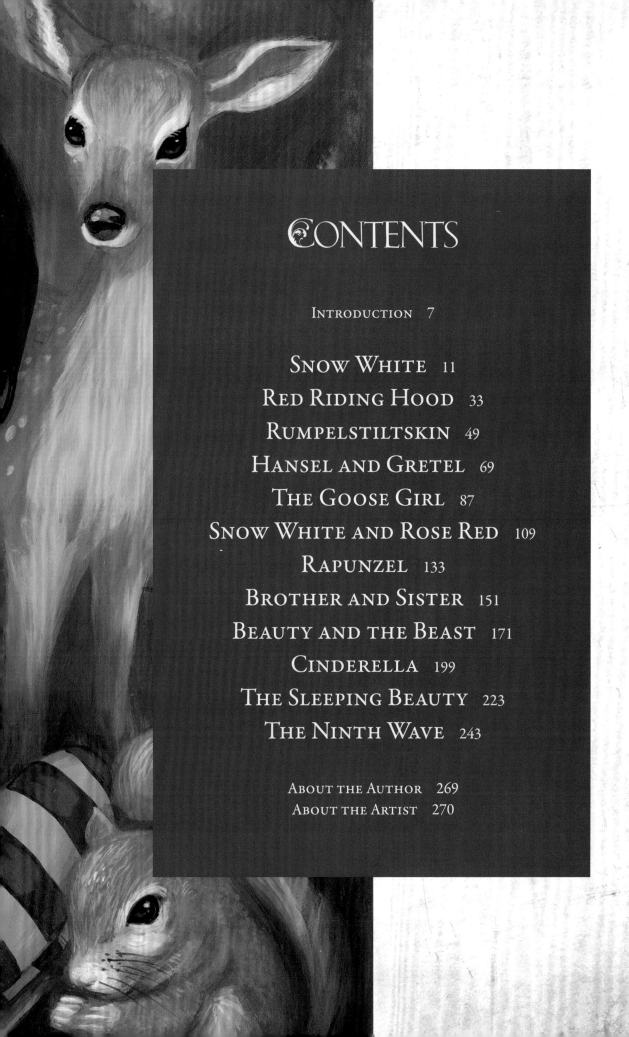

CONTENTS

INTRODUCTION

SOME DAY YOU WILL BE OLD ENOUGH
TO START READING FAIRY TALES AGAIN.
—C.S. Lewis

I HAVE ALWAYS ADORED faerytales. Some have haunted me my whole life, long since I first ate them up, my child-wide eyes hungry for these strange stories with their tenderness and terror, cruelty and kindness, death and resurrection. I cannot remember when I first read a faerytale – they seem another part of my soul. But while working on *The Faerytale Oracle*, I knew I wanted to begin writing a book of faerytales, really explore them – and perhaps be fortunate enough to return some of their lost magick in the retelling.

Faerytales have an everlasting kind of magick. They have been with us a long, long time – scholars now believe the genesis of some tales can be traced back over ten thousand years. I feel the same faerytales will be told again and again, for perhaps another ten thousand years, shapeshifting and changing, just like the people within them. They are that powerful. I hope this volume adds just a little to this marvellous lineage and magickal tradition.

You will see that within this book of retold ancient tales, I've borrowed and built upon the strong bones of that ancient past. I've also burrowed within the Hollow Hills of the faeries within the stories, and asked their permission to share more about them and the Old Ways through the tales within this book.

While these tales are based on the traditional tellings, I set out to explore the stories from a slightly different point of view. I wanted, as I kept saying when people would ask me what I was working on, to tease out the *magick* within the tales. Because they *are* so magickal, yet some of that strange old enchantment has been lost with familiarity. It's most often been stored in strange vessels, like TV shows and movies and other watered-down, palatable versions of the stories – and some of the true, weird magick within the old tales doesn't quite fit the plain containers we've placed them in. Perhaps the old, wild wisdom within them seems inappropriate today. We are nervous about speaking openly about such fearful, strange things in our world. We wonder if that is the right way to guide children, to re-teach ourselves. But the stories, with all their strangenesses, are needed, you see. Our souls hunger for the initiations and tests within each tale.

To me, faerytales are about survival. Surviving our families, most often, and being sent out into a world which is hostile, and navigating

the new worlds in which we find ourselves, without bitterness or rancour. And so, I find the tales not only frightening, magickal, and enchanting, but hopeful, too – hopeful because there is nearly always a kind of transformation that occurs at a deep level, due to the courage displayed within the heart of the children, or the princess, or the girl in the tower wondering how she will ever turn a pile of straw into gold. This storytelling inspires us with the same courage, and tells us that, no matter the hardship, we can continue to be ourselves and find our way to freedom.

The tales are alchemical stories, too – one thing becomes another, true things can only be seen clearly by those who are good at heart, and the characters within have important parts of their own soul stolen from them. Identity is abducted in *The Goose Girl*. Childhood is stolen from Hansel and Gretel. The gift of long life is taken from the Sleeping Beauty. And freedom cannot be found in the confines of the castle in which Rapunzel is trapped.

There is often a magickal helper – Falada, the talking fae horse, within *The Goose Girl*, or the faery godmother within the tale of Cinderella. With the assistance of a magickal helper, the brave characters within these wonder-tales change, they learn, and they create real, authentic lives.

Being forced into making tough decisions in order to survive is at the heart of many tales, and as a child this thrilled me. When I was young, once I read a particularly captivating story, I'd reimagine it, and relive it as best I could, gathering its magick to me like a cloak of protection and transformation. Into my basket I would gather blackberries that grew in a paddock down at the end of my suburban street, imagining that I, too, was cast out into the world and had to live upon my wits. I would peek into the tumbledown stables, wondering if they were the isolated cottages so many faerytales summon up. I would see a stranger, and ask myself if they were a witch or faery, deep beneath their human disguise. Today, I see little ones wearing faery dresses, or dressed as characters from their favourite tales, and I know they, too, are exploring the world through the stories, fighting off foes, awakening from enchanted sleeps, and finding their way through the mysterious and often bizarre world grown-ups live in.

As an adult, I have returned to the stories. And how they have helped me!

How, I now wonder, can I overcome these great tests, pass through the initiation of the forest, or meet the challenge, or achieve the quest, and emerge free and willing to still love life? When we read the stories, especially as adults, old wounds may find fresh air, and thus, they heal, leaving scars that speak of initiation.

Throughout the writing process, which took several years (thank you to my patient publisher, Toni Carmine Salerno – again), I released any notion of where the stories "ought" to go and let the people within lead me down the path through the woods. I was often surprised, and occasionally astonished, at what they came up with. As I'd write, I instinctively tuned in to the voices within the tale – those of the brothers and sisters, the faeries and the young women and men and crones and the hapless fathers the stories feature. Red Riding Hood came to life in my mind, the muse letting me know that her cloak of red was a magickal garment of initiation and protection, her grandmother a wise old crone of the forest. Snow White's dwarves became gnomes, the ones who had the knowledge of the crystals and the earth, and thus her casket becomes a magickal device, which can preserve life and charge us with energy so that we rest between lifetimes.

There is an old Druidic saying that *the same story cannot be told the same way twice.* I found this to be true. For the tales changed as they were told through me. They are not quite the same faerytales you may have heard or read before.

Who, people ask me, are they for?

They are for any of you who have ever not been seen for who you truly are. Or who have been cast out from family and community. Or who have been hunted by those who would make use of you. These stories offer you a way through – a way to transform through enchantment, which is more needed now, I believe, than ever before. Story is magick, and it is power. By reading each story, you become a part of its magick, a part of the transformation that is the miracle within the story. Read these, and I know that, at some sacred place deep within, a little of the old magick will trickle into the cracks and wounds you've covered up and work its healing and wonder, within.

It may seem a grand thing to say, but I believe story – especially magickal, enchanted story – can set us free. Stories give us back our minds, help us conquer fears, and take us away from, as W. B. Yeats so beautifully said, "this dull world".

Faery tales have come to us out of the retelling of deep, old myths – told around fireplaces, shared in communities older than our family trees, told by bards again and again, and shaped to fit the landscapes, and the communities that were the audience. Yet I chose not to modernise the stories – they do not take place in our recognisable cities and in our new families. But the protagonists do still, I think, echo our own deep instinct to survive, to become who we are truly meant to be.

I think that faerytales teach us something

very beautiful, also. You see, it struck me again and again within the stories that the protagonists don't turn on each other. Hansel and Gretel, Brother and Sister, the Goose Girl and Falada, they support each other. They also keep finding the world beautiful. They are resourceful, and resilient, even when the world is denying their true identity. In these ways, stories show us to be the best kind of human – to keep trying to build relationships, to stay loving, to be kind, to seek freedom, even if that means going hungry and lonely for a time. If you do these things, faerytales show that your life will be made anew – even resurrected. It's for that reason the stories and the blessings within them are holy as sacraments to me.

In addition, faerytales can bring us back to the sheer transcendent quality of the natural world, remind us of our connection with the woods and the sea and the unconquerable chaos that is nature. Which brings us closer to knowing things – knowing the Old Ways – which helps us to feel connected to our more primal, wild self, the self that longs to live, the self who will not be resigned to sacrifice. Even with the Christian cloak thrown over so many of the tales, the Old Ways are always there, just at the edges of the path, showing us how to overcome wolves, change back into our true form, and learn the secret names of the ancient ones, all of which gives us amazing power.

Thus, *Rumpelstiltskin* is not only about the power of names, but reveals what, perhaps, he truly was – for his name, odd as it is, means something close to "poltergeist" in the old tongue in Germany. The closest translation may be "rattle ghost", or "one who knocks", making him part spirit, part boggart – a creature somewhere between the realms, known but unknowable.

So, we see that the stories include ghosts,

and werewolves, and tormented faeries who've lost their kinship with humans. They are peopled with bad witches and good, oak trees that shield and protect, herbs that have magickal properties, horses that talk, living libraries, and boys with antlers.

After each of the faerytales, you'll find a story-behind-the-story exploring the magick of each of the tales in more detail. The symbols, tree wisdom, old spells, folklore, and evolution of each story is there for you to delve into, so that we come to know the deep, rich history that lies within all the tales – and which lies within your own ancestry, too! Discovering the magick woven into each of the stories is a fascinating and fulfilling way to enter into their mysteries and enchantment. For each story is a well of wisdom, ready for you to draw from and quench your thirst for spirited adventure.

I hope that you love these stories. They may not be suitable to read to your little ones – or they may be. I do feel they help with the difficult journeys into the dark forests that all of our lives must take. They show us how to change – and when – and they initiate us, in a deep way, into new stages in our lives, whether from girl to woman, human to animal, or spirit to flesh. They are wonder-tales that show us how to survive, how to thrive, how to reclaim our true selves. My wish is that you take your time with each one, savour the twists, explore the enchantment underneath and magicks of each faerytales, and discover the restorative power of every story working its subtle magick on you, every day, from this day forth, until your last day in this lifetime.

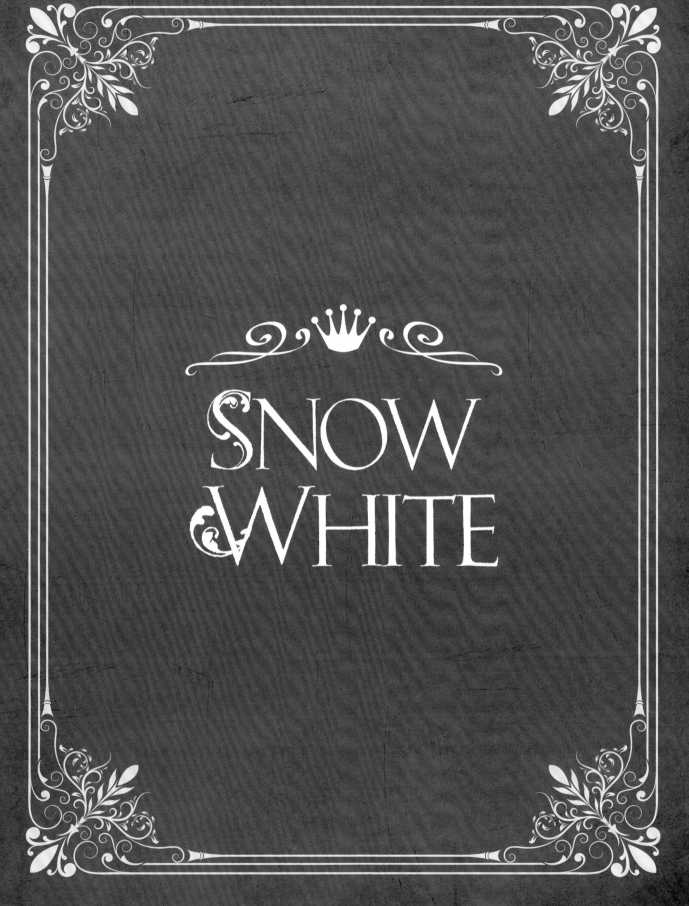

SNOW WHITE

IT WAS THE LONGEST WINTER ANY COULD recall. It was the coldest winter any could recall. So cold it was that no babes were born in the land, and the king and queen of that still, white place knew that without the birth of a child, the land would never give birth to plants or crops – nor would the animals bring forth their young amidst that frozen world.

So, the king and queen wished ... and one day, when the longing grew too much, the queen rose up as if in a trance and walked out into that cold world. Snow fell, tiny crystals, kaleidoscopes from the sky. Her lashes were white, her lips were blue, her hands were frozen with cold, but she walked, longing for some sign that new life would come.

She had with her a fine staff made of ebony, and she leant on it, after a time, for she grew tired quickly in the cold. She came to the gardens that, in summer, held great, full-petalled roses of every colour, and she saw, on a blackened branch anointed with the longest thorns, a small, perfect red rose.

She reached for the bright blossom, but her cold finger caught on a thorn, and although she was close to frozen, her blood rushed to the surface, and three drops of her scarlet blood fell upon the purest snow.

The brilliant spots of red were beautiful upon the white snow, and the black of the ebony walking stick, carved with the sigil of the royal house, stood out starkly against the alabaster land. Seeing this, the queen thought to herself, as if in a dream, *How I wish I would have a girl, her hair as long and black as this ebony stick, her lips red as this blood, her skin as fair as the snow* ... and she felt at once a great change within herself, as though something in the world had heard her and granted this wish.

And so it was that within nine cold moons, the queen's wish was granted. On the day her daughter first drew breath, a great howling gasp as

13

she sucked in life for the first time, the snowdrops pushed their way through the cold ground, the animals began to birth their young, and slowly, the green world advanced upon the white snow, and life began to return to the land.

But something had gone from the mother forever. The mysterious winter had taken too much of her to survive for long, and although there were soon summer days and warm breezes, soon red roses blooming in her child's white face, the queen lived for only a little while.

When she knew she would go back, back to the earth, she requested her child attend her. She whispered to the little princess many secrets – secrets of calling the animals to her, old knowledge of how to live when the world stops being kind and ways to survive.

"There will be times when there is cruelty," the queen said to the little girl, who stood before her mother, puzzled but attentive.

The child wanted to be outside. She itched to climb the trees and peek into the nests filled with baby birds. She longed to help milk the goats and trace the path of the tiny deer she had seen at the edges of the forest when her father took her for walks. She wanted to know everything about the world, about all the beings in it.

But she listened, and though the girl had known only kindness since the moment she first breathed, someplace deep within her understood her mother when she whispered, "Beware."

And so, the queen died, and the child's walks with her father ceased. He could not speak to his daughter. Seeing her face made him think of the brief summers he'd had with his wife, and of how the cold time had returned to his heart.

After just thirteen moons passed, the king prepared to take another wife. The woman was beautiful, so fair that all who saw her were smitten, enslaved with devotion and a cowering kind of love. She was kind to all who worshipped her – and, as all did so, no-one saw her true nature. Nor did they see the great fear that worked within her, for to this woman all power was derived from beauty.

A great wedding was held for the union of the king and his new queen, and there was feasting and revelry throughout the land. The beautiful queen was kind to Snow White, as the princess was known, for though the child was fair, she was only a child, and long years lay between her youth and her coming into womanhood. The new queen knew that when that day came ...

But no, she told herself, beating back the shadow of her jealousy, she would not think of it, now.

In a dark room, high in the tower, where once the other queen had gazed out at the endless snow, the new queen looked out upon roses, and tall trees of green, and fertile lands rich with crops. In this room, she ordered her servants to build an altar, and upon that altar they installed a great, black mirror, one she had brought with her – part of her dowry.

She kept a special silk cloth over the altar, and when the moon was dark each month, she went to the inky mirror and gazed into it. There, and only under the dark of the moon, she saw the reality of her being, how she would look if the truth within her was revealed upon her seemingly perfect face.

For when others looked at the new queen, they saw hair that fell like a golden lake all about her, light shining from her skin, eyes the colour of flowers in the fields in spring. But at the dark of the moon, when she gazed into her mirror, she saw a twisted face bearing scars and cracks and furrows caused by anger, jealousy, sadness – and,

most blighting of all, by cruelty.

Most surprising, though, was that the face she saw in the moon-dark mirror was ancient. For she was very old – so old the king would never have believed it had anyone told him.

Each month, after the queen stared at the truth of who she was, she was filled with heartbreak. If any saw who she truly was, or knew the tainted magick that kept her shining youth intact, she would lose all. All comfort. All food. All riches. All power. She would be cast out ... or worse, burned, as her mother before her had been when she had allowed herself to grow as old in appearance as she was in years.

For, the queen knew, age was a woman's death – and loss of beauty the death of her power. And she would never allow her beauty or her power to die.

She gazed within the mirror at all other phases of the moon's cycle and comforted herself with her apparent beauty, saying,

"Mirror, mirror on the wall,
Who's the fairest of them all?"

And the mirror, showing her reflection of beauty beyond compare, would reply,

Great Queen, thou art the fairest of them all.

For it could, after so many years, speak the truth to its keeper.

And during those years, the land grew stronger, and the princess grew older – she was good and bright and kind, so kind. The girl had so often climbed the trees at the edge of the forest and followed the paths of the tiny deer into the forest's fringe, but still she longed to see the great old sacred trees deep within the forest's heart, trees of which her father had often spoken.

But she knew he might never be able to show these trees to her, himself because her father had sickened with every year of his marriage. Before his daughter's eyes, he had transformed: he became bent and grey and shuffling, growing weaker and older, ageing faster than anyone could recall a person doing in so short a passage of time – although no-one knew the source of his affliction.

Meanwhile, both the land and Snow White grew stronger with every passing season. Daily, the princess became more lustrous, with her shining white skin, the great black waterfall of her ebony hair, and the roses of red that bloomed on her cheeks and lips.

The queen saw all this and knew that, when the girl came of age, her own beauty would be surpassed. Only the queen knew that she alone had drained the life force of the king for these years. With it, she had shored up her beauty. But soon the king would die. And then, without another source of life force, the queen's power would wane. And if one became more beautiful than she? The queen herself would be eclipsed. And then she would shrivel and die – or be burned.

And she determined that she would not.

A potion was made in her lonely room to aid, she said, the poor, sick king. But it was not a potion to bring good health. Instead, it sped his span of years by increasing the flow of life force the queen sucked from her husband. The king aged forty years in a mere forty days, until one morning, when Snow White went to see her father to beg him to take one last walk with her, she found him, old as the greatest of the trees in the heart of the forest, lifeless upon the floor, killed by magick.

Stricken, Snow White ran to the forest and screamed her grief to the sky. She felt deep inside that something sinister, something evil was at work. And she looked about her and saw that

something was wrong in the land, as well. All the animals had a strange look in their eyes – they were wary, watchful, ready to run at the slightest sound. Over the last forty days, the people said they could not harvest their fine crops, that the plump fruit fell from the trees before its time, rotten and ruined. She felt certain there was some wretched magick about. She must ask her stepmother if she knew its source.

She did not wish to disturb the woman's vigil, for the queen spent all her time in a lonely room, praying, she said, for the king. But Snow White knew it was time to heal the land. And so she returned to the castle, and began to climb the stairs.

***

THE QUEEN HAD ORDERED FOR THE KING'S dusty remains to be swept up and buried next to the first queen, Snow White's mother, as the new queen had no need to keep the royal couple apart any longer. Afterwards, she went to the dark mirror, and as there was no moon, she saw just how repulsive she had become within. It was more important than ever before that she hide her true form from the servants, from the court, from her people, and from the girl as white as snow.

But while she gazed into the mirror, the girl crept into the room, and seeing the fair face of the queen and the foul reflection in the mirror, she gasped in terror – and in anger. This, she thought, is the reason all has been ill. This is no good thing.

The queen turned, smiling, hoping the girl had not seen her true form. But the girl did not smile in return.

"I know who you are," she said, frightened but brave. "You are no queen. This is evil magick. Are you the one who has hurt this land? Do you care nothing for the people? Did you take my father from me?"

A soft laugh escaped the queen. "Yes," she said, smiling, pleased at the pain she could give this girl. "And your mother, as well," the new queen added, malicious and glittering in the light of the black candles. "And soon, I will take you, too."

Snow White turned and fled, but the queen simply smiled. She was still the fairest in the land. Her beauty still held power. She had that.

She turned to her mirror, holding on to that power.

"Mirror, mirror on the wall,
Who's the fairest of them all?"
And her voice was a threat.

Queen, fair thou art,
But she has beauty of face and in heart.

The queen felt as if she were standing at the edge of an abyss.

"Speak more, my mirror," she ordered, voice calm as a glacier about to break.

Thou art fair, Queen, it is true,
But there is one fairer than you,
With hair of ebony, lips red as rose,
Skin like snow, a mind that knows.
Snow White's childhood is now done.
Her reign as beauty has begun,
But it is not her beauty that is best.
'Tis her heart that can pass every test.

The queen let one crystalline tear slide down her face, and she touched the edges of the shadows she saw creeping in under her eyes. Then she covered up her mirror and returned to the great hall, where she sat upon the cold throne and called the palace guard to bring her Snow White.

But the girl could not be found.

"She has fled, perhaps in grief, my Queen," said the trembling guard.

"Oh, no! I would not want anything happening to her," replied the queen, voice laced with feigned concern. "I have lost too much, already. Bring me the best huntsman in the land."

And one man came to her, with a hound as brown as good earth and a falcon to fly above and see in all directions.

The queen saw him alone, and she told him to find Snow White.

"And what, Queen, shall I do when I find this girl," he asked, in a voice low and serious.

"You will remove her heart," said the queen, "and say she was taken by wild animals. You will bring that heart to me. And we will speak no more of her after that."

Despite his horror at these orders, the man took the bag of gold the queen handed him – for the failure of the falsely beautiful crops was creating alarm among the country folk, and he knew he must do what he must do to weather the approaching famine. So, he and his hound and his falcon began the hunt. The huntsman tracked Snow White for days, and when he found her in the heart of the forest, she was curled up within the roots of the greatest tree the man had ever seen.

The huntsman's hound bayed and called, and then he calmed as the girl beneath the tree awoke. Her eyes were wide and kind, and she looked straight into the soul of the hound. Even the fierce falcon on the huntsman's arm gentled. And then she gazed into the huntsman's eyes. And he saw her. Truly saw her.

"I've been sent to take your heart out," he said simply, reaching out his hand.

"By the queen," said the girl, as if she knew. And she did not take his hand, but huddled back into the roots a little more – and it seemed the great tree itself gathered about her, sheltering her.

"By the queen," agreed the huntsman, sitting down upon a great, old coiled root.

"Will you take it?" she asked.

"I cannot," he replied, "without losing my own soul."

They sat for a while, and finally he sighed, heavy at heart.

"Keep going into the forest, girl," he said. "Run as far as you can, and don't ever look back. She is mad, and she will kill you."

She hesitated. "What will you do?"

"I'll bring her a heart," he said. "But it will not be yours."

"You can't kill anything on my behalf," she said, fierce.

"I will not. Now go, before I change my mind. For to cross this queen is its own kind of madness."

So, Snow White clambered up from her fortress of roots and reached out, stroked the dog, who went to go with her. The huntsman turned and dashed a tear from his eye, and the loyal hound reluctantly turned from the girl and walked side by side with the huntsman.

When he was closer to the castle, he removed from his sack the young deer he had taken down that morning. He cut from its still body the tender heart, silent and small, but large enough to be the girl's.

"I am sorry, little one," he whispered to the spirit of the deer. Then he went back to the castle with the heart the queen wanted.

His return was announced, and the queen called her courtiers to her. Holding up the heart before them, she cried out, "Alas, good people! Your princess is no more. She ran, in her grief for her father, into the woods, and she was devoured

by the fierce beasts that dwell there. Do not flee, people, as she did. Stay here, safe within the castle's walls, and we will face the coming winter together."

She lifted the heart higher, so all could see, and the grief of the people was terrible.

"No-one leaves," she said to the guards. "Kill them if they try."

For she knew that if a single soul was to see her shifting between her forms, she would be exposed. The people were weak, but they were greater than she in number. What she had to do must remain the queen's secret.

And she went to her lonely tower room, and salted and ate the heart, licking at her fingers. "I am fairest. I am powerful. I am forever young," she crooned to herself, her eyes avoiding the ugly truths within the mirror. For while once she had only seen her true form at dark moon, little by little, the mirror had begun to reflect who she truly was at all times – and her true self grew even uglier, but a little of her beauty seemed revived by the hope that Snow White was dead. But she did not ask the mirror who was the fairest of them all. Perhaps did not want to know the truth.

As for the huntsman, he knew obeying any command of this queen could lead only to evil. So he stole away from the court and made himself and his family scarce. They fled deep into the forest under night's cloak and headed for the tree where he had last seen the princess.

***

In the days that followed, the world grew cold, and the girl underwent the lonely initiation of the forest. At first, she followed the tracks of the tiny deer that she knew from her childhood walks, but as she went deeper into the woods, she began to follow the path of the reindeer, eating what was good of the fruits and the roots of the forest. But Snow White could see all about her that harsh times were coming. The animals were vanishing, and those that remained peeped out at her, eyes filled with mistrust, even for the girl with the pure, wild heart.

Yet, she coaxed them out and shared her food with them, and even the wolves were gentled and came to eat from her hands. The princess wove a little home of fallen willow wood, and covered herself in rowan leaves, and her long black hair twisted into wild shadow-shapes about her perfect face, and she looked more faery than human for a time.

As it grew colder, and the first snow began to dance in the breeze, she began to search for others living in the forest. She had heard strange calls in the woods, and knew there must be more wild ones living in this ancient world. She could almost catch a glimpse of them at times, darting just at the edge of her gaze, but when she turned to look, they could not be seen. She did not know it, but she had stumbled upon the borders of Faerie, and the wild ones she had glimpsed were the faery folk, who were drawn to the strange human child, curious as to why she had come so close to their world.

She went on walks each day from her little twisted home of willow wood, and every day she walked a little farther. Until one shivering day, she found a path, narrow and so well hidden that only eyes disposed to see could find it. She followed this path until she came to a door of oak within the side of a great, round mound, surrounded by shining white rocks.

She pushed at the door, and it opened.

Within were herbs and cauldrons – and seven small beds, lined up one after the other. She was so cold, so very tired, and ravenously hungry. In a cupboard she discovered honey, good bread, and mead, and she feasted on these. Then, without thought, she dragged two of the tiny beds together and stretched out along their doubled length, her pretty feet spilling over one end, black hair falling over the other. She pulled a sheepskin over herself, and just like that she slept like she had not rested for moons and moons.

That night, the door opened, and a tumble of burly little men burst into the room, light burning from their tallow torches, sacks gleaming with stones from the earth, a tremendous clatter of small shields, picks, axes, and swords hanging from their thick, woven belts.

They were men of the earth, the dwarves, who fashion the armour of the wild ones and the most protected of princes. The stones sang to them, and they would find those ready to come to the surface. And while their wisdom was not that of the wise men of the courts, they were knowledgeable in the ways of their mother, the earth.

As they entered, they saw a fire burning in the hearth at the centre of their room, and they saw the young woman, stretched as if dead over two of their beds, and they clambered forward, gazing upon her.

Most were afraid – she was from the otherlands, the human places, and wild ones of the forest ought never trust such people. But as they argued among themselves – some saying even that they should put her out into the cold or cut her white throat, as she would kill them – she opened her eyes wide and stared at them all, and they felt something strange stir within their souls.

She was not afraid, and she reached out to touch them, one after the other, on their cheek or shoulder, and it was a blessing and a benediction,

and within moments, even the one who had said he would kill her found himself upon his knees, swearing to protect her.

Snow White stayed within the dwarves' home for one day, sleeping, and eating, and growing stronger than ever before. Then she went with them, and they taught her the ways of the earth, of smithcraft, of the secrets of the stones, and of the powers of the crystals.

But one day, instead of going with the dwarves, she stayed behind to tend the forest animals who were gathering closer to the dwelling, as the cold grew in power. And while she went about her work, she began to feel happy, and so she sang, and that song attracted more of the animals to her. They were comforted by the energy of her song, and rested within the safe space the sound created all about her. Wherever she could be heard, there existed that magickal protection.

But that same day Snow White's sweet voice was also heard by one who was searching for her. For the queen had soon learned from her mirror, from the disappearance of the huntsman, and from the return of the shadows beneath her own beautiful eyes, that Snow White still lived.

This time, she decided, she would take care of the girl, herself. So, she took on the shape of an old wise woman, and at the very time Snow White was singing, she was making her way through the forest. She looked bent and ancient, as aged as she truly was, truth be known. She fixed a smile upon her criss-crossed lips, and was sure to keep a false kindliness shining out from her crinkled eyes, near-swallowed as they were in folds of ancient skin. Humans could be deceived with such tricks, but the forest shrank back from her, and with every footstep the earth turned to dust beneath her feet.

The wicked queen followed the shining

trail of the princess's golden voice and came to the house within the hollow hill, with its circle of glowing stones ... only to find an impenetrable energy was pouring from them, and she could not pass. But she called out to the girl, whom she could see from where she stood.

Snow White was taller and lovelier than ever, her hair as long and straight as her mother's ebony staff, her skin luminous, as lustrous as white quartz and first snows, roses blooming upon her cheeks.

The queen felt the princess's power, and knew she had done right to decide to end this shining girl.

"I am in need of a drink, my dear," the woman called, her voice a croak.

Snow White nodded, and in her haste to fetch the old woman a cup of tea, of white oak bark and honey steeped in the water boiling in the cauldron, she failed to see that the animals had hidden themselves from the crone.

She hurried forth, a steaming cup and some good bread in her hands.

"Here, Mother," she said kindly. "Lean on me and drink this. It is good, pure water, with healing bark within it to return to you your strength and wellness."

The old woman drank, then, and felt the truth of the girl's words. She nibbled at the bread and clutched at the edge of the glamour keeping her disguise in place. She did not allow herself to feel the gratitude she showed, for that would make the spell fall from her.

She smiled at the girl, one lonely tooth remaining in her old mouth. "Thank you, beautiful lady," she croaked. "You are so fair. Perhaps the fairest in all the land ..."

Snow White shook her head. "No," she replied. "I know a woman more beautiful, but alas, her heart is ruined with hate."

The old woman reached into her pockets and pulled out a knife.

Snow White stepped back.

"Do not fear, my sweet," said the queen, hidden in her glamour. "Here." And she reached again into her filthy cloak and pulled out a perfect, shining red apple. "It's as red as your lips, beautiful lady. As payment for your kindness," she said, slicing one curling ribbon from it and nibbling at it. "It's summer-sweet. For your goodness, have some."

"I thank you," said the girl, taking the apple and breathing in its delicious scent. She bit into the fruit, tasting its promise of blue skies and golden fields. It was fragrant and tasted so sweet, that she wondered if it had been honeyed. She took another bite. Then she blinked a little, her eyes losing focus as she took a third bite.

"Do you feel sleepy, my dear?" the old one asked, as Snow White sank to her knees, a sudden weakness flooding through her, a dizziness, a loss of balance. Finally, the girl fell heavy to the ground, into the arms of death itself.

The old woman laughed and coughed and spat up the poisoned bit of apple she'd nibbled and left it there beside the girl.

The woman changed her form slowly, all the way back to the castle, until she appeared before the guards as the queen they knew, looking as fresh and lovely as if she were twenty years younger and had enjoyed the longest, most restful sleep.

She made her way to her lonely room and put away her poisons and stared at her face within the magickal mirror, its darkness revealing only her beauty.

She called forth the spirit that lived within the obsidian mirror.

"Mirror, mirror on the wall,
Who is the fairest of them all?"
Thou art the fairest, oh, Queen, said the dark mirror.

It was strange, but the queen could hear just a touch of sadness within the voice that issued from the dark glass. But still she went down to her supper and ordered a great feast and danced all night and took great pleasure in the knowledge that the power of her beauty was unrivalled, again, at last.

As the queen feasted, back in the forest, the dwarves returned, to find their Snow White lying upon the ground, without breath, as heavy and still as if she was made of stone. They began to fight among themselves again.

"Return her to the earth," one cried through mad tears.

Another said they should build a great fire and turn her to smoke, so she could go to the sky.

Another said they should build her a casket of magickal crystals and preserve her until they found the spell that would return her to life.

And as they could not bear to bury her or burn her, they laboured all that night and built a casket of clear quartz. Then they laid their black-haired princess within that crystal casket and heaped the whitest snow about her to keep her body cold. By nightfall, they were done. Her face was turned to the shining moon, and Snow White looked not so much a human any more, but as something beyond life, something eternal and at rest.

True winter came, then, and it was long, and the dwarves continued their work beneath the ground, and also tended to Snow White's casket – and not a thing changed within that enchanted crystal coffin. The princess remained perfect, incorruptible, and they searched and searched for answers to bring her back. At night, they pored over old runes and secret spells, rare stones and powerful herbs, their hearts aching at her loss.

And they heard, one day, of a queen who practised great old magicks, and one of the dwarves travelled to that land and offered that queen a great sword inscribed with protective charms, if only she would travel back with them and help their Snow White.

This queen was old, though, and could not journey at so bare and cold a time, and so she sent the young prince, her son, in her stead. He travelled for days with the dwarf through the snows, and finally came to the casket in the forest.

"We will need to move her," the prince told the small men of the earth.

So, the dwarves swept away the snow and shifted the circle of white quartz and lifted the casket onto their shoulders. But, although they were strong, the casket was heavier than they could bear, and it fell to the ground and cracked, and the body of the girl was thrown about within her crystal chamber.

With that, from between her lips fell a bite of apple, and with it the last remnants of the queen's spell were broken. Her huge eyes flew open, and she gasped, then shook, and her fists beat upon the crystal chamber, cracking it further, until it fell in shards and perfect points all about her.

The prince went to her and held her, and she stared at him and at the men of the forest. Every one of these earthy beings was weeping and sighing with happiness.

Then the princess climbed out of the ruins of her crystal casket and stood blinking amongst the shining fragments of earth magick. She looked into the eyes of the prince, and he gazed into hers, taking her cold hands in his and warming them

gently. With that one embrace, the truest of all spells, that of love between two good souls, wove a knot and bound them together so tightly that it would have mattered not whether they married, or, indeed, ever saw each other again, so strong was their connection.

And they, all seven of the men of the earth, Snow White, and the prince, began to journey out of the forest and into the land from which the prince came. With Snow White's every footstep, the snow melted and flowers sprang up in its place. Slowly, the animals crept forth from their hiding places, purring and whistling and leaping about. And with their long walk, the cruel winter melted away, and was only a memory by the time they reached the prince's castle.

***

MONTHS AFTER SNOW WHITE WAS AWAKENED, something strange happened in her former home.

The queen there received an invitation to a handfasting, a joining of souls. When she looked in the mirror, she cried out, for her face was beginning to resemble her soul, and she knew that there was the power of a greater beauty within the land.

"Mirror, mirror on the wall
Who's the fairest of them all?"

She trembled, hardly daring to hear the answer.

Oh, Queen, thou form, it is most fair
But another lives, beyond compare.
The princess of another land,
About to take the prince's hand,
Is fairer far than you, great Queen.
She is the fairest ever seen.

That queen was wretched with grief, and taking her magickal knife to the mirror, she stabbed at it again and again and again, until its obsidian depths cracked. Even as its magick shattered, she continued to drive the blade into its black depths, and with each broken-hearted strike, her form changed. In her fury, she grew older and older and older, until all she could do was wail and cry and crawl upon the floor, alone. Finally, surrounded by the shards of her magick, she collapsed, withered into bone and dust, and died within moments.

And that is how her people found her.

In time, Snow White and her prince returned to Snow White's family's home, to the land and her castle and the good people. Together, they brought balance and warmth back to the land. And when it grew cold, as it always does when the wheel turns, they lit great fires and feasted with their people, and they lived long and good lives, and gave the dwarves their due as great creators of shields and swords. The land was well. The people thrived. And the love of the princess and her prince was long, and good, and most blessed for all the days of their lives.

DISCOVER THE MAGICK OF SNOW WHITE

How I wish I would have a girl, her hair as long and black as this ebony stick, her lips red as this blood, her skin as fair as the snow ...

And so it was that within nine cold moons, the queen's wish was granted.

SOMETHING NEVER SEEMED quite right when I was told this tale as a little one. There always seemed to be something missing. As a child, I pored over the enchanted and deliciously scary details of the story, trying to find what exactly it was that was missing. The little men in the forest must have more magick to them than the tale revealed, I thought. Why would her coffin be glass, when the little men worked with the minerals of the earth? Why would her coffin not be ... crystal? And what if the crystal energy somehow kept her suspended, not dead, not alive, but in-between, until the queen's curse could be broken?

When I was older, it was the mirror that fascinated me, and I began to work with mirrors myself – mirrors for affirmations, and mirrors, dark mirrors, for scrying and seeing what lay beneath the surface. There was so much to this story, so much to explore, so much enchantment to bring to into the light so the story's spellbinding qualities can be fully appreciated! I hope you enjoy my take on it!

HISTORY OF THIS TALE

AS WITH MOST FAERYTALES, *SNOW WHITE*'S history is long and tangled. *Snow White* was first published in German by the Brothers Grimm, and while they did not "write" the story – they were collectors of folk tales – they greatly embellished it and gave it some of its most potent symbolism and striking detail. The first Grimm version was published in 1812, and they subsequently reworked it and republished a more palatable adaptation in 1854. Why? Because the first incarnation was really, really dark. In it, Snow White's mother was the evil adversary, rather than her stepmother, and instead of the child's heart being eaten, it was her lungs and liver. (The liver, in the Middle Ages, was considered to be the organ that housed sensuality and love, and the lungs were associated with air, and thus spirit. The next version of the tale included the heart – and you will learn below more of what this means!)

Elements of the story that we know today – the mirror that speaks, the apple laced with poison, the transparent coffin, the seven dwarves – were all included. But there was originally no magickal kiss to awaken Snow White, which I like. Love can indeed bring us back to life, but no-one should go around kissing dead girls they don't know – and who can't say, "no".

If *Snow White* has an older predecessor, it could be one of the Icelandic sagas – which makes sense, given all the ice and snow and dwarves and general bloody mayhem. In the sagas, Snafridr is a beautiful woman, who is the companion of Herald Harfager. She dies, and her body remains as pure as when she was alive. Like the seven dwarves do,

Herald sets up a vigil by Snafridr's body in the snow for three years. In the faerytale, though, while the vigilant dwarves hope their charms will bring Snow White back to life, perhaps it is the crystalline power of her coffin and the stillness and stasis of the snow that help preserve her until she is ready to return.

NEVER-ENDING WINTER: DEMETER AND PERSEPHONE

WITH SNOW WHITE THERE SEEMS TO BE a subtle allusion to the story of Demeter and Persephone playing out in the early stages of the story. The cause of the endless winter experienced by the people of the land of the as-yet unborn Snow White is exactly that the daughter has not yet come to the mother. In Greek mythology, Demeter is the goddess of the grain, and when she "loses" her daughter to the god of the underworld, Hades, Demeter's grief plunges the earth into a cold, barren winter that does not end.

In the tale of *Snow White*, it may be that it is not the endless winter that delays the birth of the child, but the mother's yearning for a daughter that is causing the endless snow. But certainly, it is Snow White's birth that breaks the spell of winter, allowing spring to come forth and green the lands once again. She brings back the light and the warmth and the heart to the land.

WHITE, RED, AND BLACK

HER SKIN IS AS WHITE AS SNOW. HER LIPS ARE as red as blood. Her hair is as black as night. And it is these three colours that are traditionally used in Witchcraft to signify the Maiden, the Mother, and the Crone, all of whom are present within the tale. Thus, in some ways, *Snow White* is a story of the Triple Goddess, albeit a truly crooked and twisted telling!

THIRTEEN MOONS

THE INTERVAL OF THIRTEEN MOONS IS THE traditional amount of time witches and other magickal practitioners must study and work their craft before they can truly be ready for initiation into the path of the wise. This is because those thirteen moons encompass the lunar year, and will cover every full-moon celebration, every solstice, every equinox, every seasonal change, and every lunar cycle from new, to full, to dark, once again. After that amount of time, the practitioner has worked through the whole wheel of the year. I wanted the king to have – or at least feel he has had – a real rite of passage before remarrying. So, he is alone for this enchanted length of time. It seemed better than a year of mourning, as thirteen moons means he has *magickally* mourned his beloved.

The Obsidian Mirror

THE MAGICKAL MIRROR IS PRESENT IN ALL versions of the *Snow White* tale: it speaks, it is poetic, it is truthful. But I wanted to add a little something here. I wondered if the mirror could perhaps have been made of obsidian, that mysterious volcanic glass, whose special powers have long been appreciated by seers and oracles. Historically, obsidian has been used for scrying since the Middle Ages. Obsidian mirrors were used by great Elizabethan magicians like Doctor John Dee – his famous scrying mirror is now housed within the Enlightenment Room of the British Museum. And most witches have worked with scrying and dark mirrors at least once, to experience the profound magick of working in this way

Mirror work, though, has now gone beyond the esoteric and sits firmly within New-Age spirituality. Affirmations are spoken into mirrors. We mouth, "I love you," at ourselves, and we work on improving our own perceptions of our bodies within their depths. We may not ask if we are the fairest in the land, but we *can* use the mirror harmfully, to criticise ourselves and to try to assure ourselves of our beauty and agelessness – despite the truth that it is fortunate to grow old and change with that precious process of ageing. But even those with no interest in such things may still gaze upon themselves, and wonder who they truly are.

Of course, it is very, very bad luck indeed to break a mirror – or so the legend says! But what of misusing mirror magick, as the queen does? Perhaps the tale gives us a warning, to not corrupt the magick of a scrying mirror.

Making Magick: Snow White Scrying Mirror Spell

THE MAGICKAL OBSIDIAN MIRROR IN MY version of *Snow White* has its roots in one of the magickal traditions of the Witch – the black scrying mirror.

You will need:
- A mirror
- Some transparent black material
- A candle
- Some time and space to yourself
- Your *Book of Shadows and Light* (see *Discover the Magick of Beauty and the Beast*)

First, create some atmosphere. I personally love to scry at the dark moon (the time immediately before the new moon). I might put on some beautiful evocative music, and I tend to scry at night – although, of course, you can scry at any time you wish.

Turn off your phone, if this is at all possible, and diminish all electric light, as I find it tends to interfere with our psychic abilities.

Position the mirror so that you can gaze into it, and cover it with the sheer, black fabric.

I like to cast a circle before I do any form of spellwork, so if you wish, you could simply imagine a protective circle of blue fire: all about you, above you, and below you, too, so you are completely protected as you enter the mysteries.

Light your candle, with these words:

May I now see all I need to know,
For the highest good of all.
Blessed be.

Be seated, or stand if you wish, so that you can see your own face within the scrying mirror. With your eyes softly closed, take three deep breaths, letting each go, steady and long. After the third, gently open your eyes and begin, for you are now in the midst of the magick!

Let your eyes gaze into the mirror, allow a shape, symbol, or feeling arise within you and say:

Mirror, mirror on the wall,
Share with me the signs in all.

Let the mirror "speak" with you – allow it to become a gateway, a door through which you can enter into the Otherworlds. If you have any questions, ask them now of the magick mirror, and let the answers float up within you, until you have answers. (I recommend asking no more than three questions at any one time.) When the answers come through, you may wish to write them down in your *Book of Shadows and Light*.

When you have finished, say:

Mirror, mirror on the wall,
Thank you for sharing with me all.

When you feel the time is right, take three deep breaths with your eyes again closed. When you open them, you are returned to the world of the everyday, in which there lies so much magick, unseen.

Blow out your candle and imagine the circle of blue fire dissolving back into the universal energy, gently restoring the everyday world.

The Heart of a Deer

A fabled animal sacred to the faery is the White Hart, and the presence of a White Hart is evidence of both faery connections and a pure heart. Snow White's heart is a kind of allusion to the White Hart. Her incorruptible heart, her goodness, and her inner beauty are what make her so powerful. If that heart can be removed and devoured by the queen, perhaps she hopes she will ingest the young women's power – and her beauty, too. But the very act of hiring the huntsman to murder Snow White ensures the queen's plan cannot work, for the powers of the White Hart can only be activated by one who is clean in their energy. And, as we have seen, our deliciously wicked queen left innocence and good intentions behind long, long ago.

THE PATH OF THE REINDEER

IT'S A VERY SMALL MOMENT WITHIN THE story, but to have Snow White walk the path of the reindeer was to put her symbolically under the protection of the goddess Elen, she of the spiral pathways, the turning points in our lives, and of powerful feminine protection. Elen is a Palaeolithic British goddess who is often depicted with antlers, and she can help us find our way when we are lost. Thus, I wanted to very quietly include her influence here, so she could help Snow White find a way through the dark forest – and perhaps find a home where she would no longer be an outcast.

THE SACRED MAGICK OF TREES

WITHIN THE TALE ARE TWO VERY POWERFUL trees – the willow and the rowan. Willow is said, in the Ogham system of the ancient Celts, to be able to help repair the soul after a great emotional wounding. It also works to balance the flow of blood and other fluids throughout the entire body, but most especially in the head. Willow soothes and restores, heals and relieves pain, and her bark contains salicylic acid, the precursor to aspirin.

Rowan is a protective tree in the Ogham. It is the tree which shelters outcasts and orphans, the persecuted and the cursed. Its berries form a five-pointed star, so it is seen as a protector of the magickal ones, in particular. It is a tree of intuitive powers, and it is said to whisper premonitions to those who take shelter beneath its protective branches. Ironically, rowan was used as a charm to protect *against* Witchcraft during the middle ages – strange, because it is witches who most often worked with this amazing tree, for its protection and its sanctuary.

DWARVES, OR GNOMES, AS WISDOM KEEPERS OF THE EARTH

DWARVES IN THE NORDIC SAGAS ARE metalworkers and alchemists. They forge protective chain mail and great powerful weapons and can work with every metal and every jewel beneath the earth. And of course, in the story of Snow White, there are seven dwarves – seven

being a sacred number. Seven-pointed stars are sacred to the faery, there are seven chakras, seven wonders, seven planets, seven musical notes, and seven colours in a rainbow.

Within this tale, these seven dwarves are wise beings who are keepers of the treasures of the earth – minerals of all kinds, including crystals, are under their protection. The dwarves work deep within the earth and are very strong. They offer inspiration that is grounded, and a calming influence, strong and solid and slow. By connecting deeply with the dwarves, Snow White can safely undergo her transformation. When we connect with that deep, earthy, root energy, we can transform and transmute, too.

The Magickal Art of Glamour

GLAMOUR IS THE ART OF CHANGE, particularly of changing our appearance, and can be learned through interacting with the faery. It can help us enhance one aspect of ourselves, bringing it to the fore physically – so a short person can seem tall, by virtue of the way they carry themselves and the energy they project. Faery glamour can make you appear to be smaller, taller, invisible, more attractive, old, young, male or female. It is an awesome magickal ability, and one which often begins with very subtle effects, which you can grow over time.

A person lacking in what we call beauty can be overwhelmingly attractive due to their ability to draw upon glamour. Glamour can also make a characteristic of one's personality become a part of one's appearance. Generally, glamour is

an energy that overwhelms our actual physical characteristics and makes us appear changed in shape and form – which affects how we are perceived.

Although glamour is not disguise, it can be used as such – and obviously is used in that way by the wicked queen in this tale. Our evil queen uses this magickal ability to change her form, but she is powerless to turn back time and completely restore her youth.

The Misuse of the Magickal Apple

THE APPLE IS A PERENNIAL SYMBOL OF MAGICK – cut one open, and you'll find a five-pointed star. It is said to be sacred to the Holy Isle of Avalon and to her priestesses, and it is also associated with Aphrodite. In love spells, we often work with an apple, and can even ask a potential love to take a bite out of an apple we offer to see if they are interested! The apple also has biblical echoes and, in this case, biting in to the apple does bring Snow White wisdom – the wisdom of disillusionment and of walking for a time between the worlds of life and death. That the queen is willing to take this symbol of magick and literally poison it shows how far she is prepared to go in her misuse

of spells. Working unhealthy magick in this way rarely – if ever – turns out well. Here, the queen has poisoned her own abilities, and her spell's eventual outcome, by her abuse of the sacred.

CRYSTAL MAGICK

OF COURSE, I WANTED THE DWARVES TO PLACE Snow White in a casket made of crystal rather than glass! I chose clear quartz, as it is an amplifier. And it is also transparent, so the dwarves could still see her and take hope in her incorruptible corpse. Around her casket, I had the dwarves place a circle of white quartz. This is an ancient tradition from the burial mounds of Ireland and Great Britain. The stones shone under moonlight and "charged" the bones of the dead with magickal potency and energy, so those left behind could receive their messages. I thought the dwarves would be likely to do something like this – to almost place Snow White in a crystal grid that had a chance of preserving some flicker of life force, until they could discover how she could be awakened and brought back to life.

THE WISDOM OF SNOW WHITE

I SUPPOSE ONE OF THE WONDERS OF THIS tale is its resonance, for it speaks to us of what we deny about ourselves. It speaks for the outcast, to anyone who has experienced jealousy or that searing bitterness at being replaced within another's life.

Also, there is a desire within so many of us today to remain young and what we call beautiful, forever – but as the queen in this story demonstrates, this can poison us. We have the potential to be the bitter queen, to cast magick, to curse those younger and more lovely than we are as we grow old. Or we can become the elder and learn how to work great magicks in good ways for the next generation.

Most of all, the story of *Snow White* shows us that we need to be able to look into a mirror and truly like who we see. That is one of the most powerful forms of magick of all.

Red Riding Hood

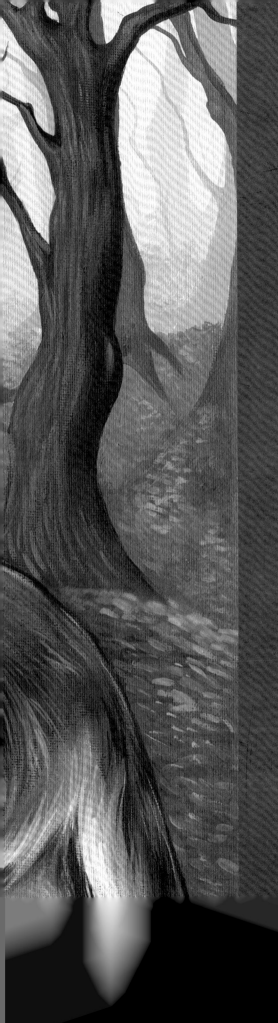

THERE ONCE WAS A GIRL WHO STOOD ON the very edge of what it is to be a woman longer than most girls. She had not grown into her moon-time, and for several years she wondered if there was something quite different about her. She began to think that perhaps being different would not be so bad, for then she would never have to be married, or have to bring babies into the world, which her mother had told her was something even the strongest huntsman would be afraid to endure. Women, her mother told her, were strong: strong enough to birth babies, strong enough to change, stronger than anyone knew. "And that is our secret," her mother said.

The girl loved her mother, but she loved no-one as much as she loved her grandmother. The girl loved her grandmother because the old woman was fierce, as fierce as the girl's mother, but courageous enough to live outside the village, within the deep part of the woods, in the very midst of everything wild.

The girl knew both the ways to reach her grandmother's home. And both of those ways were dangerous. One was the path of needles. The other was the path of pins. And along both, the thorns of the great trees protected and guarded the beings of the wood. Herbs grew along the way, as well, and she picked those that strayed onto her path. The others she left for the Wild Ones of the deep green forest.

The faery folk dwelled there, too, and the girl often saw them and left them offerings from her basket, taking care never to leave the path, should she fall into Faerie forever. She was too much in love with her life.

One day, the girl began to feel a pain and an ache and a strangeness within. Her arms grew longer, and her shirt needed to be made larger. When the silver lady next grew to full, the girl was given the celebration that all the girls in that village were given when they became daughters of the moon. She barely noticed when the red cape was placed about her shoulders, but she felt its warmth, and she knew that her grandmother had woven the cloth, that her mother had dyed the wool, and that all of this had been done long ago.

The tradition was for the newborn daughter of the moon to wear her cloak whenever the moon-blood was with her, so all could honour her and pay her respect, for it was known that some women were especially fierce at this time. They knew more and felt more and heard more and saw further and knew things, knew even more things than usual, at their moon-time.

This girl wanted to see her grandmother all the more after her moon-time came. She wanted to hear more about the ways she could live and be free and, maybe even one day, dwell in the forest like her grandmother. She did not want to find a husband, and she avoided the boys in the village, who all noticed her now she was wearing the red cloak, with its scarlet hood pulled up over her shining hair.

Perhaps because of this, her grandmother gave her the gift of a knife. "A knife that can cut away all the ties that bind, if you wish, my dearest," said the old woman, for she knew the dangers of the forest, and of the time of the red cloak, too. She, too, had been young and very beautiful, a long, long time ago.

When the next moon-time came, and the moon was full, and the sun was falling, the girl set out to visit her grandmother, who was not well. Her mother helped her pack the basket with a sweet wine to restore the blood and small cakes made in the shape of the moon that shone above the path as the light slowly crept away for the night. They were the tastiest and most tempting of treats, for although her grandmother was as brave as any hero in a book, she was growing older, and

winter would soon come, and everyone needed as much meat on their bones as they could gather before the darkness swallowed all the day's light.

The girl kissed her mother and smiled at her father, who was polishing his axe by the fire. "I'll be back in a day or two," she said.

"Don't be so casual, my child," said the mother.

The girl smiled. "I am no child, remember? I have the red cloak, now, so everyone is a little more afraid of me. I like that."

"Even so, stay on the path," her mother said, taking her daughter's chin in her hand and looking into her eyes. "You are my great treasure, and I know you will stay to the path. That is the only way."

"Which path did you walk, Mother?" the girl asked. "The path of needles, or of pins?"

"I trod the path of pins, my love," she said softly, gazing at the man by the fire. "I chose the path that led me to my destiny."

The girl smiled, gathered up the basket, pulled the hood over her head, and went out into the world, its light softening to gold.

As she walked away, she gazed at the trees turning to a dark copper, their leaves curling into scarlet scrolls. *They ought to call this time "the red month"*, she thought to herself. *All about me is the colour of what now makes me a woman.*

But not too much of a woman was she, to forego skipping and a little hop, every now and again. She smiled as the birds sang their night song flying into the trees to roost. Still, she kept to the path, and only stopped to dig a little at the roots she knew would be good for soup in the cold days that were coming.

Amidst the simple pleasure of her hands in the earth, and the song of the blood-red sky, and the colours of the forest, she could feel herself growing larger and larger. Her every sense felt as keen as the edge of the blade she hid within her pocket, her whole self was sharp and awakened. *Maybe*, she thought, *it is the moon-time, or just a place of magick, but I feel … I feel …*

As she wondered how she could describe this sense of being at one with all, the forest suddenly quieted. There was no soft slide into the silence, but a sudden ceasing of the song of life. The world, in a moment, seemed heavier, and the girl looked about her, only to see a huge, dark shape, furred and red-eyed, moving at great speed between the ancient pines, so straight and strong.

She showed no sign of the fear that shot like quicksilver down her spine. Instead, she took a deep, long breath to steady herself, and stood up slowly, putting the roots in her basket, careful not to get dirt upon the cakes, and resumed her walk, as if nothing at all felt wrong. Finally, every nerve stretched taut, she reached the point where the two paths diverged in a great fork. *This is the place where I choose*, she thought. *The path of needles. Or the path of pins.*

A voice as deep and rich as any man's, softly called out, "Which one, girl? Which path shall you choose?"

And a great shadow appeared beside her, and inside she shook. *Remember the knife*, she reminded herself.

"I am the wolf of the moon," he said, "and I wish to know which path you choose."

"I choose my own path."

"And what will you find at its end?"

His voice seemed very far away, and his eyes very close, and his scent so strong, and his size immense.

"I will find my destiny," she said, her voice strong.

"Destiny?" he mocked. "You are taking these to the old woman, the wise one who dwells deep." He laughed, gesturing with a thick, clawed hand at the basket. "Your destiny then is to live alone in this great, dark forest."

She did not say a word. So, he changed course.

"Will you give me a taste of what is in the basket?"

"I will, for the sake of sharing with a fellow traveller," she said. She dipped a small white hand into the basket and held out a mooncake.

He reached out his long, thick, hairy paw, with its curved black claws, and took the cake with grace, chewing with surprising delicacy for one so huge.

He has manners, the girl noted. That made him even stranger.

"I am a gentleman," he said. "You need not be surprised."

"I did not know wild things were taught manners," she said.

My manners, he thought to himself, *are tearing off heads.*

"Well, if it is truly your destiny to which you are going, all paths shall lead you there," said the moon wolf, for he was no ordinary wolf. This wolf was as much a man as he was a creature of the woods, and she was caught in his eyes, red and yellow and gold as the forest.

"I choose this path," she whispered, breaking his gaze. It was less trodden than the other, for it was the path of needles, and this was the way she loved the least, but this, she thought, was the way for strength and courage.

"I shall take the other path," called the wolf to her from the fork on the road. "Let us see who reaches their destiny first."

She leapt upon her path and began to run.

***

THE WOLF ARRIVED FIRST, OF COURSE. HE HAD the advantage. And this was not the first time he and the old woman of the woods had met.

He knocked at the door.

She knew it was not her grandchild, for she knew the girl's scent, which was like sunlit fields in autumn. Her visitor had the smell of the earth at night, and the cave where he slept, and the fresh blood of a new lamb. She knew who he was, and she knew why he had come.

He knocked at her door, again. Good oak it was, and strong. Wards and charms and spells protected it, but even the wise old woman's great magick was no match for the wild wolf of the moon.

"It is me, Grandmother," he said, his voice like a howl that was whispered.

And she opened the door.

***

THEN, WITHOUT MESS OR FUSS, THE WOLF took her into his great jaws, which opened wider and wider until her entire body was engulfed. Although she was old, she was a strong woman – the best kind for a wolf to sacrifice at the full moon. And when he was finished, the wise woman was no more. She had vanished into the chasm and the chaos of the void, leaving the wolf the possessor of her life force.

The wolf went to a wooden chest, hand-painted with symbols and strange sigils, and opened it up. He laughed a little at the old woman's clothes, lying there so quiet and neat. He took out a green shawl and wrapped it about his shoulders, and he pulled on a woollen cap.

Next, he climbed into the bed and waited for the girl. He thought of her beauty and fierceness, her youth and all the long life in front of her, and felt it was a little unfortunate that it should end this way for her. But the winter was fast approaching and this was too fine a chance for him to satisfy his hunger before the world's plenty grew scarce. So, he lay on the bed, pulled up the covers to complete his disguise, and waited … but not for long.

Tap, tap, tap.

She was at the door.

"Grandmother," she called softly. "It's me. Can I come in?"

He cleared his throat, and growled low and soft. "Come in, child of my heart. The door is open."

And she pushed a little and entered the room. A fire crackled in the grate, but she could smell the wrongness in the air, the scent of something wild and raw.

She knew she looked upon the wolf.

"I brought you some treats," she said, biding her time. She placed the wine upon the table, and its ruby colour winked in the firelight, dark as blood. "Some cakes. And roots, too, from the forest. Good for soup."

The wolf grinned. He would not be needing these.

"Why don't you put a little of the wine in a glass and the sweetmeats on a plate and bring them here to me, where it is warm."

The girl moved closer, knowing well what she approached. She put the plate upon the bed and sat down.

The wolf looked her in the eyes.

"My grandmother," she said, her voice full of magick, "what big eyes you have."

"All the better to see you with, child of my heart," murmured the wolf, so sure he was

that she was his.

"And," said the girl, "what big hands you have."

"The better to eat this good food with," he said, a grin splitting his great, furred face.

"And Grandmother," said the girl, her hand tightening on the knife within her cloak, "what big teeth you have."

Realising that the girl was wise to him, the wolf flung back his cloak and reared up, huge and fearsome, with hunger on his breath. His golden eyes turned red as blood by firelight, as he whispered, "All the better to eat you with." And he reached for her, opened wide his jaws, and swallowed her whole...

And she fell, deep within the belly of that beast. Into the void she tumbled, and in that place of shadows, she found her grandmother, and they held each other tight.

"I am sorry, my child, my heart," said the grandmother. "I should not have let him in."

"It is all right, dearest Grandmother. For me, it is time."

"But this is the beginning of your life as a woman. It is too soon for death to find you."

"I will not die, now, Grandmother," said the girl, drawing forth the magickal knife. "Nor shall you. For I chose the path of needles."

And the girl reached up and felt between the ribs of the wolf and found the soft skin. Then she closed her eyes and drew down all the power and magick of the moon, until the knife shone in the darkness of the void.

She gripped the leather-bound handle, closed her eyes, and thrust. Her steel will strengthened her arm, as once, twice, three times, she pushed the blade through all resistance. With the final blow, she cried out, drew the knife down, and the wolf's belly fell open.

Pushing her way out, a child being born again from the strangest womb that ever was, she went into the new world, then turned back to pull her grandmother out – the wolf howling all the while, like a great, wild wind.

"I am hurt," he cried, gathering his belly together in his thick, hairy paws.

The girl looked upon him, knowing who he was, and who she must now be.

And she ended the life of the one who had tried to take hers.

***

THE GIRL STAYED THREE DAYS AT HER grandmother's house, making soup, adding healing waters to the wine, dipping the sweetmeats into the warm broth and feeding the old woman until she was beyond the shock that had set in after the wolf's attack.

But when snow began to fall, the girl knew her parents would be worried.

"I must go back," she said to her grandmother. "I will return in a few days."

"Thank you, child of my heart," said the old woman, silver hair long and unbound.

The woman's granddaughter put on her red cloak, tucked her magick knife into its hidden pocket, and kissed her grandmother. "Stay warm," she said.

"I shall," said the grandmother.

And the young woman smiled, and pulled the great wolf fur over her grandmother's bed, knowing the fierce old woman would never be cold again.

"I AM THE WOLF of the moon," he said, "and I wish to know which path you choose."

"I choose my own path."

"And what will you find at its end?"

"I will find my destiny," she said, her voice strong.

Discover the Magick of

Red Riding Hood

HISTORY OF THIS TALE

THERE ARE FOLKLORISTS WHO BELIEVE THIS tale first surfaced in Ancient China, over 2000 years ago. And it is true that it has variants all over the world, including in Africa, India, and Asia. But the story we know so well is, most of all, French. The earliest version of *Red Riding Hood* to make it into a collection of tales was written down by Charles Perrault. That version of the story was called, *Le Petit Chaperon Rouge*, and it was published in 1697. There is an Italian version, too, which is called The False Grandmother, or *La Finta Nonna*. There is also a meaty version by the German Brothers Grimm. And Andrew Lang added his own beautiful layers to the tale in 19th century England.

In other takes on the story, the wolf is variously an ogre or a giant, or a tiger. In all tellings of the story, though, the grandmother is devoured, and, in most, the young woman escapes. Essentially, it was a cautionary tale told to children of the country folk, warning them of the dangers of the forest, of the perils of straying from the path. But it is also a coming-of-age parable. In some versions, Little Red Riding Hood gets into bed with the wolf, after he demands she burns her clothes. In other variations, he leaves parts of her grandmother's body in the kitchen, which the girl unknowingly cooks up, thus becoming an unwitting cannibal, devouring her most beloved relative.

I wanted readers of this version to experience the challenges of the girl as she undergoes a true initiation into womanhood – from innocence to experience – in one short

HOW DO ANY OF US COME TO know this story? It almost seems I was born with it inside me. So much a part of us is it, that when we are first told this story of dark forest and wild wolves, it is like we are remembering something we have heard again and again, throughout lifetimes.

For myself, I have only blurred memories of grandma's house, of the walk through the woods – and of the swallowing down of the grandmother (in some tales, and the devouring of both the young girl and the old woman, in others). These images all tumbled about me, but what stood out so very clearly was the path the girl was told to follow. In older versions of this French tale, there are two magickal paths (discussed in a section, below) – and so I reintroduced those into this telling of the story, to illustrate the idea that we must choose our own path in this life.

journey from the rites of the village to the wildness of the house in the woods. And I wanted her to escape because of her wit, her courage, and just a little inherited magick.

THE GRANDMOTHER

THE GRANDMOTHER IN THIS *RED RIDING HOOD* is a wise woman, living alone in the forest, despite her years, despite her frailty. She will face winter alone – although, by the end of the tale, I feel the young woman may just move into the forest house, to undergo a final training in the ways of the wise from her grandmother. While the mother and daughter love each other dearly, there is true kinship between the old woman and the girl on the cusp on young womanhood. The grandmother also stands in for the witch, the one who knows the forest – a female hermit, and of course, a crone. Independent, experienced, and wise to the ways of the wild world, she is nearing the end of her earthly life and preparing, I feel, to hand her role as wise woman, and perhaps herbalist, over to her granddaughter, the maiden.

TWO PATHS IN THE WOOD: THE PATH OF NEEDLES AND THE PATH OF PINS

IN THE OLDER VERSIONS OF THIS STORY, BEFORE it came to be written down, the tale was often told in rooms where women and girls did their work. In sewing rooms with spinning wheels, in the weaver's huts and the dyeing rooms, this tale of how to move through the darkness was told. In the older versions, there is not one path through the forest, there are two – and they are called, in some versions, the path of thorns and the path of needles, and in other versions, including the ones I have drawn from, the path of pins and the path of needles.

Pins are simple items that temporarily hold things together in order to construct a garment. But needles are complex: they can be threaded, can be used to make something enduring, can be used to make things last. Pins are relatively passive, solid, constructive, simple, and impermanent. Needles are more dynamic and creative, more complex, lasting, and powerful. So, when the maiden chooses a path, it is, in a sense, between these two options. We know which path I saw this maiden choose! In other versions of the tale, the pins are said to symbolise sexual innocence, and the needles, sexual awareness and activity. I prefer to think of the two paths as a choice between a kind of safety and domesticity and a kind of power and independence.

THE RED CLOAK OR CAPE

THE COLOUR RED IS ASSOCIATED WITH women's mysteries – and, of course, the onset of menarche is a great rite of initiation. I loved the idea that the red cape symbolised the girl having entered into this aspect of her feminine experience, that there was a symbol whereby others in the community knew she had moved into this part of life. It's almost a dangerous symbol, because others – including predators – would then see the girl in a sexual way. But it was also a source of pride, for it symbolised that the edge of her womanhood beckoned. It was almost as if the idea of the red cape was inspired by the red-tent movements, also the idea of safe spaces, where women's rites and women's blood were considered sacred and powerful – with respect, without the fear that led to women being stripped of their powers by a church terrified of the wise woman and the ones who had the wisdom of the blood.

A MAGICKAL KNIFE: THE ATHAME

IN WITCHCRAFT, ONE OF THE SACRED TOOLS that witches work with is a magickal knife called an athame (pronounced *ah-tha-may*). An athame is traditionally black-handled and double bladed, and is never used to cut anything on the physical plane. Instead, it is used to create "doorways" into other realms, to clear cords or bindings between people, and to conduct energetic surgery, too. So, the heroine of our tale does indeed use the magickal knife in an unconventional way – but she is also creating a doorway from the void, through the wolf, back into her life and into the forest house. I loved that this girl rebirths herself *and* rescues her grandmother with the very knife the old woman gave her. There is no huntsman, no masculine presence to set them free. Only the girl's wit and courage and willingness to use this magickal knife will bring them back from the darkness of the void into the world once again. (If you have a magickal athame, it is probably best not used in this way.)

THE WOLF OF THE MOON

COULD THE WOLF WITHIN THE TALE BE A KIND of werewolf? He is most definitely in-between, a shapeshifter growing in power and hunger as the moon reaches fullness. Perhaps the wolf was once human, but has been consumed, himself, by his wild nature. He has manners, but he is ferocious. He feels it's a pity to kill a girl with so much life before her, but will do so, anyway. He is starving when he meets the girl in the woods, and his condition means he must take in the most energy he can before winter fully immerses the landscape in its cold white cloak. He must kill in order to live – as so many of us do, even if it is not in the ways the wolf does.

I feel for the wolf – he is starving, a survivor, and alone. But I am aware of just how dangerous feeling compassion for him is! He is a potent and enduring symbol of the predators that stalk the world – charming, attractive, lethal. It is easy, and very dangerous, to be fascinated by him – as the writer of the original written French version of this story, Charles Perrault, knew: *Alas! Who does not know that these gentle wolves are of all such creatures the most dangerous!* The wolf is temptation and danger and the wild unknown. It is through the confrontation with these aspects of life that the girl will be reborn into young womanhood.

THE MAGICK OF TREES: THE OAK DOOR

THE GRANDMOTHER'S HOUSE IN THE WOODS has something very special – a magickal door that protects those who dwell within. During the Dark to Middle Ages, the great oak forests of Europe were nearly destroyed, as oak was so prized for its strength and ability to withstand nearly all shocks. It was considered to be a royal tree, and the presence of an oak door symbolised a kind of nobility of those who dwelled within the home. Thus, the oak door makes even the grandmother's humble forest dwelling a special place – as the wise woman is notable for her knowledge and courage. To knock upon an oak door was to ask to enter into a strong, safe, and special place – a door that guarded the area between the worlds.

Chanting often took place while oak doors were made, and charms were often woven into the doors to further ensure the safety of those whom the noble oak tree would guard in its new incarnation as a door. *Oak* in the old Druid language means *door* – but not an ordinary door. Rather, it means the kind of door that can either close the gateways between the worlds or open them, so that great transformation can take place. Thus, I gave the wise woman, this wonderful grandmother, a very magickal oak door. I am sure it has its own story to tell!

MAKING MAGICK: RED RIDING HOOD'S WISE WOMAN FULL MOON CAKES

NOT TO BE CONFUSED WITH CHINESE mooncakes, the mooncakes I had our heroine take her grandmother are the kind that witches might share at full moon rites, the kind that we once baked when we celebrated our cycles as wise women, the kind that reflected and celebrated the phases of the moon. The girl takes these cakes to her grandmother as a symbol of the magickal link that exists between them, and they are a nod to the full moon and to the full moon's energy, which would be absorbed by the old woman when she ate these cakes.

To make your own Wise Woman Full Moon Cakes, you will need:

- One cup of almonds
- Two teaspoons pine nuts
- Three tablespoons of delicious local honey
- One raw fig
- Three teaspoons of lemon juice
- One teaspoon water (spring water, rainwater, or your own homemade rosewater are best!)

Soak your almonds in a little warm water for about one hour, then drain and, using your magickal mortar and pestle, grind the almonds, the pine nuts, the fig, honey, lemon juice, and water until you have a nice smooth mixture. It should be a little sticky, but not too sticky, and certainly not too dry. Just add ingredients a little at a time to get the right consistency.

Spread your dough by hand, and then cut out as many small, moon-shaped cakes as you can – round for the full moon or you can make crescent-moon shaped cakes, too! Refrigerate for two hours, or pop in the freezer for half an hour, and serve slightly chilled and topped with fresh, in-season berries and cream!

TRANSITIONS FROM AUTUMN TO WINTER

THE EVENTS IN THIS TALE HAPPEN AS THE autumn gives way to the winter. As the wheel of the year cycles around, everything must change, and so, too, do the fates of the women within the story – and also, that of the wolf, of course. Perhaps the tale takes place between Mabon, the festival of the last harvest and the descent of the Maiden Goddess into the void of the dark. Perhaps there are echoes of Ishtar's descent into the Underworld, or Persephone's choice to leave the land above and go below into the earth with Hades, creating winter within this tale. Or perhaps the events take place closer to Samhain, when the veils are thin, and the spirits of the dead are at their most powerful, and walk with us, just as you and I could walk side by side.

moon, wild wolves rise up and walk the paths of the forests, and girls become women, all under her sacred light.

THE WISDOM OF
RED RIDING HOOD

I LIKE TO THINK THAT RED RIDING HOOD HAS something for all of us, no matter at what stage of life we find ourselves. We are the Mother, who must let her child go into the dark alone, for it is through that journey that they will become the person they are destined to be. We are the Crone, at the end of our years, holding fast to our independence, yet loving fiercely the young ones who brave the forest and gift us, in return, their love and support. And we are the Maiden in the forest, choosing our path, feeling the magickal knife in our pocket, and vanquishing the predators we will encounter on the way to our destiny.

FULL MOON

SO MUCH TAKES PLACE DURING THE FULL moon of this tale. The moon, like our heroine, appears to die but is reborn, and her moon-blood is of course linked with the cycles of the moon. The moon symbolises change, the night, mystery, and the wild, the nocturnal, the unknown self. It is a symbol, too, of the maiden, the mother, and the crone, all of whom are present in this story. Most of the action takes place between the maiden and the crone, of course, but the mother's presence is loving, and powerful, and has helped this young girl come to be the fine woman she is.

The full moon has long been considered a power source for shapeshifters, such as werewolves, which are symbolic of how our wild, inner nature comes out to play at full moon time, stimulated by the presence of the magickal silvery light. Everything is "more" at the time of the full moon. We feel more intensely, our intuition and psychic awareness are at their peak, and we are often more reckless, spontaneous, and wild. It is a vivid and slightly "mad" time – a time when almost anything can happen! Witches dance beneath the full

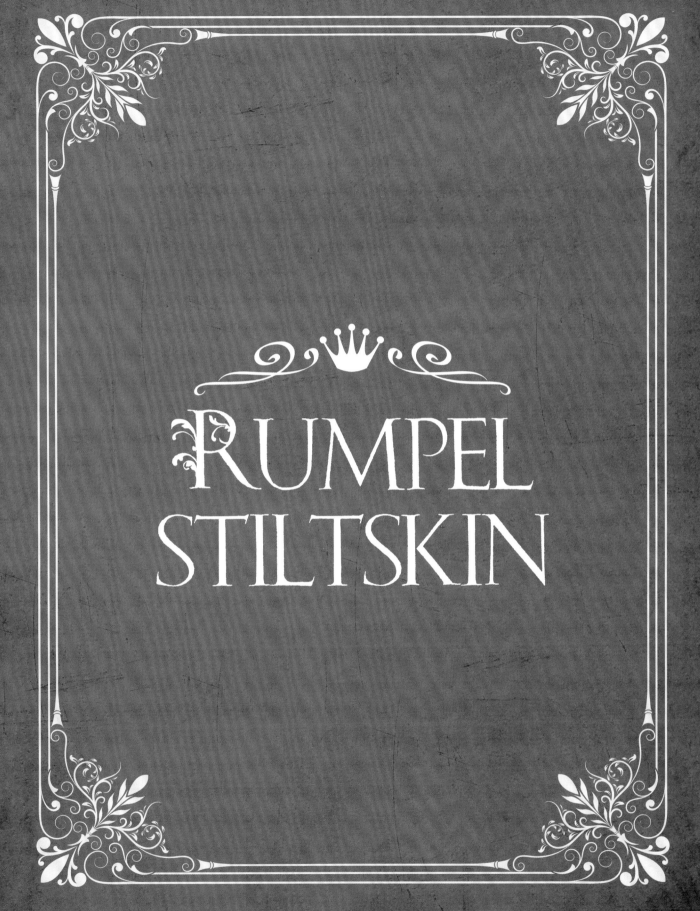

RUMPEL STILTSKIN

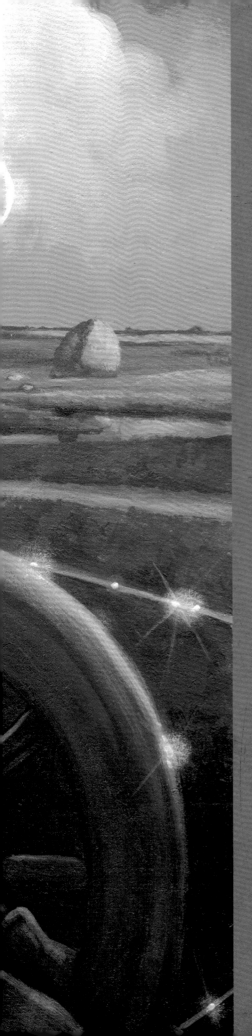

ONCE, FAR AWAY FROM YESTERDAY, there was a young girl, a miller's daughter, who could hear spirits that no-one else could hear. Although they listened closely, they heard only the rustling of the wind or the chatter of the birds or the crackling of the fire, yet they did not deny the girl was truly hearing spirits.

When the girl grew out of childhood and closer to becoming a woman, the spirits she heard grew louder and began to shake the pots and tip over the cauldron by the fire. And in time her father and their cat did hear one of the spirits. It would come a-knocking each evening, just as the sun went down, getting louder and louder the darker the night became.

This spirit took to tapping on the table while the girl and her father ate, causing them to upend their dinner from fright, at first. It would knock from above and scratch from below, and even the cat, a fierce mouser who had driven away every rat in their street, hid when this strange spirit came a-rapping and a-tapping in their mill after dark.

The girl was sensitive and an optimist, blessed with a sunny spirit. She was a realist, too, for all that she could hear those the eye could not see. She never exaggerated nor told a falsehood, for she dealt with things just as they were. In this, she was like her mother, whom she still could remember although the miller's wife – whose fine gold necklace and a precious golden ring her daughter always wore – had died before the girl could talk. She was less like her father, who was loud and foolish, yet so good-humoured he was loved by all. He was so proud of his daughter and her lovely golden hair and her ability to hear the spirits, he would often boast that she could turn straw into gold.

He did not mean that literally, of course. He only meant she could always make something fine and good out of something ordinary and commonplace. Most of the villagers laughed off the miller's boast, knowing him to be vainglorious and loud. They knew his daughter was bright, yes, and could hear spirits, but the miller and his daughter were just as poor as all the rest of their neighbours, and just as likely to go hungry in the wintertime. If the girl could spin gold from straw, they said, she and her father would not have to worry about enough food for the table in the cold times.

But somehow the story grew and grew, until one day it reached the ears of the king. Now, simply because a man is a king does not make him wise. He too was foolish, but in a different way to the miller, and when he heard there was a girl who could spin straw into gold, he sent his soldiers to every home in the village until they found the man who had made this claim.

When the soldiers found the miller, he told them that, yes, he had said his daughter could spin straw into gold, but …

And before the miller could explain what he meant, the soldiers were forcing his daughter into a carriage and driving off with her to the castle. The miller was left to be guarded by two stern soldiers holding shining, sharp swords, who had orders of what they must do when word came from the king.

After her jostling ride ended at the castle, the girl was taken before the king, who was fine in his way, and not so much older than she – but, she could tell, uncaring for anything except the gold about his throat, the gold woven into his clothes, and the gold that filled his coffers, which made his army the largest in the land.

"Are you the girl they say can spin straw into gold?" the king asked.

The miller's daughter shook her head. "I cannot do that, sire. It was simply my father who said this, as he is proud of me."

The king held up a hand for silence.

"Your father does not want you to spin gold for anyone but him. I would want the same, if I was your father. So, you are a faithful daughter and do as you are bid."

She stayed silent.

"You hide your wealth well."

She waited for the real question, which she could feel coming.

"But are you a faithful servant of the Crown?"

She stayed silent, but curtsied slightly to show respect, and she looked up at his face from under her lashes, her eyes wary and wise.

"Good. You *will* spin, for me. For your king."

And he and his soldiers led her to a room, high, high up within a turret of the castle. And within this room lay a great pile of yellow straw, a spinning wheel, a little stool, and a handful of beeswax candles.

"Here," he said. "You will stay here this night, and if you refuse to spin the straw into gold, I will have your head."

The girl turned to him, her eyes full of truth. "I cannot, sire – it is not within my power."

"And I shall have your father's head, too, if you insist on being a treasonous subject who will not aid their king."

She gazed at him. *How could he be so stupid?* she thought.

"Your choice, girl."

And he left, thinking on what he would do with all the gold the miller's daughter would spin, calculating how many soldiers he would buy, how many ships he would build, and how many gentle lands he would invade with his great, golden army.

The girl slumped to the floor and looked at the spinning wheel, shaking her head, feeling

anger, confusion, and the dreadful certainty that she would most likely die the next day, as would her father. The feelings grew stronger within her, until she was unable to contain them, and her emotions spilled out all over from her and travelled far away to the mill where her father was under guard.

That night, although no tapping was heard at the mill, as midnight approached and the girl began to weep, she heard a faint rapping in her tower chamber.

"Ah," she said. "Spirit, you've found me here. See what has happened? I am to die tomorrow, because my father boasted of what I could do, and the king believes the words and not the truth of it. There is no way through this except death."

The tapping, which had stopped when the girl spoke, began again. Three taps on the floor. Three taps on the ceiling.

Then, three raps at the door.

What's that? the miller's daughter wondered. The spirit had never knocked on the door before.

Again, three raps at the door, louder this time.

"Shall I let you in? Is that what you mean, Spirit?"

And again, louder still, three great raps.

"Come in then," she said. "I might as well know what you are before I die."

She screwed shut her eyes, and when she opened them, there stood a little man, brown and tangled like old, old tree roots, strange and wonderful, with a crooked back and huge, leaf-green eyes, and hands with the longest fingers she had ever seen. He wore red and emerald, and despite his strange shape, he moved as quick as the mice the cat had caught with ease. No-one, she could see, as the strange being darted about the tower, would ever be able to catch this creature.

"Sir," she said. "You entered."

"You asked me in," he replied, his voice full of old wisdom and crafty ways.

"I will not be here tomorrow," she said.

"Good thing, too – this place is awful! No windows, no air, no sky, no trees, no water, and no fire!"

"Just this straw," she said wryly, "which I must spin into gold before tomorrow."

The bent little man knelt down and stared at her.

She answered the question in his eyes by saying, "The king has heard I can do this. The boast went straight from my father's mouth to the royal ear, and here I am, condemned by my father's pride to this impossible task."

The little man looked at her, his great eyes narrowing with thought. Then it was as if fire danced across his eyes, as they widened, alive with sparks of intelligence.

"I can be of help," he said, his voice all croaky like a frog in a pond. "Give me your necklace," he demanded. "There must be an exchange – something of yours for this talent of mine," he added, when she hesitated.

"On my life, I hate to give it up, but I know my mother would rather have my father and I alive, than dead and me wearing her necklace in the grave."

With her heart breaking, the miller's daughter passed him her mother's fine golden necklace, and the little man sat down at the stool and began to spin. And as he did, he chanted and muttered and trembled with a power that flowed through his fingers, and she watched, bedazzled, as the room began to shine with the candlelit pile of gold that began to replace the straw.

Then he turned to her, saffron flames dancing in his eyes. "Sleep now," he said. "It will be done."

And she did, resting upon the floor, dreaming strange dreams of necklaces and promises, spinning wheels and magicks.

In the morning, she awoke with a start to a harsh knock at the door. The little man had vanished, but the gold, it was still there, lustrous and smooth as butter, hard as old wood, and she touched it in wonder.

"It's real," she said, shocked, as the guards entered, and the king stood before her.

The king's eyes grew large in his narrow face, and she could see him delighting in this turn of events.

Now, I shall never go home, she thought to herself. *He believes I can actually do this.*

"Girl, I am pleased. You are no traitor but a loyal subject of the Crown." He clapped his hands, and she was marched to another chamber, where she was brought food and wine, and permitted to wash her face and hands, while a scowling guard watched to make sure she did not escape.

Where would I run to? she thought, seeing how seriously he took his duty. *There is only one staircase up and down.*

As she was escorted back, they passed the room she'd been held in, and a new door was opened, and in she stepped to a different chamber, much larger than the last. She saw the king had wasted no time.

"More straw," he was ordering, and already it was being carried up to her new prison. "More this time – enough space for the wheel, and the girl, and a little air. Fill this room to the ceiling."

"Girl," he said turning to her, overflowing with greedy excitement. "Fulfil this task, and I

will be pleased. But if you do not, it will be the executioner for you and for your father."

She said nothing, but looked at the king and begged him silently to become wise and know this was not her doing. But she could not say so. For the gold had been real, and she and her father had been saved. For a day. And no-one, she saw, had noticed her mother's necklace was gone.

After the door to the chamber was locked and she was left alone, the girl lay down upon the straw, creating a little bed out of the great mass of it, and thought upon what she would do, and what could happen when night fell again.

***

Rap, rap, rap.

"Is that you?" she whispered into the dark. She lit a candle, careful not to drop a match on the great piles of straw all about her.

"Come on in then, sir." She blinked, and there he was.

"You lived," he said.

"I did," she replied, simply. "Thank you. But there's still no escape. I have to spin this great mass into gold by daybreak, or—"

"Or..." He made a strange noise, his long finger running across his wizened throat.

"Yes," she said with a shudder.

"What can you offer me?"

She looked at her hands and saw her mother's ring.

"You can take this," she said, sadly. "On my life, I hate to give it up, but I know my mother would rather have my father and I alive, than dead and me wearing her ring in the grave."

She pulled it off and held it out to the strange little man. "It's yours."

Then those strange eyes lit up with fire again, and he tucked the ring into his pocket, and

under his breath he began to sing, and croon, and mutter great spells and enchantments, and the fire in his eyes travelled down to his fingers, which sparkled with magick, and his skin began to shine and flicker and dance. He was small, but in that moment, he seemed taller than the sky that the miller's daughter had not seen for two days,

And he settled down upon the stool again, and again he spun the straw through those quick enchanted fingers, into pure, heavy gold.

She lay down upon the floor and began to dream of eyes and fires, rings and magick.

And again, when morning came, the king was pleased.

So pleased that he told his advisors this girl was of such value he would marry her himself, and for them to stop their matchmaking with wealthy princesses – at least for the moment.

"If she can do what I will ask of her next," he announced, "I will take her for my queen. Then her talents will be mine alone, and no other king can benefit. And besides, she is comely, with that hair the colour of gold."

The advisors agreed, and the king organised a final test for the girl, who was now craving fresh air, her foolish father, and her own bed in the mill house.

She was led to a third chamber, larger yet than the last. "One more test," said the king, as she sat before him on the stool. "But if you fail this—"

"I will die," she said, her eyes frank and open. "I might," she said. "The power to do this is not mine."

The king ignored her, choosing to believe the evidence of the gold all about her. "If this final place is filled with gold by tomorrow morning —"

"I can go home?" she interrupted, unable to help herself from saying what her heart wished for.

"I will marry you and make you my queen. My golden queen."

Her heart froze in her chest, for she did not want to marry this greedy king, with his unloving heart, who did not even notice that her mother's ring was gone from her finger.

She stayed silent and looked at the floor, and the king thought her awed with the honour, and smiled to himself. *She is*, he thought, gazing at her, *so very pretty. And quiet, too!*

He left, and the guards locked the door, and the girl, alone once again, turned to gaze at this last great chamber. It was vast, and filled to the very rafters with straw.

"He must not want to marry me so very much," she said to herself.

She sat and wondered what on earth she could do. Even if the strange little man could spin this vast ocean of straw into gold, she had no jewellery left to give to him in return for his labours. She had not a coin in her pocket to offer him. Even her clothes were worn and old, and none too clean, now, too.

Finally, night fell, and she heard, *rap, rap, rap*, upon the door.

She didn't answer.

It came again, louder this time. *Rap, rap, rap.*

Again, she looked away. What point was there? She had nothing of gold left to give the little man. Perhaps the king would take pity on her and send her home. He wouldn't kill his golden goose, would he? Even if she didn't fulfil this final command, he would keep her alive hoping to get more gold from her.

Wouldn't he?

But she knew the greedy king would kill her, just to keep her and her "power" away from others.

RAP, RAP, RAP.

"Come in," she said, quietly.

"Why are you a-sitting here in the dark?" the little man asked, as he clambered through the straw.

"Because I have nothing more for you, sir, and therefore, I will die."

The little man laughed.

"Do you know what loneliness is?" he asked.

"It is this, surely," she said.

"It is, and never having had a friend, or a family."

"I suppose that is true, sir. I had a mother who loved me, and a father whose pride may have killed us both, but he, too, loves me. As does my cat. And the spirits."

The little man nodded. "You must give me something for the power, for the energy," he said, thoughtfully. "I will ask you for something a year from this day. Knowing me as you do now, would you be willing to give it?"

"How can I say, when I do not know what it is you will ask of me?"

"Say yes, and you will live."

The girl said nothing.

"To live is to hope. Without it – there will be nothing," he said, a flicker of cunning in his leaf-coloured eyes.

So she agreed, but to what she did not know, and again he chanted and muttered and hopped and twitched, and his hands grew golden, and his eyes went the colour of jewels on fire. He sat down to his work, and from that spindle fire flew, and gold was made out of straw for the third and greatest time.

That night, she had no dreams.

When the king woke the girl up in the morning, he kissed her on the forehead. "My queen," he said, and had the girl taken to a great bedchamber and stripped and washed by maids who looked frightened of her.

"She is a witch," the girl heard one of the women whisper.

"The king is dabbling with black magick," said another.

"Quiet," snapped the third. "She will hear you and turn you into gold," she hissed.

The girl turned away and allowed them to bathe her and anoint her in the finest oils of rose and frankincense, bought by her bargain with the little man. She let them dress her body in the softest of garments and a great robe of golden thread, so heavy she could barely walk. At last, her hair was brushed out, and it shone like the gold that was her curse, and she was taken to a great cathedral, where her father, stuffed into fine scarlet robes, walked her down a long aisle. And she was watched by the eyes of all those with wealth and power, as she was married to the king who loved the gold he thought she had spun.

***

The new queen never grew accustomed to the castle or to the king, but she did use what power she had to help the people in villages like the one she had come from. She visited the poor and smuggled them gold from the coffers of the king, which barely made a dent in his great wealth. And as the moons passed, she saw her belly begin to swell, and she knew she would bring forth a child. She crooned to her babe in the womb as it grew each day, and she dreamt of a time when she could leave the castle and be free – of the king, of fine garments, and of her reputation as a witch, or a goddess, or a woman who could spin straw into gold.

When the child was born, after a great and dark labour, she cried with relief at seeing his face, for he was fine and shone with a faint gold shimmer all over. His hair was like sun, and his high, wide forehead shone most of all. She sang to him, and held him close, and refused to let the wet nurse take him, as she wanted to feed him at her own breast. The king was pleased at how closely his son resembled gold. In fact, he was so pleased with his queen that he left her alone abed with her son, and feasted for nine days and nights with his courtiers and his mistresses in a golden chamber he had built specially to celebrate the birth of his heir.

The king assumed his son would be named after him, but the queen could not bear that thought. She felt she would know her son's true name – and at just the right moment it would be revealed. So while the king feasted, and the queen watched her son for a sign, unnamed he remained.

The days took on their pattern. The queen stayed in her room, and walked in her little garden, and sang to the child. She wished she could see her father and her cat, but she especially wanted her mother and wished she could rely on her wisdom and kindness. She still could not help touching her throat, against which her mother's necklace had once laid, or holding up her hands, and seeing the white line marking where her mother's ring had encircled her finger. But her son gave her so much joy that she could feel the empty spaces in her heart slowly filling up with a new kind of love, deeper than any she had ever felt before.

And on the ninth day after her son's birth, she carried the child to the tower where her future had been spun, for she had not forgotten that she had made a promise. She sat at the little stool by the spinning wheel and told her son the whole story, explaining that it was one year since she had seen that little man and now it was time to find out what she would be asked to do.

She stayed there all day, knowing no-one, except that little man, would think to look for her there.

And at nightfall, there came at the door a rap.

And another.

And another.

"Come in," she said.

And the little man came in, his body a corkscrew of limbs and leaves and pointed shoes, his enormous forest-filled eyes fixed on her child, one hand reaching out to touch him.

"You've returned," she said, forcing him to look at her.

He glanced once, before those eyes returned to her son's face.

"May I hold him?" he asked.

She could not refuse him, for he had saved her life, and so she passed the child to him.

"You remember your promise," he said, great eyes, flickering.

"Yes. But I don't know what it is I agreed to," she replied.

"You will have more children," he said. "This is only the first. Golden, too! Such magick inside him."

And she then knew what he wanted. But she would not say so until he had.

"A year has passed. And now I have come to take this child."

She stared at him, a great rage filling her, that great fierce force that can change lives and rip the world apart when thwarted, the force all wild mothers have within them when their babes are threatened.

"You cannot take a child. He is not a

necklace or a ring. I cannot give away my child. I love him."

"But a promise is a promise, and your word is binding," said the little man.

"I won't give him up," she said. "He is precious to me beyond my life. I have not even given him his name, yet."

The little man laughed and clapped his strange long hands. "I will set you a challenge," he said, smirking with glee. "If you can tell me *my* name, he will stay with you."

"Your *name?*"

"Yes, Queen. I have a name. Just like you once had. Before you became a queen."

"I did not want this," she said. "You and my father and the king – your demands have shaped me. But I will not have you take from me this child."

"You have three days," the little man said, kissing the child on his glowing brow and handing him back gently to the queen. "Tell me my name, then, and I will have no power over you. But you won't find it out," he said, with another laugh. "Rest assured, though, I will care for your child. And he will be happy with me, in the great in-between of Faerie. And I will give him a far better name than you ever could."

The queen held her babe tight and stared as the spinning wheel began to shake, and even the floor began to shake – and as the little man slowly vanished from sight, she held her son tighter and knew she would never let go.

***

THE NEXT MORNING, WHILE ALL IN THE CASTLE were fast asleep, she rose in the darkness, dressed in her old clothes, tiptoed past her servants, and crept away from the castle before a single soul could know she was gone.

She walked a long, long way while the sun rose, talking to her son, telling him about her old village, and the life she'd had, and how much she loved him.

When she arrived at the mill, she knocked three times, and her father opened the door and held her tight. The cat purred, and she stroked him while she fed her son and explained to her father her plan.

And before the sun was too high in the sky, she gathered together the villagers, who were all so grateful at the help she had given them that they wanted only to help her and the little prince.

"A little man," she explained, "wizened and so odd as to be one of the faery. That is who we are searching for. It may be that only I can see and hear him, but all of us – if you will help me – will go to the woods, to the in-betweens, and we will travel down every path and every trail and peer into every hidden place. Because somehow, we must find this little man and learn his name. For he wishes to harm your young prince, and I cannot allow this to happen."

The villagers nodded, and put down their ploughs, and lay aside their needles, and left their milking buckets, and searched with their queen, the miller's daughter, all through the forest. And she, too, walked the paths, with her son strapped to her back, until she was far away from another human soul.

Finally, she reached a place where a great oak, a great ash, and a great thorn tree grew together. And there, within a little hole in the great oak, she saw a light.

She climbed through the opening carefully, and began to walk down a great tunnel beneath the trees, until she came to a cave beneath the earth.

And there he was, beside a fire of gold, dancing and singing, as he built a crib of twigs and bird feathers for her child.

Merrily, the babe I'll make
A little home; we'll brew and bake;
Merrily, I'll dance and sing,
For next day will a changeling bring.
Merrily, the babe I'll claim,
And Rumpelstiltskin is my name.
Rumpelstiltskin is my name!

The queen, who had almost stopped breathing, covered her son's head with her shawl and waited for the little man to say the rhyme again, to be sure she had the odd name right in her memory. And once he did, she turned quietly and went back into the world, into the forest, and followed the paths and returned to the castle.

And three days after the little man had told her the price she must pay, she climbed to the tower, sat down on the stool by the spinning wheel, and waited for those tell-tale raps at the door.

Rap, rap, rap.

"Come in," she said.

The little man strode in, grinning and bursting with pride and happiness. He stretched out his arms for her babe.

"Your promise, fair queen."

"Wait. I have a chance, remember? To name you."

He snorted. "How ridiculous! Give him to me, Queen. I will make him happy and feed him on nectar and sugar wine. Your princeling will no longer be human. But, as you know, being human is no great thing."

"I will name you," she said, quietly.

"Three chances, then," he said, shrugging,

already planning what magick he and the babe could create together.

"Is your name ... Pointy-toes?" she asked, knowing it was not.

The little man smiled. Ready to be a faery-father, he moved closer to her and the babe, clapping his hands.

"It is not, Queen."

"Is your name ... Twisty-ears?" she asked, staring at him and holding her child close.

"It is not, Queen," he said, a great grin breaking out across his strange face.

"Is your name ..." She paused, as the man danced and giggled, seeming quite mad with glee. "... Rumpelstiltskin?" she asked.

"What did you say?" he asked, so suddenly still she began to grow afraid.

"You heard me. I asked if your name is Rumpelstiltskin."

At that, the room began to shake, and the little man began to grow red, and he began to cry out loud and gnash his pointy teeth and stamp his long feet upon the floor. And the floor shook and shook, and the queen held her babe closer than ever before, as the bricks began to shake loose from the wall, and the spinning wheel toppled over, and the queen fell to the ground, protecting her child. And the little man howled, and grew smaller and smaller, until in his place there was a whirlwind that tore through the entire castle, upending bookshelves, chasing mice from their holes, ripping curtains from the windows, and even the tiles in the great floor began to fly loose from the floor. And the castle finally began to fall, down and down, all about the queen and her child, and she clung to her babe as she heard screams and cries, and then she saw the little man and the whirlwind he had become finally vanish into the might of the storm of his anger ...

She stared deep into her son's eyes, hoping that his gaze would be her last moment. And in that second, when all seemed lost, she heard his name, clear as sunlight through clean water. And as she whispered her son's name, she smiled, and fell into darkness.

The queen awoke three days later, to find herself lying amidst the great golden rubble of the castle. It was her child's cries that brought her back. She checked him over, hurriedly, whispering his name like a plea, and began to weep with relief when his lusty wails told her he was without any harm at all, except hunger.

A soldier came towards her, picking through the rubble, and lifted her from the wreckage, and she was taken back to the village, to her father's mill, with her child. She shared his name, and her father smiled, and cared for them both while they recovered.

The king, she was told, had died, crushed by the gold that had fallen all about him in the feasting room. His was the only death – and all the courtiers, one by one, and the king's advisors, all together, came to her and told her that she was now their queen in truth, and must rule, must decide what to do.

And so she did. The queen rebuilt the castle and invested the gold in crops and in a strong group of knights who honourably led the army, and she built a school, and a hospital, and she never, ever married, again.

And so the miller's bright and lovely daughter became a great queen, and, in time, her deeds outshone her reputation as the girl who could spin straw into gold. Her son became a good man, with all that was best and bright within her, and he was nothing at all like his father. One day, when his mother had lived a very long time, he became the fairest, and strongest king the land had ever seen.

But until then, she ruled.

Discover the Magick of
Rumpelstiltskin

THE LITTLE MAN sat down at the stool and began to spin. And as he did, he chanted and muttered and trembled with a power that flowed through his fingers.

Then he turned to her, saffron flames dancing in his eyes. "Sleep now," he said. "It will be done."

HISTORY OF THIS TALE

ONCE AGAIN, WE CAN THANK THE VERY busy Brothers Grimm for writing down this tale sometime before 1812. There are so many tales that have similar themes and characters – *Tom Tit Tot* (a French version), *Titty Tod*, a Scot's take on the tale, and the curiously named *Whoopitie Storie* from Norway. There's a Hebraic version, a Spanish version, and an Icelandic version, too – and this is barely even scratching the surface.

AS A CHILD, WHEN I READ this story, I would worry for the girl. I felt strongly how unjust it was that she was asked to do this impossible thing, to spin straw into gold. I think that may have to do with how often we are asked – as children, and all throughout our lives – to do things we think are far beyond us. It is daunting, even terrifying, to be asked to do something we have no idea how to accomplish – and the threat that hangs over the girl is of death if she fails. I truly felt her anguish, as a child. And while I was glad she'd found a way to survive with the help of Rumpelstiltskin, I knew there would be a price to pay, so the tale had a great deal of foreboding energy to me. It stayed with me, and now and then I still think about what I would have done if I had been in those rooms in the castle tower, asked to do the impossible, just to live.

WHAT IS RUMPELSTILTSKIN?

WHEN I WAS PONDERING WHAT LAY BENEATH the tale, I discovered that the root name *rumpelstilzchen* had several meanings. One was of a kind of poppart, or poppet, which also broadly translates as "goblin". However, there was also an interesting clue to the little man's nature in the word *rumpelgeist*, or "rattle ghost" – very similar to meaning for the word "poltergeist". So, the idea formed of the girl being able to hear and see spirits, and, as is so common, when she reaches mature adolescence, to have the activity increase, ultimately allowing Rumpelstiltskin to enter her life in a very real and tangible way. I like to think he is a little out of the box. For me, he remains really hard to define. I see him as being part faery, part gnome, all forest being, very real, and yet very "other".

Spinning Straw into Gold: the Alchemy of Rumpelstiltskin

With the king's command for the girl to live up to her father's boast, the theme of alchemy is brought into the tale. Alchemy can be used metaphorically, alluding to the creation of gold within the spirit through adversity and purification. But alchemy was also a very real science, a series of bizarre experiments whose aim was to create gold out of something very unlike gold.

I do see the father's boast as being one of loving pride – but unfortunately, his metaphor for her ability to turn a bad day good was taken quite literally, and the king, in his love of gold (a kind of reference to Midas), threatens her with death if she won't use her supposed gift for him.

The Enchanted Number Three, Again!

You'll see the number three recurring in lots of stories and tales – simply because the number three is so magickal. This time, the girl hears three raps when Rumpelstiltskin first comes to her; she is led to three chambers, each with an ever-increasing amount of straw that must be spun into gold; and finally, she has three chances to "guess" Rumpelstiltskin's name.

Also, three magickal trees create the entry to Rumpelstiltskin's underground abode – the oak, the ash, and the thorn. Faery lore tells us that when these three trees are found together, an entrance to the land of Faerie – the otherworld – is created.

Three is a binding number, as well as an increasing number. I like to do certain things in threes within spellcasting to reflect the adage of the threefold return – the belief that whatsoever we send out will return to us threefold. When I open a magickal circle, I walk about it three times, and when I close it, I do the same. Three times is, again, the charm within this tale.

Is Rumpelstiltskin a Faery?

Well, the truth is, I don't really know. He may or may not be, strictly speaking a faery. I think he is much more like a boggart (a legendary and very troublesome house faery) than a kind and

helpful faery – but he is definitely from the deep heart of the Faerie realm, which is a home to many magickal beings, including this very strange, very lonely, very powerful forest being.

It could also be that he is kin to the mighty dwarves, who were, in the ancient sagas, the great metal workers. His ability to create the precious and pure metal gold speaks to me of a time when the dwarves fashioned the swords and shields of the gods of the Vikings. Perhaps he is a very, very distant cousin, who has, with his loneliness and lack of kin, grown desperate for a family of his own.

CROSSING A MAGICKAL THRESHOLD

WITHIN MUCH SUPERNATURAL LORE IS THE belief – or the natural law – that in order to enter into a dwelling, a supernatural being must be given permission. We see this particularly within the vampire canon, whereby a vampire cannot cross a threshold without explicit permission. It is also a magickal law that we must work with consent, except under extreme circumstances. Rumpelstiltskin does not really begin his work with the girl until she gives her permission for him to enter the chamber in which her first test is being conducted. When she allows him to enter, she is also allowing magick to begin to work more deeply and powerfully within the tale.

THE POWER OF OUR NAMES

WHAT IS YOUR NAME? IT'S A QUESTION WE ARE asked over and over throughout our lives, yet we rarely think of the power we give others by letting them know our name. Within this tale, there is a girl whose name is not shared with the reader (one of the few powers she retains in the story) who must make a promise to survive – and then must find a way out of that promise through the discovery of a magickal name.

Such names have a long tradition in spiritual traditions, including Witchcraft and most indigenous paths. And while all names are very powerful, magickal names are perhaps even more potent. Thus, the magickal name the miller's daughter seeks won't simply be told to her – she must hunt it down before it is revealed.

But even "ordinary" names give people their identity and their "belonging". When we know someone's name, we may also know how to search for them. We know, in very real ways, where they are from. In Tarot and oracle card readings, the knowing of a name can lead to the unlocking of the energy held within the name, which can help a reader "know" their client.

That names have this power is interesting, because most often we do not choose them for ourselves. Names are given to us by our parents and our cultures. Names can define us and, in some cases, enslave us, so people often change a name that no longer feels in accord with who they truly are. And those of us who have connected deeply with our soul know there are names of the spirit, names which are spoken to us by our soul's whisper during ritual. In these ways, name changes can be important to the establishment of

our true identity.

So, we name people, and we call them by name, and we write down their name so that they are known within the world – from birth certificates to gravestones. In many cultures, babies are not given names until they are strong enough to survive. In others, they must be named, or risk imperilling their soul. And in yet other cultures, if a person transgresses against their community, their name is taken away. Thus, they become "no-one".

The queen in this story does not name her baby until a moment of great crisis – and she will not allow anyone else, most especially the king or her magickal adversary, to name her child and thus take him away from her. She wants to know what he wishes to be called, his true name, and so she listens and waits and watches for signs. In what could be the last moment of both their lives, their souls connect, and she learns his name.

In some ways, I was suggesting that we ought to wait until our children tell us their name. But instead we name them, and within that naming there is also, often, a wish to shape them. This is something our heroine does not seek to do. Instead, she respects and honours his free will and his soul, even though he is but a babe.

As this tale shows, knowing a magickal being's name may give us power over them – but the hiding of our own name can keep us safe from those who would do us harm. When Rumpelstiltskin dares the girl to discover his name, and thus break their enchanted pact, he cannot believe she will be able to learn it. But her tenacity, which is driven by love, not by the desire for power, prevails, and her eventual discovery of the secret of the name sends the magickal creature into a rage that destroys the castle that once was her prison. Such is the power of names!

CHANGELINGS, FAERIES, AND LOST GIFTS

IN FAERY LORE, THERE IS A STRAND THAT includes the theme of stolen children. The idea is that faeries would steal human children, and in their place leave poppets made of moss and twigs and bundles of earth. These would sometimes be animated and become like children – but very, very strange and otherworldly children.

The idea of faeries stealing children may have originated with the experiences some children have of being able to see and hear the faeries, while their parents have learned to fear and reject them. Faeries may rescue children, but it would be rare indeed that they would steal a child. Within this tale, I augmented the reason for Rumpelstiltskin's desire to take the baby. To me, he is perhaps the last surviving member of his magickal clan, and his loneliness is so great and he has grown so desperate that he leaps at the opportunity to have someone of his own, someone that he could care for and love, and who would love him back.

THE FALLEN TOWER

THE FALLEN TOWER IS AN ARCHETYPE THAT makes an appearance in the Bible with the Tower of Babel, and in the Tarot with the image the Tower, one of the Major Arcana. Within the Tarot, the Tower card is often seen as ominous, speaking of the destruction of an aspect of the seeker's life. And sometimes it is said to symbolise the destruction of a source of power and influence, an old regime, or even of constructs of the ego. This imagery intuitively inserted itself into the story – and I loved the idea of the place that had been the scene of the girl's imprisonment and enslavement finally being destroyed when she finds the means to free herself. I also had her become a queen and rule the land herself. It seemed the least that could be done to restore dignity, freedom, and choice to a girl who had been robbed of so much.

MAKING MAGICK: RUMPELSTILTSKIN'S GOOD FORTUNE FAERY SPELL

TRADITIONALLY, WE HUMANS WENT TO the faeries for help with health, healing, and good fortune, as well as in matters of love. The fae are especially kind and supportive to good people who, through no fault of their own, find themselves in difficult circumstances. And, unlike Rumpelstiltskin, the loving faeries you will attract to you with this spell will not ask for very much at all in return.

If you make this offering on a regular basis – say, once every three full moons – you will start to develop a very strong connection with the elemental realm.

You will need:
• A little chalice, cup, or bowl – or an eggshell or a nutshell would be wonderful!
• Bread
• Honey
• Milk or cream
Optional additions:
• Fennel
• Thyme (Thyme is known as a "faery flag". When faeries smell and see it, sense its energy, they know they are in a safe place.)
• Frankincense

On a waxing or full moon, go outdoors into the starry-lit world of the night. Take your little cup, or eggshell, or leaf, or nut casing, break up some bread and place it within, and over that drizzle some honey. Finally, sprinkle this with milk or cream. If you wish, you could add a few seeds

of fennel and a touch of thyme. Hold your faery chalice up for the fae to see, or smell, or sense. Call to them, saying, if you wish, these words I work with:

> Faeries sweet and faeries wild,
> Come to the aid of this human child.
> Spin good fortune all about,
> Bring me luck and banish doubt.
> May your blessings circle 'round,
> Keeping ill-luck back and bound.
> Faeries, may you blessed be.
> As I do will, so mote it be!

Offer them your service in cleaning up and caring for the environment. Ask them for assistance, and leave the offering out for the faeries. Do this regularly, and you will find good fortune coming to you in surprising ways, at exactly the right time.

In return, be sure to keep your side of the promise. And always have a little patch of your garden kept wild for the faeries to play within!

THE WISDOM OF RUMPELSTILTSKIN

THIS TALE RETURNS US TO AN OLDER BELIEF – that our name and our identity are intertwined, and that this interdependence means we can choose who we share them with. In today's world, this could extend to ideas about who our personal information belongs to. Within the tale, there is a sense that we need to keep some aspects of ourselves private, or be sure we share them only with those we can truly trust.

There is another kind of warning within the story, too – to be sure that, when we interact with spirits or otherworldly beings, we know with whom we are working. We must at least know their name, at least have some idea of who or what they are, so we can be safe while they are part of our lives.

We also find the message here that others making boasts on our behalf may place us in very awkward situations – particularly if it is someone close to us, a parent or a sibling or partner, who makes the promises that others may ask us to live up to. And, in another sense, the story tells us that even when we have been given supernatural help which produces a positive outcome, we ought to be wary of giving promises to beings we do not know. Of course, the miller's daughter has no escape from her tower prison and the demands of the king but to make that promise – but many of us, fortunately, have more freedom. So, if and when you communicate with spirits, be sure to whom you speak, and be very, very cautious about making oaths or pledges to those whose desires cannot truly be known.

Finally, the story advises that when we have been placed in terrible circumstances, we can still, with determination and the use of our wits, overcome the power that seems to bind us. When circumstances seem to corner you, and there is no clear way out, go deep into the forest – or deep within your own wild self. Those are the places where you may discover the secret that will break any power over you, break any chain, and dissolve any false obligation.

For none of us need keep promises that are forced from us.

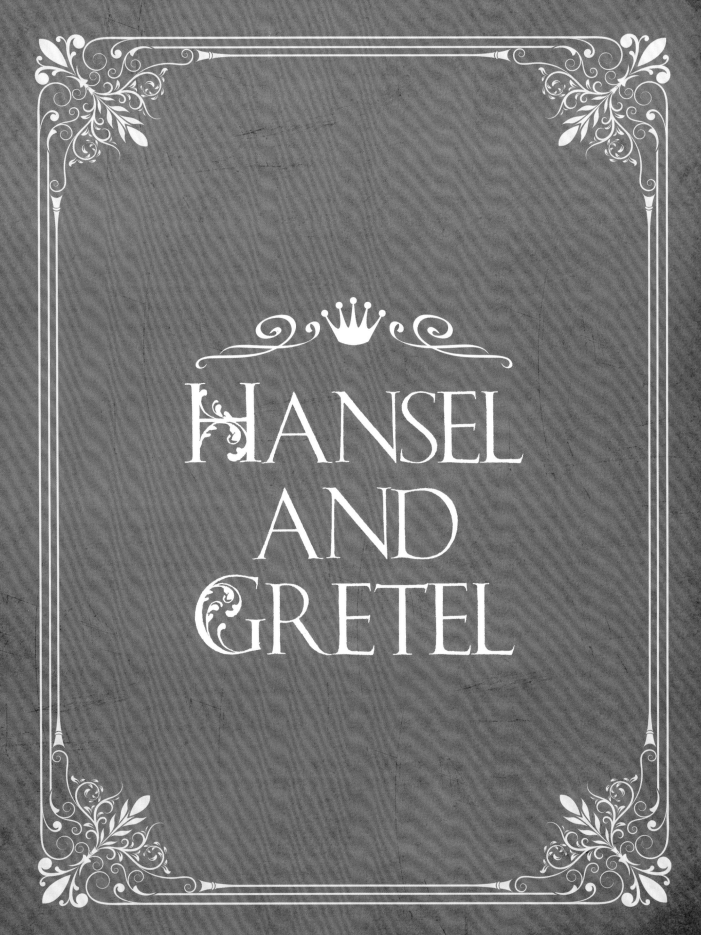

Hansel and Gretel

T**HE FOREST IS SAID TO BE BEAUTIFUL.**
"Oh, the forest," people say, speaking from their safe homes and their warm fireplaces, with their round bellies full of food, their family nodding, only half-listening. They've seen three trees and a flowerbed, and they think they know what nature is.

"I would love to live in the forest," they sigh, imagining buttercups and dragonflies and clouds skidding across blue, blue skies.

And I think, *Would you? Would you really?* Because the forest is not what they imagine it to be. They don't know it from the inside. They are just visitors, who at best, live on the forest's edge.

But those of us who have been into the forest's bleak heart, we know it, as well as any human can. And you do not want to live in the forest we went to.

Because there, people take you into the woods to lose you – and let you die.

M**Y BROTHER AND I WERE NOT HAPPY, BUT WE** were safe. We even had moments of joy, it's true, mostly with each other – and our father told us story after story, for a long time, about how happy we had been when our mother was alive.

I can remember her, but my memories are soft and blurred, like a dream dreamt long ago. Her smell, rainwater and mist and flowers and gingerbread. Her smile, like daybreak. Her hair, not soft like they say in the stories, but rough and brown and strong, curled and tangled as tree roots.

Our mother told us stories, and sang us songs, and taught us many little things that seemed to have no use once she was gone.

"The forest took her," our father said. He came home one day, and we were there, standing by the front door, waiting for her. We couldn't remember where she'd said she was going. But she had always left us – for hours at a time – to find food, to forage and hunt, to bring home a small animal for the three-legged pot by the fire or acorns to grind for flour, and herbs and roots for sweetmeats. Sometimes wildflowers, which we'd wind into a garland for the door, "To invite the elves in," she'd say.

And Father was happy. I don't remember being happy, myself, but I remember our father and mother's smiles and their laughter, and how often we four sat together. I slept safe in Father's lap, and he rocked me till I dreamt, and we were loved.

We *were* loved, once.

So, our mother was taken by the forest, and my father, whom I'd never seen without purpose and industry and a quest – to make a good fire, or build a home in the town far away, or split enough wood to make a dent in that great forest – he was never properly alive ever again. He was felled, just as if he was a great tree and her disappearance was the axe that brought him down. And there were no more garlands, and no roots for the soup in the three-legged pot, and never again were there sweetmeats for us.

With dead eyes, he took the lumber to town to get some coin – and he returned with Her, a great, huge, golden woman with a crooked smile and a rotten thing in the place where other people have hearts.

We knew that, for she laid down her law right away.

She sat down, spreading herself wide across the chair, while we were told to stand up, told that there was to be no more idle time with our father – for he had work to do, and to waste his time was a sin. Told there was to be no speaking from us, none at all, without us being spoken to first, and that we had to do as she bid, when she bid, or she would beat us – for the good of our own souls. And if we displeased her, which soon proved to be often, we would be locked in a dark place under the floor, without food, until we had learned our lesson.

In addition to our "lesson" (learned again and again), we also learned that she had brought our father back to us even more changed than before. He was now filled with the things of the town, and the wildfire they drank together made them sleep all of the day and stay up deep into the night, and my brother and I started to walk farther and farther into the forest each day, avoiding them both, thinking, perhaps, we might find our mother there. Every day, we stayed out longer, and sometimes we found wild things to eat, and while the sun and the oak were still on the throne, we lived just with each other.

Soon, we built a little shelter beside our father's house, weaving it from willow and other winding trees, and we would creep in there when the roaring and the fighting and then the beatings began. They beat each other, and we would leave and lie within the little house we'd made, and we said we'd like to run away and find our mother, and then we could all live in the forest together.

Soon, winter came, and it was cold, and nothing grew, and we, all of us, got very, very hungry. The kind of hunger that is like something else is living in your belly, and your flesh is its feast. We grew thin and weak, and there was no more creeping out at night, for it was too cold. But all the wildfire they drank replaced any of the grain or the root vegetables we needed for winter.

And because we were inside, we found

out why they fought.

They fought about us.

"They will take everything we have," she would hiss. We would be lying in the corner of the room we shared, with our hands over each other's ears, telling each other not to listen, but we heard her, anyway.

"They can go to the forest. We don't have to hurt them. They can go live there. They spent all their summer days there. And I've heard them say they want to find their mother. Maybe they will. Or maybe they will just live wild till spring. Then, if things are good," she'd wheedle, her soft hair like butter falling down around her face, "they can come back."

Our father said nothing. He'd gone as dumb as old wood.

"It would be a kindness to us both. We could live. And have our own."

Still, our father said nothing.

"And if they are meant to live, well, then they will," she said.

We stared into the cold darkness and began to plan.

***

Hansel had the first idea, to save our bread so we would have a supply to eat. But she snatched us and took us away before we could even put our jackets on that day, and we walked with only our rags to keep us warm. She laughed when we shivered, saying we would warm soon, when we had walked enough.

Hansel walked a little way behind, weeping and sniffling – and picking up white pebbles, pretending to wipe his nose on his sleeve and tucking the stones into his pockets. And as we left the familiar track, she blindfolded us, so

we would not know how to return, but she did not check Hansel's raggedy pockets, and so he dropped the pebbles, one at a time, leaving a secret trail we would find.

Deep in the forest, she left us without word. We only knew she was gone because the world was silent for a while and her tavern smell was gone.

We sat down and released the rags that were tight about our eyes. And we waited a while, and then, when the moon rose, and the owls were about, and the forest seemed still to be our friend, we crept home by moonlight, and nestled next to the fire, caring not what the two them thought.

We weren't going that easy.

The next day, when they found us, our father wept, and held us tight, and rocked me in his arms, and sang Hansel a song.

But she sat in the corner and stared at us, a knife in her hands.

"I could blind you both," she said after he left to cut down the wood to keep the fires burning.

"Or cut off your hands and feet when we get to the next place I am taking you."

And so she took us out again. Our father wasn't there when we left, but we think he let her take us. He was weakened by her, somehow, and though he could still swing an axe and fell a tree as tall as twenty men, all his power and pride was gone.

This time, though, we had the chance to snatch our raggedy jackets with their pockets which Hansel had filled with old bread, and we dropped little bits along the way. But when we reached the next point of abandonment, even deeper into the forest than before, she took out two lengths of old rags and tied us to the roots of a tree.

"Stay," she said, like one would to their dog. We didn't say a word. And she walked away, leaving us there in the cold and the gathering night, and we took each other's hands, and after a while we began to find a way to untie ourselves from the tree.

Once we were free, we fell asleep in each other's arms, the only place there was any warmth, and when we woke, we began to follow the breadcrumbs back to our house. But the birds were rising, too, and even as we followed the crumbs, the birds found them, and starving as they were, they took it, and the path was lost to us forever, and the forest closed in about us, all the trees looking alike, and although we knew our way around its kinder parts in this, its dark heart, we were lost.

Hansel's hand was warm in mine, though, and we found a way to keep our spirits lifted. We spoke of all the good things in the world, and of what we would do when spring came, what kind of house we would have, and how many dogs, and how we would keep a cat to hold the mice at bay, and we teased each other, as brothers and sisters do. We didn't know where we were going, but we had to move – to stay alive we had to find someplace where we could find food and a place to shelter.

Just as we thought we must rest, we could smell smoke in the forest, the kind made by a woodfire. I thought we must be dreaming, or going a little mad, for who could be here, tending a fire, in this great, dark, cold place?

But as we walked, a path began to clear before us, and grass grew underfoot, and the air felt a little warmer. It was as if things were somehow different in this part of the forest. Soon the path opened up to a grove of great old oaks, and amidst that circle of immense oaken ones lay a little cottage, sweet and tidy, with a neatly stacked woodpile to one side.

Hansel's eyes grew wide as we came closer, for the cottage was covered in embellishments that appeared to be breads. It was as if the little home was made out of the gingerbread of our memory – gingerbread lined the windows, in place of eaves, and the tiles on the roof were layers of cake, it seemed. It was a vision only starving children would see, and we gazed at it, and then at each other, unable to believe what appeared to be before our eyes.

Hansel broke first, his thin legs wobbling as he ran, and he rapped on the door in a way that broke my heart. I am his older sister. I should have been able to take care of him, and there he was, pleading in a high, thin voice for help at the door of this strange and wonderful cottage.

I reached him just as he broke off the door handle. We gazed at it together, and he pushed it into his mouth, for it was not wood, but something sweet and full of sugar. Every part of the house was glazed and good to eat, though we did not know the names for all the treats, for we had never seen their like before. I reached for the confections that formed the shingles on the roof, and pulled one off, and ate, and ate, and ate.

We did not eat so much of the house that it would be noticed – but, somehow, we knew that there would be a payment. For there is never something taken without something needing to be given it return.

"Perhaps," said Hansel, hopefully, crumbs falling from his lips, "it's a gift from the birds we shared our bread with. Maybe a good faery lives here, and saw our kindness, and how things were at our father's house, and now wishes for this place to be our home."

"That may be," I said, though I did not

think so. "Let's wait. We will see who lives here, and we can tell them what we have done. Perhaps we can exchange our labour for food this winter. Perhaps," I said, beginning to dare to hope, "it is a kind person."

"Perhaps they are like Mother," Hansel said.

"Perhaps," I said, though I knew no-one could be like Mother.

So, we waited, and we resisted eating all we could, but we did keep eating, and we felt something close to happiness. It may have been the sweetness of everything on offer. Or it may have been that we thought we had found a new home.

We slept awhile, slumped against the door, and so we did not hear the boots falling on the path – but we felt their kicks when she arrived.

The witch of the forest.

She was small and hunched over and had a staff, which we felt before we saw it.

"Stupid children," she said, her voice full of creaks, like an old gate in a sly wind.

"Get in, get in," she wheezed. "I see you ate my door handle," she said, laughing in a strange way. She pushed the door open. "But you didn't go inside – better manners than the mice, then!"

We got up, dazed, and I hastily wiped Hansel's face with my sleeve. He was a beautiful boy, face still plump with childhood and good to look at. I hoped she would take a liking to him.

The witch brought us in and fed us more milk, from where I did not know, and good bread and butter. And we began to wonder if she was just harsh of tongue, but kind of heart.

She put us to bed, and we slept all the night long, and in the morning, she put me to work. But Hansel, she put in a cage.

The cage was hauled up by a rope. She made me do it. She said it was a young person's work. And she promised she would feed him up – and then eat my brother whole when he had more fat on his small bones.

And this I knew she would do. For I began to find bones about the place. Large bones. And I noticed she wore about her neck a locket, one I had seen before – only then it had been on the neck of my mother. And so I knew whose bones they were, and wept briefly in the yard while I swept it.

Back in the cottage, I passed a bone to Hansel in the cage to show him the truth of her threat. "We will find a way out."

He slumped to the floor of his cage, looking at the bone.

"Did you see the locket she has?" I asked.

He nodded.

"You know whose it is?"

This time, I saw one fat tear slide down his dirty cheek.

"Sweetheart," I whispered, "I will get us out."

So, the witch fed him up, and day after day, he grew plumper. But she was as blind as she was hungry for his flesh, and each day she asked him to stick out a finger so she could see how tasty he was becoming.

But Hansel was clever, and would stick out the bone of our mother, and the witch would scowl and frown and tut-tut, and urge me to feed him more.

Then finally, she said, "I'll have your sister this night, you skinny boy."

"You can't," he cried out.

"I will. And she will prepare herself for my feast," she replied, her milky eyes crinkling with laughter. She looked like she could have been my grandmother, a kind woman who rocked children by the fire.

Instead, she ate them.

"Turn on the oven, girl," she ordered, and I got up, slowly.

"Where is it?" I said. The stupider I was, the slower this would go.

"Come girl. It's here." The door was wide enough for me to fit into, and I opened it up. It smelled of grease and fat and bones.

"Clean it," she ordered, and I scrubbed and washed until all trace of our mother was gone.

And when the oven was clean, she said, "I shall cut your throat first, girl, if you do not fuss. That will be a kindness." She laughed to herself, soft and dark. "The last one there, she fought. I was not so kind to her."

"Thank you, old mother," I said. My voice shook, and I sounded frightened. I was, but something else was in me, too. It was fury. It lit the light within me, and sparked my mind into action.

"I shall then, child. Fetch me my knife – it's there, on the wall. Do not think to cut me with it. It cannot hurt me, for it is enchanted."

I fetched the blade and handed it to her, right way round, by the black handle, like my mother had taught me.

"Light the oven, child. Then we'll finish this, quick and kind."

As I peered into the depths of the oven, it was as if my mother's strength filled me, and I could smell her rainwater smell and see her pale green eyes and brown hair like tree roots.

"You are clever, my girl," the witch said. "You know what to do."

"I cannot see how to do it, old mother," I called from within. "I am trying, but I cannot find the place to light it from."

"It's there, girl – up the back, in the centre."

"I'm sorry – please say you'll kill me quick.

I am stupid, and ignorant, and I cannot see it. My hand shakes so."

She spat with disgust and stamped her foot with its pointy toes, and pulled me out of the oven with such force I was stunned at her strength.

"Idiot girl. I may have to cook you slow."

"No, no," I cried, cringing from her.

"I'll do it," she snarled. "Stay there, or you'll cook slow, and it will be hard on you, girl."

"I won't move," I whispered. And the witch crawled deep inside the oven, and lit it. "Hah," she gloated, her voice echoing back to me. "I can taste you now!"

Before she could back out, I leapt up and shoved that door closed. I pulled down the handle and locked her fast inside. And when she realised what I'd done, she screamed with outrage and hammered with her fist on the oven door.

"Let me out," she pleaded. "I won't eat you, nor your brother if you do."

I said nothing, only moved to lower the cage and let out Hansel. As we held each other silently, we felt the heat rising from the oven, and the more the witch pleaded, the harder we hugged each other, and finally we covered our ears at her screams, not because we pitied her, but because we knew our mother must have screamed so, once.

We never opened the oven again, but we stayed in that cottage for the winter, and we searched every crevice and corner of that neat, awful little house, and, in so doing, we found a chest filled with jewels – rings, and necklaces that belonged to those she'd devoured in that horrible place. We learned where the milk and the butter came from, for the witch had left offerings for the faery people, and they had brought her their gifts in return. So, we did the same, and their faery cows' sweet milk and butter was ours, and we ate and ate, until we were fat, so fat we would have

fed two witches like her.

Then, we took all the bones and buried them, deep in the forest, but not near where the witch had lived. Our mother, and all the rest of those whose lives she'd stolen, deserved to rest far away from where that hateful creature had spent her days.

And when the world grew warm again, my brother and I filled our pockets with all the treasure we could take. We slipped rings all the way up every finger of both our hands, we looped necklaces around our necks and hid them beneath our rags.

Finally, we took the cottage apart and made a little cart from the wood and filled it with food. The faeries offered us one of their cows, and that cow pulled our plunder, as we followed the faery lights through the forest.

We reached its edges, and were once again at our father's house, what once had been our mother's home. And we watched until we saw he was quite alone. There was a fresh dug grave out the back, and when we peered closer, we could see a rough carving of Her. We looked at each other, and wondered if it had been hunger, or wildfire, or our father who had ended her life.

But we did not care.

And so we went to the door, and we knocked.

And our father opened the door, and he wept, and we watched him as if from a great distance as he made his apologies, and we told him of our mother.

Hansel may have forgiven him. But I, Gretel, his daughter, never did. He had let us be taken into the deepest, darkest heart of the forest, and he had let her leave us, same as if it had been by his own hand. But I lived with him, and cared for him when the years of sickness came before

he passed, and I cried a little when I buried him deep in the earth.

And all these years later, long after my brother and I bought a house in the village, I still hold my children close before they go to the trees that are on the edge of town.

And when our neighbours learn about out where we grew up, they say, Oh, they wished *they* could live within the forest. "How peaceful, how lovely," they croon. When they do that, I look over at my brother, and at his children and mine, and we know we will keep our kin in the town, forever and ever and ever.

For we were taken into that forest's dark heart to die.

And I say, "Do you. Do you really want to live in the forest?"

And maybe it's the way I say it, or the look in my eye, but they never mention a word about it again.

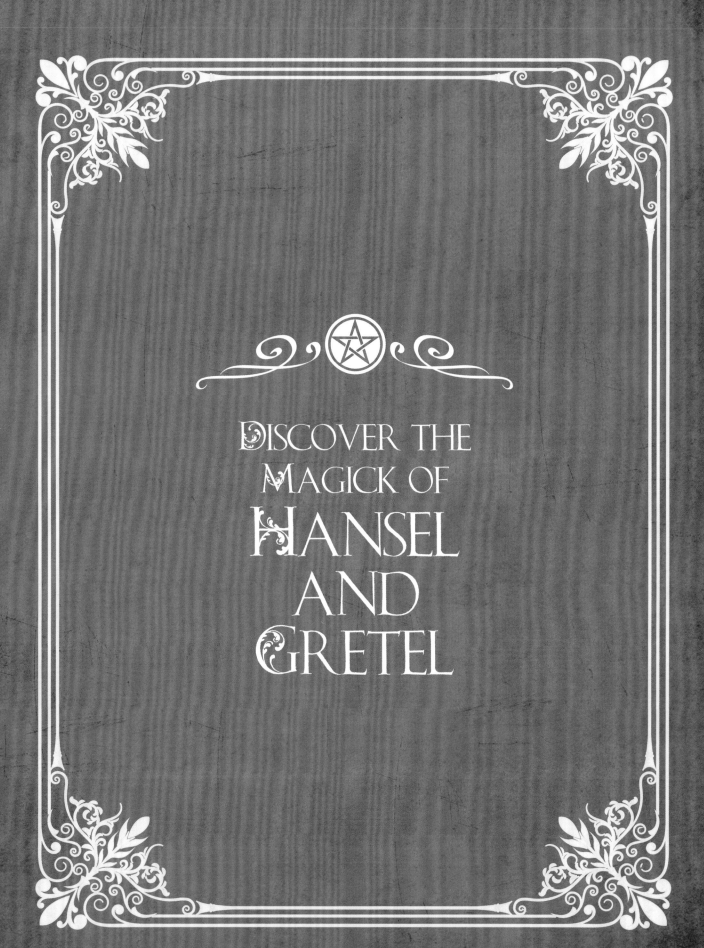

Discover the Magick of

Hansel and Gretel

THIS IS SUCH A POWERFUL tale – it takes my breath away every time I enter its spine-tingling world. I ask myself again and again, how could the father have allowed himself to be talked into abandoning his children? Did he think that as the forest took their mother perhaps the children were inevitably destined to die there, too? It is a frightening story to me – as the abandonment of the young and vulnerable, those who ought to be able to depend upon their parents, seems a great crime of the heart, a crime against our own instincts. The tale is saved from being just too cruel, too terrible, by Hansel and Gretel's love and care for each other.

In this version, I explored the story from Gretel's point of view. I imagined an older Gretel looking back, recollecting the tale from the inside. I hope you enjoy her take. She is a very strong heroine – a child who survives using wit and cunning, and who ultimately becomes a killer in order to defeat her enemy. That is a choice which changes people – and I can only imagine how much the necessity of killing would change a child.

Just as an aside, I have often wondered if the stepmother and the old witch in the forest are one and the same person, moving through forms, leading, finally, to that ultimate showdown in the forest.

HISTORY OF THIS TALE

THERE IS A CHARMING BACKSTORY TO *Hansel and Gretel* – strangely enough given the gruesome nature of the story! Jacob and Wilhelm Grimm first heard *Hansel and Gretel* from Dortchen Wild, who in time became Wilhelm's wife. (Imagine if talking over the story is how they met!) In the original version they recorded, it was the children's birth mother who abandoned them, which really heightened the horror of the story. That first 1812 version was tweaked over the years by the brothers to address their own concerns. They Christianised the story to a large degree by having the children pray and by including symbols of Christ. I've faded these out of this telling, in an homage to its pagan roots, and because the story to me is not about Christian children vs. evil witch … it is much more complex and subtle in its ethics and belief systems.

As is always the case with these tales, this story has many cousins from other countries. In France, there are two stories, one called *Finette Cendron*, the other, *The Lost Children,* that work with the same themes of paths in the forest, abandonment, and supernatural, cannibalistic foes who are ultimately cooked in their own juices – literally. And another story, *Hop o' My Thumb*, features an ogre who wants to devour children. There is also a lovely link between the Russian Vasilisa stories, which feature Baba Yaga, and Gretel and the witch in the forest (discussed further, below).

There is a theory that suggests *Hansel and Gretel* has its origins in one of the great famines of the 1400s, which saw people across Europe abandon their children and cannibalise members

of their family to survive. In light of this, it's fascinating to learn that, in the earliest tellings, the witch's cottage was not made of gingerbread. This was a later embellishment, perhaps added to act as an irresistible trap for starving children, and as a temptation for children with bellies full of good food to continue listening to the tale being told.

THE DARK FOREST

IN MOST OF MY WORK, I'VE ALWAYS MAINTAINED that the forest and nature are glorious, healing, and a part of us – as you find in *Snow White and Rose Red*. But perhaps because of the trauma Hansel and Gretel encounter there, and the perversion of the forest's magick by the old witch, these children do not wish to live in the forest, nor do they rhapsodise about the woods as grownups. Instead, they avoid it because, for them, the forest brought only horrors.

This is a different take, indeed, but it is also realistic. How many people get lost on bushwalks, or fail to read the ocean, or assume that nature is some sort of pretty picture postcard, not the immense, powerful, and complex relationships of elements and forces that it is? In this version of the story, the children know the darkest part of the forest, and because of this, the town is their friend. They don't harm the forest – although perhaps their father did. As a woodcutter, did he cut down one sacred tree? Maybe. Or is the forest blighted due to the presence of the witch? I like to think so. To me, she has perverted the natural magick and bent it to her unkind will.

THE SUN AND THE OAK: THE WHEEL OF THE YEAR IN HANSEL AND GRETEL

IN THE WESTERN PAGAN CALENDAR KNOWN as the Wheel of the Year, there are eight festivals. These mark the turns of seasons, the solstices and equinoxes, and days set aside to observe ancient ancestral and fertility rites. Each festival has its symbols – and the oak, which is the summer symbol, presides over the warm parts of the year. In *Hansel and Gretel,* we find the witch's cottage within a grove of oaks – known as a *nemotom* – sacred to the Old Ways, and within which sacred rites were enacted. This grove, though, is perhaps blighted by the witch's perverted use of natural power.

However, the Wheel of the Year begins not with the oak's summer season but with the festival of Samhain, which is celebrated to venerate the dead and whose modern parallel is Halloween. The Wheel ends with the festival of Mabon, or the autumnal equinox.

In older times, people would have marked the changing of the seasons carefully, as winter's coming was a serious matter, and festivals like Lughnasad were spent preparing for winter's

arrival – just as the winter solstice festivals celebrated the return of the light and the clan's survival through the darkest months. In *Hansel and Gretel*, each member of the family knows that winter means potential loss of life, lack of food, and a struggle to stay warm – it is, in part, the coming of this struggle, combined with famine, that leads to the abandonment of the two children. It is also what leads to their return in spring, at Imbolc, when they have transformed into survivors, heroes, and agents of justice.

THE ABANDONED CHILD

WE ALL HAVE WITHIN US A GREAT FEAR OF abandonment. No matter how old we are, or how healed, safe, and fearless we seem, we all have that inner child, and that inner child fears they will perish without their parents. In spirituality, there is much work done to reassure this inner child they are safe. Perhaps, though, we would be better off working on encouraging our inner child to be wise, to use their wits, and in the grownup us learning how to protect ourselves and thus our inner child. Life can be strange and challenging – and it is not always "safe". This tale, with its theme of terrible, criminal abandonment, shows us we must, at some stage, parent ourselves and look out for each other, in order to emerge safely from encounters with the hostile forces we may encounter in our lives.

FEMININE AND MASCULINE LEADERSHIP

WITHIN THE TALE *BOTH* CHILDREN TAKE TURNS being the leader. They swap roles within the story very naturally, and there is no sense that Hansel is dominant, simply because he is male. He does come up with the ideas for the pebbles and the bread path, but when he is caged, Gretel steps up and fights for both her freedom and that of her little brother. It's very unusual in such an old tale to have gender roles be so irrelevant – at least with the children – and I love how both children carry within them the love of the other, the need to protect and nurture the other, and the desire to fight for and save the other. It shows a balance of masculine and feminine energies within the children, and it occurs without the usual stereotypes.

TO FAIRLY TAKE AND FAIRLY GIVE

WHEN THE CHILDREN EAT PARTS FROM THE cottage, they know there will be some kind of natural balance required – for what is taken, something will be given.

When Gretel tells us, *We did not eat so much of the house that it would be noticed – but, somehow, we knew that there would be a payment. For there is never something taken without something needing to be given it return*, she is echoing the lines of *The Wiccan Rede*, a long poem by Doreen Valiente

and Gerald Gardner. Part of the *Rede,* which documents various laws of modern paganism, states, *Live, you must/ And let to live/ Fairly take/ And fairly give.*

The *Rede* does not condemn taking, but it acknowledges that we must do both – take and receive – to keep the balance of energy. The children instinctually know this, perhaps Gretel more so than young Hansel. And what is taken? Perhaps the last shreds of their tattered innocence.

THE WITCH OF THE FOREST AND BABA YAGA

THERE IS A BEAUTIFUL RUSSIAN FAERYTALE called *Vasilisa the Brave,* which I included in *The Faerytale Oracle.* Within it, the heroine, Vasilisa, is banished to the forest to bring back the light from Baba Yaga, an iconic figure from Slavic folklore, a crone possessing immense powers, who lives either at the edge of, or deep within, the forest. Baba Yaga is a really ambiguous being. She can be a harsh teacher, yet strangely kind, as she is to Vasilisa. Or she can be immensely cruel and malevolent, as is this version of her archetype, the witch within

Hansel and Gretel.

Baba Yaga is also the personification of death and winter, and she is said to live in a cottage that can walk around on its chicken legs. If you have ever seen the Miyazaki/Studio Gibli film *Howl's Moving Castle,* there are several references to Baba Yaga, including the way the castle moves about on chicken legs and the curse an ancient witch puts upon a young girl, who loses her youth and becomes old overnight.

While the witch in the forest, the *Hansel and Gretel* version of Baba Yaga, is cruel and very frightening, she does serve as a catalyst for change, impacting Gretel in particular. When Gretel murders the witch to save her brother and avenge her mother, she is facing the instinctual part of herself, and making a primal choice in order to survive. She chooses her youth, and her life, and the wisdom that comes with this initiation. Thus, the witch in the forest, the shadow side of Baba Yaga, pushes Gretel through her childhood and into a kind of premature adulthood. In this way, at least, the witch serves as a teacher.

I also love how "baba" in old Russian translates variously to "old mother", "sorceress", "midwife", and "fortune teller". It even made its way into the Russian word for grandmother, "babushka". When we grow old and impatient, perhaps, with youth, we may all have a little Baba Yaga in us – but hopefully we will share our wisdom mixed with a little kindness!

The Story of the Bones

Bones abound in *Hansel and Gretel*, as the children in my version find their own mother's bones, as well as the bones of many other victims of the witch within her cottage in the cursed grove.

In all indigenous cultures, the bones of ancestors were considered to hold powerful magick. Similarly, in this case, when the children find their mother's bones and work with them to fool the witch, their earthly mother is still with them, helping them, and sharing her strength and wisdom in a deeply shamanic way.

In Australian aboriginal cultures, to "point the bone" is to curse a member of a clan, or an outsider. I like to think Hansel is pointing the bone at the witch when he offers her what she supposes is his finger to feel – but which is, instead, the agent of her own demise.

Finally, it seemed right to have the children take their mother's bones and the bones of all the others lost to the cottage into a sacred part of the forest and return them to the earth so their spirits could find peace. I love that as numb and traumatised as the children are, they still have that deep compassion within them.

The Oven: From the Womb to the Tomb

To me, the oven in the witch's cottage is a kind of perverted cauldron. Not only is it much larger than a standard cauldron, but it has become a place of horror, rather than one of nourishment. Of course, much of this is about perspective – no creature would wish to be placed in a pot to be cooked to death, and I very much doubt plants, with their sensitive life force, would volunteer to die within a cauldron, either. But within the oven of the gingerbread cottage, cruelty and murder have taken place. The sacred nature of the cauldron, symbolically the womb, has been turned into the tomb. It is no longer the birthplace of nurturance and long life, but a dreadful place of most dreadful deaths. It is not good that the witch perishes within the oven, that it becomes her own resting place – there is a frightening echo of the burning times in that death – but there is a kind of balancing within it that could almost be considered justice.

Making Magick:
Hansel and Gretel's Spell to
Summon Courage

Both Hansel and Gretel show so much courage as they face their ordeals. We all face people, times, and situations which are threatening within our lives – and we need to find the inner valour to draw upon. But we do not have to face the hard times alone – we can cast this spell to create courage.

You will need:
- A cauldron, or a fireplace, or somewhere where you can safely burn what you will cast into the flames
- Matches
- A small cutting of your own hair
- Paper and pen
- Water, to put out the flames

Now, visualise a magickal circle of light, all about you, beneath you, above you, which will protect you as you work your magick. Take your pen and paper, and begin to write what frightens you in your life. Once you have done that, take a moment to read over these, and ask yourself, *Do I want this to change?*

If the answer is yes, put down the paper and pen, and light up your cauldron, fireplace, or fireproof container. Be sure to have water nearby, as a safeguard.

Take three great breaths in and out ... and cast your hair upon the flames, saying:

Know me now, great Spirit.

Wait a moment for the flames to absorb your hair. Now, say:

I call upon courage, will and power
To help me in my darkest hour.
I ask for these flames, this bright fire,
To burn through all unlike my desire.
(At this point, place your paper into the flames.)
Burn away the fear inside
A warrior's heart within me rises!

Feel the strength and power flowing through from the Universe to you. Know that you need only ask, and you will be more daring, more intrepid, than ever before.

Now, take another piece of paper, and write how you will always be there to protect yourself and do what must be done. To really bring this home to yourself, you can read this out loud, and say three times:

And by the powers of three times three,
As I do will, so mote it be.

Thank yourself, thank the Universe, and be sure to act on this promise to yourself. Now, put out the flames, and when the ashes are cold, bury them within the earth, so that what once you feared can be transformed.

Close your circle of magick by imagining it shimmering brightly, then gradually dissolving back into the Universe, from whence it came. To complete the closing, simply say, *Blessed be.*

The Wisdom of Hansel and Gretel

Ah, this is a terrible tale, so full of cruelty, but what is miraculous is that the children survive. They do so because they use their wits – they are clever, and they are cunning. They plan and they prepare. They take advantage of moments when people underestimate them. And when they return, they have learned, and they are a little cynical. In fact, the way grownup Gretel reflects upon other people's romantic notions of the forest seems to me to warn us against idealising.

Surely, these children were disillusioned at a very early age – but they were clever, and they were wise, and they had each other. That they held each other's hands, covered each other's ears, and, finally, emerged from the dark forest together, all this is a testament to the power of teamwork and to mutual concern and care. If we, too, can use our disillusionment, which will inevitably come in life, to bring us freedom, and if we, too, can have at least one close friend or ally who cares for us, as we care for them, then we, too, will emerge from the dark forests in our life and find ways to survive. Perhaps, even, as Hansel and Gretel do, we will ultimately thrive.

THE GOOSE GIRL

ONCE THERE WAS A QUEEN IN A LAND far to the north who ruled alone for many years. She had one child, a daughter, who reminded the queen of her husband, very much so. Her daughter was sweet, loving, and bright, with a love of animals that exceeded even her love of humans – which was great. But she was so gentle and so deeply kind that the queen worried for her child. She had already lost her king to harder things. And so she protected the princess from the harshness of the world. Well, she tried to, for a time. It was simpler when the princess was young.

And then the girl grew up.

By then, the queen's realm had become vulnerable to the greedy neighbouring kingdoms, and so, to shore up her armies and protect her people, she contemplated an offer of marriage for the princess to wed the prince of a powerful land far to the south. Knowing this alliance would offer great strength to her people, and warmth and comfort to her daughter, she felt it would be the decision a strong ruler would make. But the price for her realm's protection was the loss of her sweet daughter, and so the queen cried at night, thinking she could not bear to be alone and without her beloved child.

Troubled and torn, the queen had a great and dear friend whom she trusted beyond all others. This friend was one of the faery folk, and always spoke the truth.

"Should the princess marry this prince?" asked the queen. "She is a sweet child, and naïve in some ways."

"Nothing, my queen, can protect your princess from her own nature," said the faery. "Yet her vulnerability is not a weakness. In time, it will be a strength and source of great wisdom within her new kingdom."

The queen nodded, although her worry remained. "Still, she wants too much to please," whispered the queen, who knew her daughter well. "She puts others before herself, which is admirable, but it means she can be exploited by cunning, greedy people."

"She would do well to go out into the world and discover who she can be, away from all who have known her in her most sheltered life," encouraged the faery. "But she should not go alone."

"That is the truth," agreed the queen. "She needs someone to go with her – to protect her in this new land."

And so, the queen chose for her a young companion, several years older than the princess. This girl pledged her life to care for the princess, and swore she would never betray the queen's trust in her. For this, she and her family were to be rewarded with fine things – the companion girl's brothers and sisters would learn at the finest academy, and her parents would be gifted a rich plot of land and good seed for their crops.

But the faery saw something twisted in the heart of this companion, and to counteract this, she asked if she could give the princess a gift of her own.

"What do you most love in this world, Princess?" asked the faery.

"I love my mother – so strong, and noble and wise. I love, too, the animals – the birds and the dogs. But most of all, I love horses. They speak to me, you know. Their eyes say so very much. I would like to be more like them than I am myself."

And so the faery gave the princess a parting gift – a fine horse, called Falada, who had the gift of speech. But Falada's speech was rare and guarded, and the horse chose carefully who could learn of his ability.

The companion and the princess prepared to leave their homes and their families, and the

queen aged ten years on the eve of her daughter's departure, so worn by grief was she at the loss. But she knew this could be the key to the realm's safety, and so she bore it, hard as it was, for the good of the people of her land.

As her daughter mounted her horse, the queen in her grief wrung her hands so tightly that her nails drew blood from her hand, and three bright drops of noble red lifeblood fell onto the handkerchief she was holding as a parting gift for her child. She walked to the princess, seated high above upon her horse, Falada, who stood silently next to the companion, upon her steed.

"Farewell, Princess," the queen said in a strong voice, meant to reassure her people. "Go forth, and be well, and give us news, always, for you are most loved by all of us." She stepped closer and reached up to embrace her child. "But most of all by me," the queen murmured, as they held each other close one last time. "Take this," she whispered, passing her child the scrap of white cotton stained with the three drops of blood. "They say a mother's blood can protect her child. Take this, and know that, wherever you go, there I am, through my blood on this, a mother's charm for her child. And there I am in your blood, too. Be brave. Be wise. Be well, my love."

Then the queen thanked the companion for protecting her daughter, and the companion gave a pretty speech. The princess held up her pale hand and waved farewell, and together, the two young women rode from the land on the journey to the realm where the princess would one day be a queen, just like her mother.

The distance was not so long, but the summer sun was hot and bright. The princess was quiet, and though her head was low, the companion could see her weeping, and she began to feel a bitter glee in her heart. *She is weak*, the

companion thought to herself. *Spoiled child. I've had to fend for myself my whole life. And now I am supposed to look after her?* she thought, keeping a tight smile on her face to disguise her feelings.

After a good distance, the princess broke the silence of the path along the river, "Are you hot?" she asked. "I would like a drink. Let us quench our thirst and rest awhile."

The companion snorted. "We've barely begun our journey, Princess," she scolded. "We don't have the time to be soft. Let's keep going."

The princess was so parched, she could not help but plead. "Can we not just stop for a drink, then? Only to quench our thirst. It is so bright and hot."

The companion shrugged her shoulders and turned away, a look on her face like she had smelled curdled milk.

The princess climbed down from Falada, puzzled at her companion's disgust. But her mother had told her that this girl was her protector and companion, and so the princess did not question the girl, but went down to the river's edge and sank to her knees amidst the purple-stemmed angelica.

She cupped her hand in the clear, sweet water, and drank deeply. Then she gazed at her reflection for a moment, and saw her tear-stained face. "Ah, faeries," she whispered to the song of the waters, "this leaving is harder than I dreamt."

She laid a gentle hand on the little charm with her mother's blood that she wore over her heart, and as she whispered her troubles to the river, just for a moment, she fancied she heard the river whisper back ...

Alas, alas, if your mother knew it,
Sadly, sadly, would she rue it.

"Do not be so sad, river," she whispered. "Surely things will get better." But the river did not reply.

She splashed some water on her face to dash away the tears that threatened again, and clambered up the bank to Falada, with some water for her steed. He dipped his head and drank from the golden cup she offered him.

"You're letting a horse drink from such a cup?" sneered the companion, whose temper seemed to worsen the farther they rode from the castle.

"Why should I not?" asked the princess. "He is blessed with great powers, and I will care for him always, as a gift from the faeries. He is my dearest friend."

And what am I, then? thought the companion. *Nothing. People like me are always nothing to people like her.*

They moved farther along the river, which grew wider and stronger, and the travelling was hard and the heat was thick about them. The princess asked again for a drink, and this time, the reply was harsher than it had been at first.

"Drink? You want to drink? Then get down to the river with yourself. I'll not be your servant."

The princess slid off Falada, and went to the water. She knelt again and wept into the waters, and this time she heard her mother's voice whisper up to her from the waters ...

If I only knew it,
Sadly, sadly, would I rue it.

"What's that?" cried the companion, climbing down from her horse and striding towards the princess. "Are you moaning again?"

"Nothing," said the princess, turning to

the water. "I'm just hot."

"Then cool yourself," said the companion, and gave the princess a shove, and into the river she fell. Her head sank beneath the surface, her clothes blossoming in the deep water, and as the cold currents rushed through the space next to her heart, her mother's charm was lifted up like a leaf, caught up in the flow, and twirled away on the waters. In a twinkle, it was lost forever, floating downstream like so much flotsam.

Falada started, and waded into the river after the princess, who grabbed onto his golden reins and pulled herself back to the shore.

She held on to Falada, shaking. "I lost my mother's charm," she whispered to the great horse, her voice soft with sadness.

The faery steed nuzzled her softly, his eyes staring into hers. And he said, as clear as any man, in his fine, deep voice:

Alas, alas, if your mother only knew it,
Sadly, would she rue it.

The companion was watching closely and had heard the great horse speak, and knew now that he could tell of many things. *I will think on that more,* she said to herself, a little knot of cruelty gathering itself within her.

"See?" said the companion aloud, pretending not to have heard a thing except the river's rush. "You're not hot at all, now, are you?" And as her laughter rang out, she noticed a change in the princess. Meek before, now the girl seemed a little broken.

Now was her chance, the companion felt. Did she dare?

"Take off those fine clothes," she ordered the princess. "You're wet. Besides, if someone were to come upon us, it would be better for them to

think you were the servant … because that is what I am, call it what you like. Safer for them to think me the princess. And this horse," she said, grabbing at Falada's reins cruelly and pulling on his tender mouth. "I'll ride this one. It needs some breaking in, I see."

So, the princess changed and mounted the horse that was not hers, and while it was lovely, it tore at her to see her lovely Falada being kicked and pulled and beaten.

He protested and bucked, and the companion turned and said to the princess, "How funny would it be if they mistook me for thee? I have the horse. I have the clothes." *And I have the will,* she thought to herself.

"What say you? Should we try it? Just for fun?"

The princess grew sombre, for she felt the threat in those words. Gentle she was, but stupid she was not. "Halt," she cried, and stilled her mount. "Take off my clothes," said the princess. "And give me my horse."

The companion was a little stunned. *So, the kitten has claws,* she thought. Her pride could not bear this order, so she climbed down from Falada and strode towards the princess, and, with the back of her hand, she struck the girl from her horse, and brought her to the ground.

Looming over the princess, she said, "You have done nothing with all that you have been given. You are weak, weak as water, my girl. I have the hunger and the strength and the fight in me to become a true queen. You … you shall be silent, or I shall kill you, here and now, and feed your body to the fishes."

Falada startled and reared. But the companion grabbed his reins. "And if you do not settle, fine steed, I will kill you and leave you on the road for the crows. So, obey me now, both of

you, or you *will* suffer greatly."

She swung back on the chastened faery horse, and the princess climbed onto the companion's horse, fearful for Falada's life, as well as her own.

The companion knew there was no turning back from this point, and she was at once thrilled and filled with an awful fear. She had gone too far, she knew. Further than she had intended. In that, there was a dreadful freedom. Because now she had no choice but to see it through, wherever it would take her.

It was not true of course. She could have apologised to the princess, and kept the promise she made to the queen. But she had already broken her sacred vow, and besides, a terrible cruel part of her had risen up, and it relished the power she had over the princess and the faery horse too fine to be hers, ever.

After a restless night, and another long day's travel, the princess was slumped on her steed, kept upright only by her concern for Falada. She watched him through half-closed eyes, and sent him messages with her mind – of love, to have courage, that she would right this wrong, somehow.

But I am so weak, said her own mind.

I will find a way, her spirit replied.

When they reached the walls of the city, a guard awaited them.

The companion drew herself tall atop of Falada. "I am the princess, and your future queen, your prince's only love and royal bride," she announced in a clear, strong voice.

She glanced back at the true princess and smiled.

"And this is my servant. She is weak, and has need of care."

The companion dismounted Falada, and

as the guards took the princess away, thinking her to be a maid, the cruel companion passed the faery horse to a guard.

"Tell me," asked the false princess in a tone that would brook no resistance. "Who is your best swordsman?"

The guard looked startled, but steadied himself and frowned with deep thought. "Swordsman!" he cried out, and a man of middling age, with arms like two great tree trunks, strode towards the royal party.

"This ill-spirited creature," proclaimed the false princess, gesturing to Falada, "did me great wrongs on the road. It near brought me to death several times."

"Do you want us to take the creature to the horse master, Princess?" asked the head of the guards. "He has a way with them."

"No. Bless your soft heart, but it is too damaged and dangerous to live."

She turned to the swordsman.

"Strike off its head."

The true princess, shocked from her stupor, screamed out, "No! No!"

And Falada reared, wild eyes rolling in protest.

"See how wicked he is," cried the false princess, a gleam in her eye. "Kill it now, before anyone else is harmed. Pay no mind to the servant. She is a simpleton."

And while the guard held Falada's reins tight, the swordsman raised high his terrible broadsword till it shone gold in the dying light and brought it down upon the great faery horse's neck, striking Falada's head from his shoulders with one dreadful blow.

"There," said the false princess. "That is done."

The true princess wept, crying Falada's

name, and of course none knew at all what she was saying, or why she was so distraught. But the head guard saw her distress.

"Little maid," he said sadly. "The horse was dangerous. It's best for thee if he cannot hurt anyone ever again."

The false princess, then, went to hug her servant, the true princess. And she whispered into her ear, "Did you see how easy that was?"

The true princess made a sound somewhere between a sob and a moan.

"If you ever breathe a word of what took place on the road to another soul, I will have done to you what I just had done to that creature of yours. Do not doubt me."

And she pulled away, and straightened, and said, "Now. Take me to the king, and to my future husband. My new life awaits." And quietly, so only the poor weeping princess could hear, she added, "Let's see how yours unfolds, shall we?"

The false princess was taken to the king, whom she impressed with her proud stance and her strength. But he could not help feeling that something was amiss. *There is an incompleteness in the girl*, he told himself.

"Did you travel the roads alone, Princess?" he asked.

"No, I had with me a servant girl," she replied.

"And where is this companion now?"

"She is no true companion, sire. More like a slave, well-meant, but poorly chosen by my mother. She is something of a simpleton, given to delusions and moments of fantasy. I wish for her to find good, honest, hard work, the kind that leaves people too tired to make mischief."

How sudden she is to rid herself of any memories of her old life, thought the king.

"Bring the girl to me," he said, and the

true princess was brought before them all. She was dressed in simple clothes, and she was, he saw, a gentle soul, but there was something fine and good about her in her quiet dignity.

"So," he said. "You are the servant of this princess."

She remembered the threat. "I am, sire."

"What do you enjoy doing?" he asked kindly.

"Oh, sire, that is good of you to ask – I love animals."

And he smiled. "Then we shall make you the goose girl," he said. You will herd them from their stalls each dawn, and watch them in the fields, then bring them back to us. See she meets Callum," he said to a courtier. "He will show her what to do."

"Thank you, my king," she whispered.

"Farewell, and enjoy your new duties."

She sank in a graceful courtesy, quite unlike the way any servant knew how to move, and the king looked after her, still curious.

"She is a strange one, sire," said the false princess. "Wisely done."

How quick she is to banish this sweet companion, he thought again, and wondered.

The goose girl, our true princess, was shown to her new quarters, a small chamber she was to share with other servants. She was given a narrow bed of hay, a tin candleholder, two drab dresses, undergarments, a rough cap for her hair, and a crook with which to herd the geese. She smiled, and one of the other servant girls smiled back.

"Do you know the head guard?" the true princess asked.

"Yes," the girl said. "He is my sister's husband."

"Can you ask him, for me, the servant girl

who arrived with the princess, if I can see the horse that was killed yesterday before they bury him?"

What a strange request, thought the other girl. But, sensing there was more to this than she could see, she said, "I will do what I can."

"Thank you," whispered the true princess, and she went to her little hay bed and lay down.

"I am now a goose girl, Mother," she whispered, as one great tear fell to her pillow. "How I have let you down."

In the morning, she was awakened by the other girls readying for their work. The head servant girl came to her softly. "The guard has said you can see this horse. But hurry now, he is waiting outside."

The guard took her to Falada, whose head lay there, still trembling, his eyes open and shining, as brown and kind as ever.

"Looks almost alive, still, don't he?" said the guard gruffly. "Gave me no pleasure that. Beautiful creature like this."

"May I ask you something?" murmured the goose girl.

"Go ahead."

"Could you take his head and put it up, there, under that little bridge I will pass beneath with the geese?

The guard was a little shocked, but he had heard stranger things.

What the goose girl and the guard did not see was the young man watching them as they spoke – but it was the prince himself who witnessed their exchange, as he had decided to walk that day very early to clear his mind. He was readying to meet his new princess, and was very thoughtful. Marrying someone without knowing them at all was not what he had had in mind when he'd imagined taking a wife.

The king had encouraged him, kindly

enough, but without bending at all. "This girl is said to be something special," he told the prince. "Something we need in this kingdom. It is said she brings with her the magick of the faery. And her mother is a fine woman, whose husband was one of my dearest friends. It is a wise choice, my son. Your princess has the most noble of bloodlines flowing through her."

Even with this reassurance, the prince felt unsettled and strange. He'd been thinking on this when he saw the girl with the guard, who was holding the head of a great horse.

Up he stepped to discover what was going on. "What have we here?"

"This girl wants this horse's head to be nailed up, sir."

"Why?" the prince asked, as the true princess sank into a graceful curtsy.

When she rose and met his look with her own, he saw her eyes were very beautiful, with an open, violet-coloured gaze, like that of one with nothing to conceal.

"He's all I have left from my old land, your highness. He is my dearest friend, even in death. If he is there, on the bridge, I can talk to him and, for a moment, believe he is still alive."

"It's a strange request, but I think I understand. I love horses too – all animals," he said. He turned to the head guard. "Let it be so."

To the true princess he added, "May he continue to be your very good friend." Then, noticing how pretty she was, with her silvery hair, he smiled into those great, wide-open, lavender eyes and said, "I don't know your name."

"I'm just the goose girl, my prince."

"Well, I am sorry for the loss of your friend. It's been good to meet you. Greet the geese for me," he said, hoping to bring a smile to those sad lips.

Which it did, and he walked on, feeling suddenly quite right inside.

* * *

THE WEDDING WAS HELD THAT EVENING, AND it was grand, they said, and the false princess was splendid and regal and quite gorgeous, indeed. The prince was handsome, but he seemed very serious, and the king looked concerned. For he saw signs in the new princess that troubled him. An unkindness in her, a lack of care for those who seemed less important. He noticed so much, this king.

He noticed, too, how the new goose girl got up each day and took the geese out to the fields. What he did not see was that she stopped each day and spoke with Falada, whose head was still just as it had been when he was alive. The look in his eyes even more alert, perhaps.

In the sweet light of dawn, she gazed up at Falada and told him how she missed him, how good he was, and how she would always do her best to treasure him and his memory – she would never, she said, forget him.

On the third day, while she spoke with him, she startled a little. She was sure she had seen Falada's mouth move. And as she stared, he spoke:

Alas, alas, if your mother knew it,
Sadly, sadly would she rue it.

She stepped back. "Falada?"
His wise face seemed so very alive.
"Falada, can you speak? Is it true?"
The beautiful creature's eyes glistened with understanding

Bride, Bride, it is true.

Fate will still be kind to you.

She stepped quickly away, for Callum, the boy with whom she shared the geese-herding duties, was nearly with her, just a moment behind her. But as he approached, it was clear he *had* heard and was looking at her most curiously.

"What was that I heard?" he asked, suspicious.

"Nothing at all," she said with a laugh. "Just the breeze. It's so strong today, don't you think? Let's be going."

And so they took the geese to the field.

While the geese were in the meadows, the goose boy lay back and slept, and when he seemed fast asleep, the true princess took off her cap, pulled out her comb, and brushed her silvery hair, while also keeping the geese from quarrelling and pecking each other – for she loved them, though they could be bad-tempered. It made her smile to be out in the open, with the air and the sky and the sweet earth. She took off her boots, too, and felt cool and comfortable again. And as she began to feel a little lighter, she sang a sweet ditty, and her voice drifted across the fields to the prince, who was out walking – again.

He moved towards her voice. And he saw it was the goose girl.

That strange girl again, he thought, smiling. There's something about her. He watched her awhile, and felt delight in her song and the sun shining on her hair and her bare feet and her love of even the ill-tempered geese. He watched as she ate some cheese and bread and drank some water from a stream, and he noticed her cheeks were rosy with the fresh air and the breeze and the company of simple things. He found some comfort in watching her. Then he walked on, trying to shake the sense of things being not right, not right at all,

that had been dogging him for days.

* * *

AT THE END OF THE DAY, THE GOOSE GIRL plaited up her silver hair, put on her cap, pulled her boots back on, and prodded Callum gently with her crook. "Come on, sleepyhead," she said soft and low. "We need to get the geese back."

And together, they drove their herd back into town, the goose girl gently teasing Callum. "Have you a sweetheart? That would account for your doze. Do you stay up all night, lovesick?"

He blushed furiously and stalked ahead, wondering how she could know. But the true princess was glad to have Callum so far before her, as it meant she could steal some moments alone with Falada on their way home.

"I won't believe you're dead, Falada," she whispered, gazing up at him. "Not while you can talk. If that can happen, anything can take place. So, I'll be brave. And I'll change this. You'll see." She gave a little nod in the faery horse's direction, and walked away before anyone could catch her conversing with a horse's head.

Again, the next day, she met Callum at the pens, and together they drove the geese before them as they passed under the dark bridge where Falada's head was mounted. This morning, the troubled prince was walking, too, saw the goose girl again, with Callum, who the prince knew well was so love-struck he was said to be sleepless.

Then she stopped, and let Callum move on with the geese.

What are they doing? the prince wondered to himself. Watching, he saw the goose girl glance up at the horse head.

And then he heard her whisper, "Oh, Falada, there you hangest."

And he heard the horse reply, "Oh, Bride, there thou gangest."

The goose girl moved a little closer. "I feel braver today, Falada," the prince heard her say. "I can bear this, if you can bear that. It's beautiful, being out in the fields. It's what happened to you that I cannot forgive myself for. If only I'd been stronger!"

Her fists clenched, and she stood a little taller. "My mother, the queen would know what to do," she said, her sweet voice drifting to the prince.

"Alas, alas, if she only knew it," said the horse's head.

* * *

THE PRINCE WENT STRAIGHT TO THE KING, and told him of what he had witnessed.

"Something is not right here, my father," he said, his blue eyes clouded with puzzlement. "This girl is strange, yes, but there is magick about her. I swear – and do not doubt me, for I have questioned myself – that she spoke to a horse this morning."

"That is not so strange son. I've heard you speak to your own horse many times."

"But Father, this horse spoke back. And this wasn't all of a horse. It was only a horse's head."

The king knew his son to be a good man, and a truthful one, too. So, before the day was much older, he had Callum brought in from the fields to speak to him.

"How do you like your new goose girl, goose boy?" the king asked with a smile, for the boy was the son of his own servant, and he was tender-hearted towards the young man, who was said to be so deep in love he could not sleep at night, and instead dreamt all day in the fields.

"She is strange, my king," Callum replied. "She talks to the geese. She talks to the wind. She

sings. And she thinks I haven't seen it, but she talks to a horse – a horse's head."

"What does she say to the horse's head?" asked the king.

"Something strange … she tells it that she is sorry for what happened to him, and the horse calls her Bride and Princess."

"The horse speaks? Tell me the truth, now," said the king, in his sternest voice.

"It is the truth. Perhaps … perhaps it is an enchantment. It's too strange for me. I want only the simple life. That and Meg from the tavern. Meg thinks the goose girl may be a witch!" the boy cried, eyes wide with fear.

"She is certainly a strange one," said the king. "But let us not get swept away with fancies. Thank you for sharing this with me. Watch her closely. But be kind, mind you," ordered the king.

With that, Callum knew he was not to lay a hand on her. He knew that tone from the king. He'd heard it after a stable boy had been caught kicking a dog.

The king had the true princess brought to him that night, after the geese were put in their pens.

"I have heard that you speak to a horse," he said.

"I cannot say, sire. On my life, I cannot."

"Are you saying you do not?"

"I am saying, sire, that I cannot say. That my life will end if I speak of this."

"What happened on the road between the land you came from and here?" the king asked, his voice serious as deep water.

"I cannot say, sire. I cannot."

"Then go," he said, and the harshness with which he spoke those words stunned the true princess. She wept, for she liked the king and felt he would understand, but she had sworn on her life not to share the story.

She went from the chamber, feeling that she had displeased the king, and might never again see him.

But she had not displeased him. Her honesty and her courage were impressive – and the king knew there must be a reason for her silence. The king himself awoke the next day even earlier than his son, who had been keeping himself very busy for a man newly married. Dressed in the clothes of his servants, the king stood quietly near the head of Falada, where it hung upon the dark bridge. He stared into the eyes of the horse and knew there was magick about. He also knew that something deeply wrong had been done. By whom, and how, and what, he did not know.

But he would find out.

Before he saw the goose girl, he heard her song. When she appeared, she was with Callum, who was frowning and thin-tempered after another sleepless night.

"Leave off that noise, ninny," the boy grumbled. "It's not even a nice day."

"Oh, you've just not had your porridge," the girl said wryly. "You won't know yourself after a snooze in the fields."

Callum frowned and rolled his eyes and stalked ahead, looking disgusted.

"Go on, I'll be with you in a minute," the girl said cheerily, at which he shrugged and began to move the geese through. The true princess waited till Callum was out of earshot before she went to her dear Falada. She drew in a deep breath and gazed up into his handsome face.

"Today's the seventh day since we arrived, Falada. It's been strange, has it not? I thought to enter here a princess. My mother sent me here to marry. But I'm caring for the geese, instead. And you, my friend, were murdered. There's no pretty

way to put it, that's the truth of the tale. But I'm feeling strong, Falada. Something will happen to change this. I am quite sure of it. For, if you can talk, then anything is possible."

Falada gazed upon her, his brown eyes shining with love.

But alas, alas if your mother only knew it,
Then princess true, how deeply would she
rue it.

"But she doesn't know it, Falada. And she may never know. I hate disappointing her. She is such a great queen. Why can I not be more like her?"

"You are, Princess," said the faery horse kindly. "You will have your chance to shine."

She smiled. "I think I must just make the most of this day. But I will find a way to avenge you, I swear it. I have to go – the geese need me. I love you, Falada."

And she gathered her skirts and ran off to catch Callum.

The king was stunned, but he now knew the truth. He stepped forward into a beam of dawn light. "Falada is your name?"

"That is so."

"And the goose girl is the true princess? The one my son was meant to marry?"

"That is so, King."

"Time for this wrong to be righted," the king declared, and he returned to the castle, changed his garments and told all he had witnessed to his son.

The prince was surprised at all his father had learned, but not so surprised. He'd known there was something about that goose girl. And his bride was cruel. Whatever beauty there was in her, her cruelty drove it out.

The king next went to speak to the false princess. He found her with a servant cowering before her. "Leave me," the false princess hissed through lips tight with anger, then spun to meet the king, a false smile shining out. "Yes, my king?"

"I have some need of counsel," he said, sitting down on a great chair.

She sat by him, smiling that tight, hard smile.

"And I need your perspective – it is fresh and young, and may help me make a difficult decision."

The false princess looked attentive, as the king put the case before her.

"What if you knew that someone was false – that they had broken an oath, taken what was not theirs, oppressed and cruelly treated a gentle heart, and finally, sent to slaughter a noble creature? What would their punishment be?"

Looking indignant, the girl said, "Sire, I would have them put out into the woods for the beasts to tear apart."

When she saw the king appeared disappointed, she spoke again.

"No ... no," she said, warming to the task. "I would have them stripped and put into a barrel studded with nails, and rolled in that barrel until they died."

"No mercy?" he enquired softly. She was, he could see, quite unhinged.

"No, sire. What mercy is deserved?"

"Indeed," he said, sadly. "It is the truth."

"Guards!" he called.

And the false princess was taken away and sent into the forest, where no wild creature would go near her, not even to eat, for every one of them could feel her cold heart. None wished to taste her bitter flesh. They left her to roam, and become quite mad, and finally fade from memory.

Although, some say she turned into a wraith, and the faery folk found her, and danced around her until she lost all sense of who she was.

And the goose girl? Well, she became the princess, once again. But she was different now. A little stronger. A little wiser. A little more serious.

But far, far more joyful. For in her union with the prince, she found a living companion, and in the king, the father she never had. And she finally wrote to her mother, and told her all that had happened. Then the faeries came, and took down the head of Falada and spun him a new body from the energy that is all around us, so that he was returned, whole, to life and to the care and love of the princess true.

Callum married Meg, and they opened a tavern together, and they both stayed up all night long whenever they wanted, and he never had to look after a goose again. And the princess, and the prince, and the kingdom were full of good magick, kindness, strength, and protection.

But never again did Falada speak. Instead, he just shone with the light of a thousand lamps. Some said that when the moon was full, they could see a shining steed soar high into the sky, a princess upon his back, a flock of geese flying close behind them.

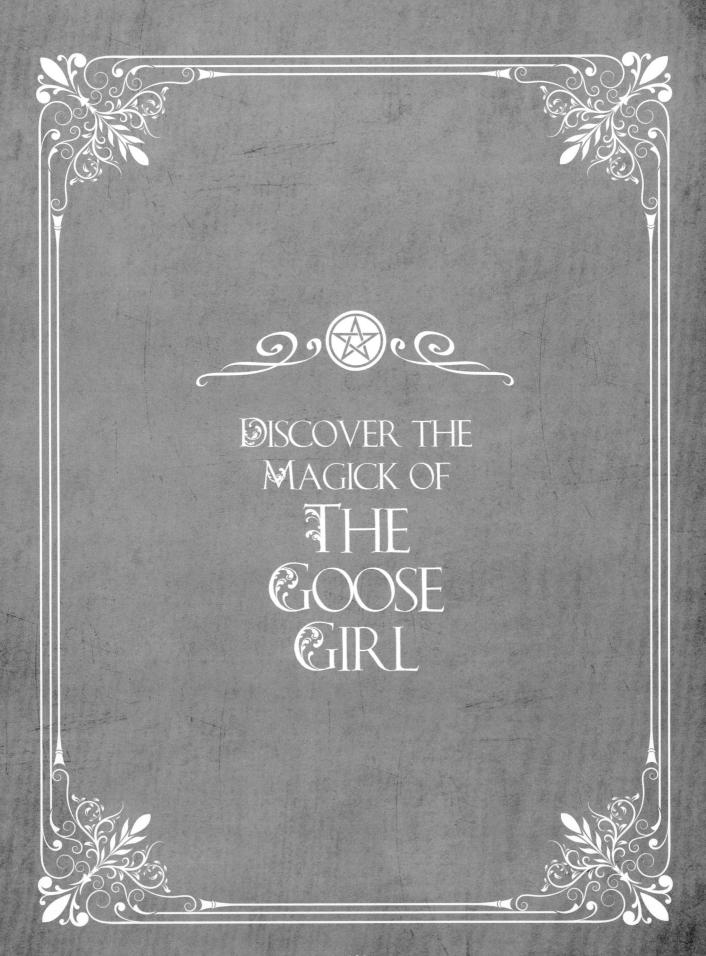

Discover the
Magick of
The
Goose
Girl

SHE LAID A GENTLE HAND on the little charm
with her mother's blood that she wore over her heart,
and as she whispered her troubles to the river, just for
a moment, she fancied she heard the river whispering
back to her ...

SOMEWHERE AMIDST THE patchwork of stories that made their way into my head and heart as a child was *The Goose Girl*, a story that featured, in a very strong way, injustice and domination, the exploitation of the vulnerable and the theft of identity. Most of us can identify with experiences in which someone tries to take something away from us – but the *Goose Girl* folk wisdom takes this to such a frightening place. The possibility that your whole "self" can be stolen is a daunting reality to face – and such theft often begins when you are made to feel ashamed of any softness, are coerced into exchanging the power of your vulnerability for a disempowering self-perception of weakness.

As much as I feel for the true princess's loss, paradoxically, I feel for the companion within the tale, too. In the telling, I tried to include some moments where the reader can sense that her resentment has its origins in hardships she has experienced at the hands of those born into privilege or power. Although her actions are cruel and reprehensible, there is a sense that the resentment that motivates this character could be born of life experiences to which the princess would be oblivious.

There's something within this story that makes my heart sing. When the princess loses her identity, her sense of self is reborn, and she gains the liberty that comes with that – really giving herself over to the wildness of the fields and the care of the geese. There's a freedom and a transformation that takes place because of this contact with the wind and the wildish creatures.

HISTORY OF THIS TALE

THE TALE WAS FIRST COLLECTED BY THE Brothers Grimm, as they travelled and listened to the oral folk tales of the Germanic people of the countryside. It was initially published in 1815, and the renowned British folklorist Andrew Lang included an adaptation in the *Blue Fairy Book* in 1889, although there are earlier English translations. *The Goose Girl* is a story that works across cultures, and there are echoes of this tale in French folk tales and in Celtic stories, too.

THE QUEEN'S CHARM

DRIVEN BY THE GRIEF OF SEPARATION, THE queen creates a magickal charm, impregnated with her energy in the form of three precious drops of her own blood, thus creating a link between her daughter and herself. Three, of course, is a magickal number, and the three drops offer the child a degree of the mother's presence, binding them strongly across the great distance that will separate them.

Because blood is the very essence of life itself, the queen has offered her daughter courage, energy, and her own wisdom and life force. The number three suggests that, in a very spontaneous way, a spell has been cast and

infused into the fabric the princess will carry next to her heart as she begins the journey into her own transformation. The number three could also represent the Maiden, the Mother, and the Crone – the three stages of the feminine divine, the maiden princess travelling into marriage and sexual maturity, and on into a rich and rewarding old age.

The loss of her mother's charm signifies the loss of her mother's protection – yet it also brings the princess a very challenging opportunity. She is now out on her own and between the worlds. She must rely on herself – and on her new ally, the magickal horse Falada.

The Gift from the Faeries

I wanted Falada to come from somewhere special – and to me, this is where the connection to the faery folk takes place. I loved that the old queen had this connection to the faeries, and sought her faery friend's advice on her daughter's arranged marriage. To me, the faeries bring the princess Falada to protect her and accompany her, but also to remind her of the faery folk, so she will think to keep them safe, too. In this way, Falada is a bridge between the human world and the faery world.

However, a gift from the faery belongs to the faeries' chosen one. A gift from the fae cannot be stolen or taken – not for long, anyway, as we can see from the tale.

Stolen Identity

The princess is shamed, mocked, and, finally, all that is of value that she possesses, including her identity, is taken from her – and her gentleness becomes a weakness in this moment. This, then, becomes her opportunity to change, to transform and discover what truly lies within her.

She does not set out to do this, but the theft of her old self is the catalyst that opens up the possibility of her discovering who she truly can be, when she is no-one. She starts by finding the courage to ask for Falada's head to be placed where she can still speak with him. She finds freedom in the fields, too, and a true friend in Falada, an ally in the king, and humour and laughter in her teasing of Callum, the goose boy. She finds purpose, and a new princess arises out of the loss of the old self.

The Magick of Horses

The horse is associated with the faery through the Wild Hunt. Horses are beloved of the faery folk, and some are said to be faeries, themselves. The presence of Falada has an echo in the white chalk horses of Britain, the beings who speak through symbols and signpost the way for travellers, helping those who have lost their way.

Horses are under the protection of two goddesses in particular, the goddess Rhiannon and the goddess Epona. Rhiannon is a goddess who works with restorative justice, and also with

our personal sovereignty and independence, with the finding of our own voice and its expression. It is Epona that chooses who will be king or queen. In this case, through Falada, Epona reasserts the public sovereignty of the goose girl, and oversees her second transformation, from goose girl to a much wiser, stronger princess.

SPEAKING WITH ANIMALS

THE ABILITY TO SPEAK WITH ANIMALS, TO communicate with them, is the domain of wise ones and sages. This princess loves animals – but it is her ability to speak with this magickal being Falada that changes her life completely. The companion's failure to respect the gift of the faery and to underestimate the magickal horse's enchanted powers leads to her downfall. Those who do not respect the wild ones, the faerie beings and the sacred animals, oftentimes come to a sad fate in these tales. The companion's bitter heart leads to the wild world rejecting her, and the faeries completing her journey by disabling her ability to ever hurt another of their kind, or anyone under their protection.

THE GOOSE AS A TOTEM FOR THE PRINCESS

THE GEESE SEEM TO OFFER SO MUCH TO THE princess. Geese are migratory beings, and so too is the princess. She has left one life and finds herself in another life, far away from her old one. The goose is a creature whose medicine is about protection and maternal nurturing – so while the princess has lost her old family, she takes her place in new family, that of the common people and the geese. She becomes one of the flock, but she also leads the flock through the darkness and into the day, into the open. Likewise, she must journey through the darkness and into the day, herself. She is a leader of the flock and a nurturer of the flock, which gives her a chance to practice being a leader and princess of humans!

She must, like the geese, let her instinctual wisdom guide her. From them, she will learn how to care for her future flock, and she will understand the power of care and nourishment. She will protect the old – geese never leave a family member to die alone; and she will nurture the future young – geese are amongst the most caring mothers to be found in all of nature.

Through her connection with the flock, she develops a sense of flight and freedom; she finds her own family and comes into connection with the deep mother-earth energy that she once found in her mother, but which the princess can begin to develop from within.

JOURNEYING BETWEEN THE WORLDS

CHANGE TAKES PLACE WHEN WE ARE IN-between. The transitional zone is its own space, and in this story, it begins with events that deliberately take the true princess away from what belonged to her old life. She steps from the world she knew to the world between her old world and the new world she has yet to enter. There, in the in-between, an initiatory journey unfolds, and she will emerge from between the worlds a very different princess, with a great deal more to offer, than she would have if the journey to the new kingdom had been uneventful.

MAKING MAGICK: THE GOOSE GIRL'S FAERY-FRIEND JUSTICE SPELL

OUR DARLING GOOSE GIRL STARTS OUT SO very vulnerable to the unjust forces around her. Luckily, she has the protection of the faery horse Falada, so we will be working with the faeries to help us with this spell. Of course, if you are currently experiencing injustice you can work this spell with your own personal situation in mind. But you may also wish to cast this spell on behalf of a group of people, or a cause you are drawn to. This spell works on both individuals and can have a true impact on bringing about positive change in society.

You will need:
• One piece of green cloth, about fifteen centimetres (six inches) across
• One quartz crystal, small
• Four coins of any denomination
• Sea salt (around a tablespoon)
• A few sprigs of thyme
• Some earth or clay
• About thirty centimetres (twelve inches) of golden thread – or, if you have a flowering vine, this could work well as a thread, too. I like to use jasmine vine if at all possible!

Lay all the items on your altar for about an hour, just to let them "cure", soaking up and charging with sacred energy.

Then, go to your altar, or to your place outside, and visualise a circle of silver fire completely surrounding you: above, below, and beneath. Take your cloth and place the crystal, the coins, the salt, and the earth in the centre. Gather the cloth up, so it forms a little pouch, then take the golden thread and wind it three times, closing up the pouch securely. While doing this, chant:

> *By the power of three by three,*
> *May faeries restore justice to me.*
> *As the fair folk will, make it so.*
> *Let my natural justice flow.*
> *By the power of three by three,*
> *As I do will, so mote it be.*

Now, visualise justice coming your way. Imagine how good this will be, how you will benefit. Reflect also on what you have learned and what you can do with this wisdom. See those who did you harm as disarmed and no longer having any power over you.

Finally, thank the faeries, and let them

know you will help them in return, simply by being more appreciative and caring for the earth.

Once you have truly felt all of this, let the silver fire surrounding you shimmer and be reabsorbed into the universal energies all about you.

Suspend the pouch in a place that is significant to the issue you wish for justice with – over work papers, near the telephone, or anywhere where it would best do its work.

Within three moon cycles, there will be change.

THE WISDOM OF THE GOOSE GIRL

The Goose Girl REMINDS US THAT SOMEtimes in our lives we'll encounter people who steal, or lie, or attempt to profit from our loss. They may bully us, or threaten us with punishment if we break our silence. But in this loss, there can be a true discovery of the self – who we are – when what we identified with is taken from us. It doesn't justify the bad things that people do, but it opens up a way through the suffering into reclaiming ourselves and asserting who we are from within.

If we connect with the wild, if we keep on going and remember we are more than what has been taken from us, we can rebirth ourselves and, ultimately, take back what was once stolen and incorporate it into a rich, good life. We are more than our clothes, our titles, and even our relationships. When terrible things happen, it is my hope for us all that, ultimately, we will remember that we are wilder, more wondrous, and more worthy than we ever knew.

SNOW WHITE AND ROSE RED

I{N A VERY DEEP FOREST, THERE CAN BE} found a very, very old cottage. Once upon a time, that cottage was the most shining and happy home you could imagine. So, let us begin there – when this little cottage was the happiest place in all the world.

Within that cottage, so very long ago, dwelled three people. A woman, who loved her garden and who took great care with her flowers and plants, especially of her herbs of comfrey and sorrel and radish and rhubarb. But she had two plants she favoured above all others – a red rose bush and a white rose bush, which sat either side of her front door, and grew and grew, until they covered the whole home in thorns and sweetness, in protection and in love, and in the holy colours of red and of white.

The two things in the world she loved most of all, though, were named for those two rose bushes – the first, her daughter Snow White; the second, although not in order of affection, only in order of birth, her daughter Rose Red.

The family was poor, and ever so alone, but they dwelled happily in that little home and cared deeply, each for the other, and not one of that sweet trinity ever knew what it was to be lonesome or afraid or without someone who cared for them.

Snow White was a gentle soul, quiet and introverted, content to write, to draw, and to read to her mother. She loved listening and solitude, and was so kind that the littlest of wild creatures crept to her, knowing she was the safest haven of sweetness they ever would see. She was not dull, though. Oh, no – she was funny and caring and so clever with her hands. Snow White could sense what was about her. She knew more than she said and felt more than most, for she could read people's thoughts, and took comfort in knowing how kind her own family was.

Rose Red was a different girl altogether – changeable and sudden, like the wind. She raced the deer in the forest, leapt like a frog by the riverbed, and climbed trees to see the great eagles that flew high in the sky near the cottage. She sang at the top of her voice, and danced like the faeries themselves. And even though she was daring and savage, all the animals loved her, too. Rose Red was like pure, unexpected joy, and no-one could ever feel anything but happy in her bright company.

The two girls were utterly different, but they loved each other so. They took each other's hands, every morning as they walked through the forest, and they shared everything they had, gladly, for they knew there were other girls who had no mother, or whose family did not love them enough to even keep them – and they knew how very lucky they were.

"We will never desert each other," said Snow White to Rose Red, as they lay in the field, gazing up in the sky.

"No, not as long as we shall live," sang Rose, leaping up and twirling her arms to the sky. "Look, Snow," she said, "the sky is whirling," and she collapsed to the ground, laughing. Snow just smiled. Then she saw a strange shape emerge in the clouds … "That's a little like a man with a long, grey beard," she whispered to Rose, but her sister had leapt up again and was too busy whirling to hear.

Later that night, they told their mother of their pledge never to desert each other.

"That's right, my loves," she said, stirring the cauldron that held their supper. "And you must always share. For we are only as strong as each other. And when we share – trust me on this – so much returns to us. Look at what nature has given us this day: food for our table, a glad day to brighten our hearts, and good wood for the fire. We are blessed."

The girls nodded and ate their dinner of wild greens – Snow White quietly, Rose Red in a rush, both of them content.

Where they lived was very wild, and they saw all manner of creatures, but they never felt danger, for their mother had taught them that all creatures belonged alongside each other on the earth. The girls knew just how to speak to the animals, with both their gestures and their minds, so they felt safe. So safe that, sometimes, when they had spent the day wandering far from the cottage, foraging for hazelnuts and mint and strawberries and the good starchy roots that would feed them in winter, they would find a bed of moss beneath a great old tree and, together, the sisters would curl up and sleep.

And their mother never worried, for she felt sure her daughters were protected by the old, strong spirits of the forest, and that as long as they had each other, no harm would come to them. So, the mother slept sound at night, even when her daughters were not home. And on those mornings that the girls awoke in the wild, they would share what they had with the creatures of the forest, who would feed from their hands, and then the sisters would return home, always with plenty for their larder.

One night, though, the girls awoke in the forest with the closest thing to fear they'd ever felt. They looked about in wonder to find themselves only a breath away from the edge of a great chasm. If they had chosen to walk just three more steps, they would have plummeted to their death. They gazed in awe, one at the other, and then Rose pointed a long, pale arm, breathing out in amazement.

"Look."

In the distance was a small boy, all glowing, shining like he was made of light. "He may be an angel," breathed Snow White.

"He may be a spirit of the forest," sighed Rose. She clasped Snow's hand tightly, feeling astonished at their good fortune. Whatever he was, they knew now beyond any doubt that they were protected and had seen something truly of magick.

When they told their mother, she thought a while, gazing into the fire. Finally, she spoke. "Daughters. That was a messenger – for 'angel' simply means 'messenger' – and the message was that you should have no fear. Fear would bring you to the kinds of cruelties others create in their lives. But since you, as you know, have nothing to fear, you will choose instead to be kind."

Then she said, with a heaviness in her warm voice, "That boy also showed us that change is coming. As it does. It could be the onset of winter, or the advent of new people in our lives, or some great event in which we will be caught up. But we will work with whatever is sent our way, and we will remain ourselves."

Rose Red loved summer, and the flowers and the blossoming woods, and she kept house in this season, decorating it with red and white roses every morning. Then the seasons changed, as they do, and it became autumn, with leaves as red as Rose's hair, and the clever girls – who always thought ahead – collected wood for the winter and gathered the food they would need. And then autumn changed, and in its place came winter, and snow fell, as white as the older sister's skin. And in winter, it was Snow's turn to take care of their home.

This suited them all. Snow White loved winter. She loved its stillness and its comfort and the time they could all spend together. Although she loved the forest, she loved her family and their closeness more, and cherished the nights when they gathered about the fire.

And winter was lovely for them. All summer long, the sisters had harvested the wild foods and by winter they had plenty. The cauldron hung over the fire, shining like gold, though it was made of bronze, and Snow White and their mother read aloud, while Rose Red danced, and they were all three very content and happy during the cold times.

One cold evening, the sky was welted with angry clouds. That night, a great storm tore through the forest. The girls worried for the animals and crept out to see if any needed their help. They found a little lamb lost in their garden and a sweet dove sheltering under their eaves, and they brought them back inside.

During the worst of the storm, Snow White and their mother read aloud a story Snow had written, while Rose Red acted out all the parts, keeping them laughing. The fire danced in the hearth, and the soup was warm in the cauldron. The wind tore at the windows, and threw itself at the door, but they knew this was simply nature raging and changing, as she must from time to time.

As they settled in to eat their dinner, a great boom shook the house, as if a massive weight had been thrown against their cottage. An eerie howl followed it, and then there were three sharp taps upon their door, as if made by a great claw, from a great paw.

The mother stood and went to the door. "Someone is lost in this storm," she said. "We will share what we have."

She opened the sturdy old door, and a massive, furry, black head thrust its way into the cottage.

"I am lost and so cold," the bear cried – for it was indeed a huge, black bear.

The mother started, and the girls' eyes

widened with shock. They had never seen their mother afraid before. The bear moved inside and howled, its huge teeth gleaming scarlet in the firelight.

Rose Red ran at it with the fireplace poker held before her like a sword, and Snow stepped back, pale. The dove fluttered madly, and the lamb hid behind their mother, who moved carefully towards the great creature.

"Girls," said the mother, after gazing into the bear's eyes for a moment. "There is nothing to fear. Is there, bear?" she asked their visitor, strength in her voice despite her years. "He means well, I can feel it, and is a good, honest, wild creature. Come in, Sir Bear," she said with quiet dignity. "Come by the fire and warm yourself."

The great bear lumbered to the fire, and collapsed in a shivering, furry heap, groaning a little with relief and pleasure.

"Thank you, dear ones," he said, more gently, for he saw how his loud roar had frightened them. "I roared with my agony. I am not used to ... I am not used to being alone, and I have never felt such cold."

"Poor bear," said Snow, whose tender heart quite melted, and she found the bear so very strong and handsome.

Rose Red tilted her head to one side and lowered her poker.

"Could you," asked the bear to Red, "replace that poker with a broom, and help me get the snow off?"

Rose grinned, thinking that would be fun, and also thinking just how brave she was. "This is almost as good as your stories," she said to Snow White.

"It is," said her sister, with a laugh, and together the girls brushed the bear's fur till it was dry and fluffing up nicely in the warmth of the fire. "It is better than any story I have ever read!"

"I would like to hear one of your stories," the bear growled softly to Snow. And so the sisters performed for him. Red enacted the story, while Snow read it out in her gentle, deep, and beautiful voice, and all were delighted at the new friendships they'd made that surprising evening.

The next morning, the bear headed out into the cold, blue day. "I will catch myself some fish and find a little food for you all, and then I will take my leave of you," he growled gently.

"Oh, bear, no, do not go," protested Snow, who was quite taken by him.

Red saw how Snow loved him, and looked at her mother, her red eyebrows raised in question.

"Dear bear, won't you stay with us tonight, as well? This is surely more comfortable for you than the cold, snowy woods, and you can sleep and sleep, all night long," said the mother, seeing just what Rose Red saw.

The bear smiled, if a bear could smile, which he seemed quite able to do, and ambled out the door. "I will return," he said with certainty, and went on his way.

That night he returned, and the sisters were overjoyed. They climbed on his back and tickled him, and Rose Red even pretended she was a knight and he was a dragon, and she poked the bear with hazel twigs.

"Spare my life," he cried. "Save me," he pleaded to Snow, who smiled and laughed at their antics.

The bear even came up with funny rhymes for them.

Oh, Snow White and Rose Red,
Do not kill your lover dead.

From that night, he came at the same time every evening, and as winter grew deeper and colder and darker, he stayed for longer and longer.

Finally, the solstice passed, and the days became longer. Then Imbolc arrived, with the ice-melt and the snowdrops and the deer and the sweet small rabbits. When the girls took the sheep into the fields, and when the dove fluttered from within and flew back into the warming world, the bear, with tears almost falling from his great brown eyes, sniffed the air and knew the green time was coming.

"I saw a great eagle while I was out, today. All the world is melting, and these ladies are everywhere in the meadow," Rose said, chatting to their furry friend and pushing a bunch of sweet, new snowdrops into a cup in the centre of the table.

At that, although, Rose did not see it, the bear looked even sadder.

But Snow had seen, and she went to him and put her arm a ways around his great furred shoulders.

"What is it, bear," she asked. "I can feel the sadness on you."

"Ah, my friends," he replied. "This will be our last evening together. For spring is come, and now is the time when the great dwarves rise up from beneath the earth. And one such dwarf has taken from me a thing of much importance."

"Treasure?" breathed Snow White, her head in storyland.

"Treasure, yes, but better," said the bear.

"Magickal treasure," said Rose Red.

"Indeed, it is. I cannot tell you more, but I must go and find the stones and the pearls and all that once was mine. Dear friends," he said, nuzzling them one by one, "I thank you."

And in the morning, he tried to leave early, so he would not disturb them, but also, truth be told, because he could not stand to see Snow cry.

But Snow heard him, and leapt to the door. "You cannot open the door, bear," she said, with affection. "Your great paws are not made for doorknobs. Let me."

He smiled with his eyes. "You are as lovely as your namesake," he said.

She smiled back, great clear tears forming in her beautiful eyes.

"I must go," he said, and stumbled out the door in a rush ... and in his haste a little of his fur caught on the latch and tore away, and Snow thought she saw gold flash, just for a moment, beneath the torn fur.

Then he was gone, and she felt very sad, although she knew, *knew*, they must see each other again. This was their forest, was it not?

And he was their bear.

* * *

THE DAYS GREW LONGER AS THE WHEEL OF THE year turned, and the Bone Mother, who brought winter, sank back into the earth. Snow White missed the bear, and Rose Red barely had to coax her outside, so eager was she to lose her sorrows in the forest.

"I keep hoping I will see him again," Snow White sighed.

"He'll be back," said Rose, picking up firewood for their cooking pot. "He's our friend," she said, with a definite nod of her scarlet head.

But Snow White had noticed a change. "There's something strange about the forest today," she said, quietly, looking about.

"There are so many fallen trees," agreed Rose.

"The storms," they both said at once, and laughed.

There was one great fallen tree, farther up ahead, and both girls ran to it. Rose Red danced along its side, while Snow peeped into the hollow within it.

"A world within a world," she breathed to herself, seeing the mushrooms and the moss and the little lights that danced about them all. "Faery magick," she murmured. She saw an empty cocoon, and touched it gently. *A caterpillar changes into a butterfly*, thought Snow. *What else can change its form?* she wondered.

And she called softly to Rose to come look.

Rose Red climbed down, and the two peered into the log, gazing in wonder at the lights that sparkled about the moss and the little fungi forest.

"It's a faery forest", said Rose. "Sure, there is magick everywhere."

"Especially in the forest," agreed Snow.

They walked a long way that day, as the sky opened up to blue, and flowers seemed to unfurl about them in the groves. They found all kinds of wild foods to eat, fresh new strawberries and sweet herbs of basil and mint and thyme, the fiery-headed dandelion and scarlet nasturtium flowers, and they gathered these and their firewood, and then made their way home.

On the way, Rose, who adored a fire, said, "We need a little more wood. Let's visit that great tree nearby that always sheds."

As the two girls approached the tree, they could hear a strange sound – a yelping, half-barking, tearing, growling sound. "It's not an animal," said Rose, staring ahead.

"Someone may need help," said Snow, and both girls ran towards the tree.

They saw there the strangest sight.

A tiny, wee man, with the longest, whitest beard, was hopping to and fro, and straining backwards, and as the girls got closer, they could see his magnificent long beard was caught tight in the cleft of the tree. The strange fellow was chained by his very own beard, which seemed determined to hold fast to the tree and never let him go.

The girls ran forward.

"Oh, no!" said Snow. "You're caught quite fast!"

Rose looked sceptical. There was something about this little man she did not like. He may have been small, but his glare could burn through walls. There was something mean and vicious about him. She did not feel fear. But she wished she had her poker from the fire, just to be sure.

"Wait, Snow," Rose said. "Maybe the tree is holding on to him for good reason."

At that, the little man glowered, his eyes red with fury. "Don't just look at me, you loathsome creatures," he spat.

Snow raised her pale brows. *How rude*, she thought.

"Here," he ordered them both, "help me!"

"How is it that you're so stuck?" asked Rose, who was inclined to trust the tree, and let the little man be its captive, so he could do no harm.

"Stupid, curious creature! She wants to know how? I was taking my axe to this vile tree, to nick just a little of its trunk for wood for my supper, for I don't need as much as you great giants," he said nastily, looking at the kindling Rose and Snow had in their bundles. "You are greedy, disgusting creatures."

"Why didn't you take the fallen wood?" asked Rose, sensibly.

The little man's eyeballs threatened to erupt from his forehead, so outraged was he at this question. "I wanted the new wood, not the old wood, fool!"

"But it burns badly," replied Rose, feeling a fight coming on.

Snow stepped in. "None of that matters now. Here, let us help you get out."

So, the sisters pulled and pulled at the little man's beard, but the tree refused to give up its silver prize.

Snow had her little sickle-shaped steel knife in the pouch she always wore. Taking it out, she said calmly to the little man, "This is the only solution." And she sliced clean through the long silver beard with the moon-shaped blade.

The little man screamed, as if in agony. "My BEARD!" he cried, rushing at Snow and knocking her over. "You cut my beard," he raved, standing over Snow as if he were a demented doll.

Rose helped her sister up. She watched carefully as the little man scurried about the roots of the tree and found what looked to be a huge bag. It clinked and clanked as he dragged it – and she saw it was full of golden coins and sparkling jewels.

"Never shall you know wealth like this," he muttered at the girls, who stood back, watching him.

"These jewels look like they are for kings and queens," said Snow, carefully keeping her distance.

"Oh, they *are* for royalty! But they are not meant for humans, not for their sceptres and their crowns and their chalices! These are for the shining ones, who kept them beneath their mounds, in their hoards, for their glorious afterlife! They are not for you, or for you," he spat, his voice growing louder and louder. "You are foul human monsters and not worthy to touch my splendid beard, let alone these stones. You shall rue the day!"

Overhead, a huge eagle wheeled about in the sky and hovered right over where they stood. Snow was too busy wondering who the little man was and why he was so hateful to notice the great bird.

But Rose tilted her lovely face to the sky and her scarlet locks streamed towards the earth, as she thought to herself, *There is the eagle, again*.

Snow and Rose went home, the eagle flying just a little way behind them, and they told their mother about the spiteful little man.

In response, their mother explained that dwarves were sometimes seen in the forest in spring. "But usually," she said, between bites of the wild cherries the girls had found, "they are to be found on the borderlands. Their treasure holds great power, and most dwarves are good souls. But this small man seems hateful. Be wary of him, my children."

She said nothing more about it, but she cast a little protection spell about them that night, for she did not trust this dwarf, and she did not like him being so close by.

The next day, the girls followed the stream to a sweet, small waterfall, in the hope of finding some water chestnut and cress for their supper.

"I know the bear loves fish," said Snow, wistfully, as they waded into the waters and the fish tickled their feet. Soon they were deep within the waters – and Rose had just come up for breath after diving beneath, looking for the sweetest plants, when they saw something that looked like an enormous grasshopper leaping backwards and forth on the bank.

"It's not a grasshopper," said Rose, matter-of-factly.

"No," said Snow. "It's that little man, again."

"What are you doing, sir?" called out Snow, who couldn't help but want to come to his aid, even though he'd been so foul to them both the day before – and despite their mother's warning.

"His temper will be the end of him," said Rose, shaking her head. She placed the cress and water chestnut in the bucket they had brought along, and then went over to the little man.

"Ugh, you slimy, wet things," he said to them both, for they were dripping from their hunt for water greens. "Staring again? Causing trouble again?" he mocked, just as he was yanked forward. A terrible scream rose up from him.

"Where are you going?" asked Rose. "You're surely not going to jump into the water?"

"I'm not such a fool," screamed the dwarf. "Don't you see that cursed fish is trying to drag me in?"

"What is the trouble?" asked Snow, although she could see perfectly well what was happening. The little man's magnificent, curling white beard was caught fast once again – this time, within his fishing line, which had caught a splendid trout.

"Poor fish," breathed Rose, and she plunged into the water and freed the silver-scaled one from the line.

But still the horrid little man's beard was caught – almost all of its length was dirty, slimy, and tangled hopelessly with fishing wire and weights and hooks. The girls tried patiently to disentangle it, enjoying the challenge at first. But after an hour, with the dwarf screaming at them to hurry, that they were stupid, that they were clumsy, that they smelt bad, and all sorts of other colourful insults, Snow handed Rose the crescent-shaped knife, and down its silver curve fell, and even more of the little fellow's fine beard fell to the soft, good earth.

And what a scream he unleashed. What a keening! What a mournful roar!

"You have mutilated me," he accused them. "You MONSTERS," he said, whirling free of the fishing line, his eyes lighting on a sack nearby. "Don't you look," he cried, "else I will poke your ugly eyes right out of your hideous heads!"

The girls left him to his sack and his horde of jewels and wound their way home, carrying the cress and water chestnut with them, not speaking at all for some time.

"I don't know if I like him," said Snow, after quite a while.

Rose smiled at her kindness. "He's an ungrateful little man," said Rose. "He takes, but he does not give in return."

Snow looked thoughtful. "I suppose we took some of his beard though," said Snow, and they laughed, although they felt he was so awful.

"Do you notice? None of the animals are around whenever he is. They don't come to help him. The fish was trying to get away from him, and it wasn't just because it was caught," Rose said, looking puzzled.

"No. Even the trees don't seem to like him," said Snow.

The very next week, their mother asked the sisters to go even farther afield, to a village far away, to barter their kindling for needles, pins, and new cloth – for the girls had so grown over the winter that their old summer clothes were too short and dreadfully tight in all the strangest places.

They set out early, and the wild creatures walked with them nearly all the way, until they reached a great heath. Then, the deer fell away and the rabbits held back, but the girls, puzzled, walked on, Snow all the while peering this way and that for a sign of her dear bear. Rose noticed her sister's preoccupation, and she looked, too, but she did not say anything. The path led by strange, rocky outcrops and an old stone circle the girls had long wanted to visit.

They ran to the stones, and Rose danced among them for a moment, but their joy was disturbed by a long, loud cry, and they whirled about to see a great eagle falling again and again on its prey.

"We must help!" gasped Snow

"But it is nature," said Rose, thinking the eagle had nabbed a rabbit or a stoat for its dinner.

Then they heard a familiar voice call, "Help me, you vile imbeciles. What is the matter with you? Can't you see I'm under attack!"

It was the dwarf. Snow ran to help him, and Rose ran, too, shaking her head. The eagle had him fast in great, steel talons.

No-one wants him in the forest, Snow thought, and she leapt high, reaching for the little man's legs, just missing a foot. Rose, who was stronger, leapt higher still, and grabbed the little man's ankle. She fell back to the rocky ground, but held tight, tugging at the dwarf's leg.

"Come now, darling eagle," she called out. "He would taste horrible, anyway! He is dreadful bitter!"

The eagle shrieked, and thrust its beak at Rose, just avoiding her beautiful eyes.

"I know, it's annoying," she agreed, as if she and the eagle were having the most ordinary conversation. And, indeed, as the magnificent bird stared into the girl's luminous eyes, there passed between them one of those sublime moments of perfect understanding.

The eagle shook its great head, two, three times, as if in exasperation at such an unreasonable request, but its claws unclasped the little man, who fell onto Rose with a heavy thud – for though he was small, he weighed a great deal.

As he fell, from his clothes tumbled sparks of fire, fragments of ocean, milky white pearls and the coins of gold. Sparkling stones fell onto their hair, and caught on their ears, and settled about their shoulders, and the sisters began to glow, as if they were faery princesses themselves, while the rest of the glory was scattered on the rocks, leaving both girls staring in open-mouthed awe.

"Get your coveting, ill-wishing eyes off," the dwarf snarled, snatching up one jewel after another. "Have you not done enough?"

"We saved you, you foolish thing," protested Rose, rubbing her elbow.

"Saved me!" He spat on the ground. "You destroyed my beard, and now you want my stones, do you not? I will see you die before you steal them from me," he said, rushing forward to strike them, a pointed rock raised in his long-fingered hand.

The girls dodged the little man, and Rose took up her own rock. "What is wrong with you?" she roared, her eyes fierce, and defiant. "We have saved you from starvation, and drowning, and now from being eaten alive by an eagle. And yet you attack us?"

The little man's only reply was to turn from Rose and rush towards Snow, his rock still raised to strike her down.

At that very moment, a great bear rushed out from behind the rocks. And the bear roared a fearsome, stomach-turning sound, full of the force of the fierce wild creature he was. He stood on his two hind legs and shook the earth with his might, claws close as a whisper to the face of the hateful little man.

"Spare me, Sir Bear," whimpered the little

man, one long finger pointing at the sisters. "You will, won't you? Why have me for your dinner, when these two tender morsels could be yours?" He leapt to his feet and grabbed Rose and Snow, and thrust them towards the bear.

At that, the bear raised its great paw, and struck at the little man with slashing claws and tearing teeth in such a frenzy that he dropped the girls, who fell to the stony ground, shuddering, holding each other, shaking each in the other's arms. Until, at last, all was quiet, and they looked up, and saw the little man, dead, quite dead on the ground, bloodied and torn, and the bear standing, panting, swaying a little, and beginning to shake in the most frightening way.

Snow stared at him. "It is you, isn't it? Our bear, our dear bear," she whispered, but the bear couldn't seem to hear her – and, shaking and jerking, he fell to the ground.

"What's wrong with him?" cried Snow, rushing to his side, and Rose joined her, as the bear began to tremble all over.

"He's dying," cried Snow, and the girls wept together into his fur.

And as the bear stilled, the whole world went quiet, except for the low sobs of the sisters, who had lost their best friend, just as they'd found him again. They began to pat his body. "Bear, dear bear. Come back to us. Remember? Come back to us, as you promised," the sisters murmured, tears flowing down their faces.

And as they stroked him, something strange began to happen. With every touch of their hands, the bear's thick fur began to come away. Stroke after stroke, the fur, then the bear skin, then even the bones began to pull away, until a great hole opened up within their bear, and within this hole lay a dark-haired young man, long of limb, and fine to look upon. Then he opened

his brown eyes and stared straight into Snow's golden eyes.

"Snow," he said. "Rose." And he smiled. "You have broken the curse," he said, and then he fell fast asleep.

Nearby, the great eagle landed and Rose stood, still shaken by what she had seen, and walked over to her new friend on trembling legs. She reached out her hand, and touched him. The eagle shrieked.

"What are you?" she asked.

The eagle shuddered and shook a little. Then a great trembling overwhelmed the bird. Seeing this, Rose began to stroke him, too, as she and Snow had stroked the bear – and soon, feather after feather began to fall.

"You're not an eagle at all," Rose Red said, and made all manner of soothing, small sounds to comfort him as he changed.

Feather after feather she stroked away, until before her stood a young man, the bear's brother, with broad shoulders, a strong nose, and piercing eyes, and fine chestnut hair that gleamed in the sun.

She smiled.

A brother for a sister.

***

SO, THIS IS HOW SNOW WHITE AND ROSE RED met the men whom they would one day make their husbands. But that came much later, of course.

First, they all went to the cottage in the forest, carrying the jewels and the gold. These they spread out upon the earthen floor, and watched as the faceted stones glowed as bright as fire, delicate and marvellous and varied as rainbows.

The girl's mother took her time looking over them all, while the two men shared the stories

of the stones.

"This," said Bernard, for that was the true name of the Bear Prince, pointing to a great glowing ruby, "came from my mother's sceptre. And this," he continued, holding up a sparkling diamond to the light, "is from my father's crown. They were gifts, long, long ago, from the faerie realms."

"Most of the others," said Aleron, for that was the true name of the Eagle Prince, "are from the royal coffers."

"*Your royal* coffers," said Rose, pointedly.

"Well, they belong to the kingdom, not to us, personally," he said with a smile.

Rose shook her head. She wasn't so sure she wanted to like someone who was *royal* so very much. She sighed. For like him, she did.

"Others, like this," Aleron continued, pointing to a luminous, milky pearl, "and this," to a deep-green emerald, "and these," gathering sapphires like pale sparks of blue fire in his hands, "we have never seen before."

"What about this," asked the mother, hands reaching out towards a great green-and-black stone, an obsidian. Before the princes could warn her, she touched it ever so softly, and immediately, one pale hand flew to her head, as she cried, "Ah," and flinched in pain.

"Yes," said Bernard. "Take great care with that one."

"You know this stone?" asked Snow, for she could feel its power.

"I do. It is the most powerful jewel here. It has magickal properties, many. Amongst them, the power to make others change shape. And the power to bring them back to their original form. Strong enough to harm, or to heal, it is a blessing, and a curse in one."

"What will we do with these?" wondered Snow, aloud.

And they sat and thought.

Then their mother began to speak.

They all listened quietly to her wisdom, and when she was done, the young people knew what to do. They took the great ruby and diamond and set them aside. The emerald, the pearl, and the sapphires were placed in small baskets of their own. The gold was to be carried in their pockets. And the green-and-black obsidian was wrapped carefully in black cloth, and placed within a small box.

Then the girls, carrying carefully all of these earth treasures, left the cottage and walked together to the tree where they had first met the dwarf, and placed in its hollow, the great emerald and a little of the gold.

They stood before the tree. "Thank you for your gifts to us, and to the forest," said Snow.

"We trust that you will know what is best for this treasure," breathed Rose, reverent and still for the first time in a long time.

Then they went to the river, where they had seen the little man the second time. "Where shall we put the pearl?" asked Snow of Rose.

"I know," replied Rose, and she went to the riverbank and kneeled right amidst the mud and the waterweeds.

"Show us, river, what we need to do," she whispered to the waters.

And a great trout rose up, the very same fish that had been caught upon the dwarf's hook. The glittering trout opened its mouth, and Rose placed the pearl within its lips, smiling with delight, and it sank back beneath the waters, gracefully.

They stood by the riverbank a while.

"Thank you for your gifts, waters," said Rose.

"We trust that you will know what to do with this treasure," whispered Snow, filled with love.

They buried more gold at the riverbank, and then went to the log where they had seen the faery folk, the tiny ones. They gazed within, seeing the lights, breathing in the magick. Gently, they scattered some gold coins and nestled the tiny sapphires upon a little mound of moss, close to the mushrooms that rose like tiny houses within that world.

"Thank you, little folk, for all that you do," the sisters said together. "We trust that you will know what is best to do with this treasure."

Seemingly in response, the lights within the tiny world seemed briefly to glow a little brighter and to dance for a moment or two around the stones.

After a quiet moment or two, the girls looked at each other, knowing there was one more thing that must be done. Rising silently, they began to walk to the stone circle where the last dreadful encounter with the dwarf had taken place. Along the way, they gathered wildflowers and herbs, lavender and wild rose, artemisia and marigold, bark and leaves. When they reached the stone circle, they saw the body of the little man, pitiable in its stillness, lying quiet and torn upon the harsh ground.

They gathered him up and gently bathed his body with water from the river. Then found two great sticks with pointed ends, and with them they dug a grave where he lay. They wrapped him in oak bark and rowan leaves and scattered artemisia all about him, to help him through to the next world.

"He goes back to the earth, now," said Rose, as they placed him gently in the cold ground.

Then they unwrapped, from its protective layer of cloth, the black obsidian, lit from within by its green fire – and both were very careful not to touch it, not once, not at all, for they wanted no part of its magick. They placed this stone – this wishing stone that could do great good, or great evil – upon the little man's chest.

And they thanked him for his lesson, and blessed him.

They blessed him with wisdom enough to let go of his hate.

And they blessed him with the hope that one day, perhaps in his next lifetime, he would do only good with this stone.

But they also laid a curse, which said that if that day was never to come, they asked for the stone to stay as hidden and quiet as the dwarf's lifeless body, and never again to unleash its great power upon the world.

Finally, they covered the dwarf with a bed of earth and placed rocks upon his grave, should a wild one come in the leaner times – for even an ungrateful dwarf deserves dignity in death.

Then the girls went home to their mother and to the men they now knew were princes.

After many moons passed, they all left the cottage – the girls, their mother, and the two rose bushes, too – and moved to the castle that was to be their home.

And no-one within the kingdom ever harmed another animal. Nor could anyone mine the earth for riches while these four shared the throne. And they were happy, and busy, and good, all the rest of the days of their very long lives.

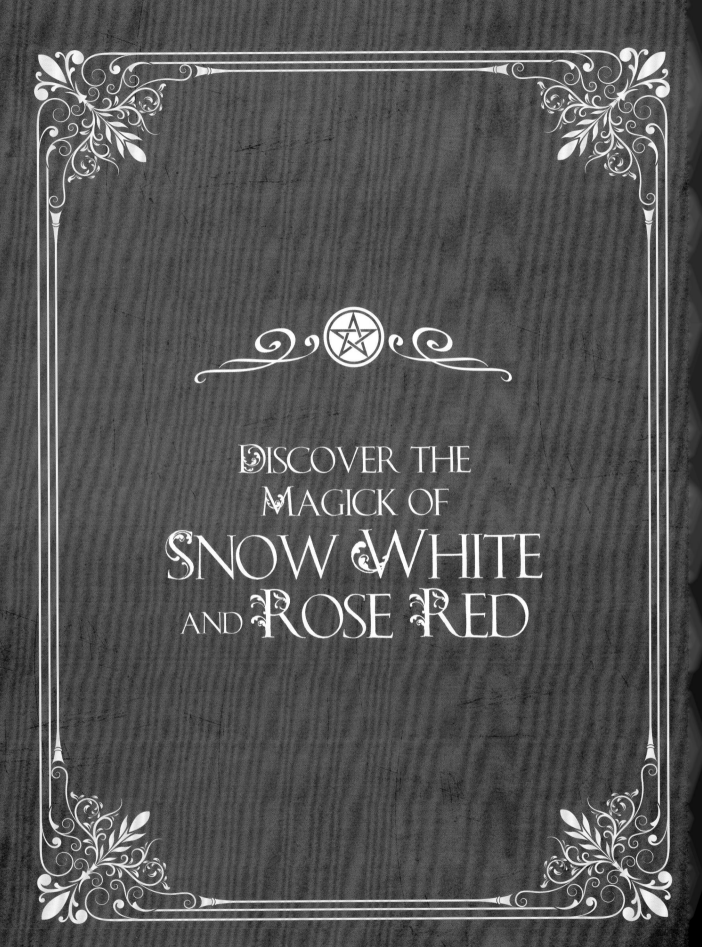

Discover the Magick of Snow White and Rose Red

AS HE FELL, from his clothes tumbled sparks
of fire, fragments of ocean, milky white pearls and the
coins of gold. Sparkling stones fell onto their hair, and
caught on their ears, and settled about their shoulders,
and the sisters began to glow, as if they were faery
princesses themselves, while the rest of the glory was
scattered on the rocks, leaving both girls staring in open-
mouthed awe.

A HAPPY FAMILY IS A RARE jewel in faerytales. In this tale, it is the father who is absent, and never a mention is made of him. This leaves the three women to form a kind of trinity of feminine contentment and wisdom, each with their own abilities and skills. I always loved the sisterhood aspect of the tale – that two sisters could be so different and so contented and joyful in each other's company was utterly refreshing after all the less-than-generous siblings we encounter in so many other faerytales. Though such siblings have their purpose and their part to play, with this story, I think we experience a world of womanhood that is really idyllic, even if it is not a conventional happy family.

I was always drawn to the shapeshifting part of the story, which is seen with the bear and the eagle. In many legends, throughout many cultures, there are tales of humans being able to change into other creatures – known in some magickal traditions as skin-changing.

Most people stay away from bears and eagles, and mostly they have good reason, but the girls have courage and wisdom enough to see beyond these animals' fearsome exteriors. They bring the bear right into the hearth of their home and stare the eagle in the eye. And, although the dwarf is frustratingly despicable, they are *still* kind to him!

When I was little, I had a very battered, rather grand book about geology, and within it were spectacular images of gorgeous jewels and their locations around the world. I stared at them, enraptured – and now, of course, being grown up (in a way), I can now stare at a few very special crystals of my own, collected over the years, and work magick with them, when they call to be used in spellcraft. The jewels in this story sparkled brightly as the tale began to tell itself, and so their particular powers have been explored a little more deeply than in the original stories.

I love this tale, and I hope you find it as enchanting as I do.

HISTORY OF THIS TALE

THERE ARE SHADES OF GREEK AND CELTIC myth within the tale of Snow White and Rose Red – a little Eros and Psyche, and a little Blodeuwedd and Lugh. And of course, there is the Nordic aspect, too. The story has a feel of the sagas, with its dwarf and treasure and curses.

There's a story called *The Ungrateful Dwarf* by Caroline Stahl, that was published in the early 1800s, and which precedes the form of *Snow White and Rose Red* collected by the Brothers Grimm. The Brothers Grimm version was published in German in 1815, and an English version, by the great British storyteller Andrew

Lang, followed in 1889.

Snow White and Rose Red is often confused with *Snow White*, but despite the two tales sharing a name, and the fact that both feature a dwarf, they are completely different stories.

A White Rose, a Red Rose

THE LOVE OF FLOWERS HAS ITS ROOTS IN ancient times. Roses were sacred to the Egyptians, and flower festivals were a part of the pagan calendar. Throughout time, the combination of their velvety softness and lush petals and the thorns that protect them have made them a powerful symbol of the paradoxical nature of love, with its beauty and pain. So, it is not surprising that both white roses and red roses are associated with Aphrodite, the Greek goddess of beauty and love, and with her love for Adonis.

The red and the white are colours that have been associated with spirituality, too: the colour red as the wisdom of the blood and the memory of the ancestors, the brilliant intuition of the body and the sensual knowledge of the world; the colour white as more the wisdom of the spirit, the connection with the psyche, the genius of the mind. The red and the white springs of Glastonbury are revered for their different qualities, and often the colours red and the white are associated with the goddess traditions of the Isle of Avalon.

Likewise, traditionally, and particularly since the heightened fever regarding roses in Victorian times, white roses are associated with purity, unconditional love, and the bride, while red roses speak of passion, physical vitality, and sensuality. In this tale, each girl's personality is represented by the rose they are named for, and each is as beautiful and skilled as the other. Both of the girls within our story, that of the white rose and that of the red, are also definitely under some kind of enchanted protection, as well – perhaps that of Aphrodite ... who loved roses so well.

Making Magick:
Snow White and Rose Red
Rosewater to Draw Love

SNOW WHITE AND ROSE RED ARE NAMED FOR the beautiful roses their mother grows, the white and the red. This magickal Snow White and Rose Red rosewater will draw love of all kinds to you – including that of lovely creatures – and make you feel like you are always surrounded by the kindest of friends.

You will need:
• Five handfuls of a mix of white and red rose petals. They can be dried or fresh, but organic is best, as roses tend to be treated with many commercial sprays.
• Pure water
• A cauldron (or a pot) to simmer the water in
• If you are fortunate enough to be picking your own roses, it's best to pluck them two to three hours after sunrise, to assure the dew has dried. (If you want to visit them earlier, you can collect the dew on them, too, for future spell use. Yes, that is difficult. I know only too well! If you cannot

collect the dew, just anoint your face and eyelids with some of this magickal natural beauty tonic and healing skin elixir.)

• A lovely bottle

Separate the petals from the core of the flower and from the stems and leaves. Place the petals in a large pot, and add just enough pure water to nearly, but not quite, cover your rose petals.

Cover your pot with an airtight lid and bring the water to a simmer on a low flame or setting. You do *not* want this to boil – you want it to very gently simmer, so that the surface is steamy. Imagine your rose petals are having a really lovely, very shallow bath.

Keep checking until your red roses have been leached of their colour and the water is changing colour. You may see some rose oil floating on the surface – don't get rid of this! Rose oil is very powerful and can be used to anoint candles for love or be added to shea butter for a beautiful moisturiser with magickal properties. So, skim the oil from the surface when it rises and pop it into a separate container. Then remove the rose petals and let the water cool.

When your water is cooled enough, pour it into your bottle, let it get to room temperature, then keep your rose water in the refrigerator, as it will stay fresh much, much longer this way.

Sprinkle your rose water in a wash, dab a little on a pillow or a love letter, and even include a drop or two in the cooking of cakes and offerings to a beloved.

SEERSHIP AND SCRYING WITH CLOUDS

SEEING FACES AND SHAPES IN TREES, CLOUDS, waves, or even pieces of toast is a part of our humanity. Once, this ability was revered as a "seeing" and was a part of seership and oracular work. Today, science has labelled this ability "paraeidolia", the tendency for the brain to create patterns.

In the story, I included a reference to this seeing with a subtle instance of scrying with clouds – known as aeromancy or nephelomancy. Snow White seemed the most likely sister to have this ability, given her affinity with air and the mind, and so she notices a little precognitive sign of the dwarf's presence in the clouds. I like that Snow White, with her stillness, is able to take a moment and truly see in this way – and perhaps prepare, psychically, for the sisters' battle-like encounters with their foe, the ungrateful dwarf.

The Cauldron at the Hearth

To add a touch of witchery to their story, the mother of Snow White and Rose Red stirs a cauldron above their fire. The three-legged cauldron is synonymous with Witches, from the three weird sisters in Macbeth, to modern Wiccans who use their cauldrons for sacred fires and spellcasting. Magickal cauldrons also appear in the Celtic legends, like the cauldron of the Dagda, which can restore life to fallen warriors after battles. Other magickal Celtic cauldrons may hold endless supplies of nourishing food – and the goddess Cerridwen has a cauldron that is rimmed with pearls and stirred with an apple wand. Just the presence of that cauldron at the hearth of this family means we know there is something witchy about each of them – except these girls are not going to cast a spell. They are going to break one.

Fearless Nights in the Forest

What freedom these young women have! They are allowed – and able – to stay out overnight in the forest! They are unafraid, for they feel they are a part of the forest, a part of nature. Therefore, they need only know it, and trust themselves, in order to stay safe. It's an extraordinary change to the faerytale patterns we see in other tales, those in which children are cast OUT of their homes and into the dangers of the forest.

Instead, in this story, the girls see the forest as an extension of their home; they feel embraced by it. Their mother, knowing her daughters' intelligence, their intimate knowledge of the trees and the plants and the animals of the woods, and their ability to rely each on the other in a way few humans can, is comfortable with their exploration of the wild.

This aspect of the tale is about trust – deep, exquisite, yearned-for trust between humans, between humans and nature, and within ourselves.

The Angel at the Edge of the Cliff

In the Grimm version of the story, the girls have a vision of a small boy while they're walking in the forest one night. Stopping, they make their bed at the place where he appeared – and in the morning, they arise to see he had stood at the very edge of a cliff. In this version of the tale, I include that vision, albeit at a different time – they see him upon awakening at the edge of the cliff. This emphasised to me that they innately knew when to stop, and also the magickal protection of the forest. I also wanted to tease out some of the meaning. Yes, he is an angel (he "rescues" them with his gentle warning in the

original version of the tale). But "angel" means, as the mother points out, "messenger". To me, he is a sign that there will soon be great changes in their lives. It was also another lovely opportunity to illustrate the difference between the two girls – Snow sees an angel, in the spiritual sense, but Rose sees a spirit of the forest. Neither is wrong – it's just that what they see reflects their differences.

THE LAMB AND THE DOVE

THERE'S A LOVELY MOMENT IN THE STORY where the all-female family take in a lamb and a dove. Now, of course, these can be seen as Christian symbols. But from an older, more pagan perspective, lambs could be said to represent the season of Imbolc, which is when the Maiden "rises" and takes her power. The name of Imbolc translates to "ewe's milk" – a time when the lambs are born, and feeding. Looked at this way, the lamb seems a symbol of a time of new times and nourishment, a time when young women come into their own rebirth, and power. The dove, which is a symbol of peace, of course, is also associated with the goddess Aphrodite – making the dove a harbinger of love to come.

THE SACRED NATURE OF HOSPITALITY

IN MOST CULTURES, AND CERTAINLY WITHIN the Celtic and the Nordic traditions, there is nothing so sacred as hospitality to a guest. With the bear's three (that number again!) knocks at the door with his great claw, the family has a choice. Will they turn someone away in the cold of winter because of fear, or will they open their door, share what they have, and let their guest warm themselves by the fire?

In this case, the being seeking shelter is a bear – a creature most humans are terrified of. And the family is definitely wary, but ultimately the bear's need seems too important to ignore. (It's an added bonus that he can speak!) So, their compassion is more powerful than their fear or caution, and without perhaps knowing these ancient customs, still, they enact a great rite that will in time see them rewarded. That is not their motivation in helping the great bear, of course. Their generosity extends to the dwarf, too. But by keeping the old laws of hospitality, they inadvertently create their own great good fortune, for the keeping of these rites never goes unrewarded.

The Eagle and the Bear

WHILE SNOW WHITE FORMS AN UNBREAKABLE bond with the great bear, Rose Red shares a deep connection with an eagle, which turns out to be another prince who has skin-changed!

The story takes places throughout the end of autumn, the deep winter and its solstice, and spring and the festival of Imbolc, and it is at winter that the bear comes calling. There is an old Celtic legend about the goddess Artio visiting chosen leaders at winter solstice in the form of a bear. Bear is also said to remind us to stand up, to be willing to fight for what we love, and for the future we wish to have. Bear's totemic energy is considered strong medicine, indeed, governing discernment, true wisdom, and healing. Snow, the more gentle of the two sisters, shows with this visit from the bear that she may be sweet, but she has a fierce spirit and leadership potential.

The eagle's energy is different – while the bear is grounded and goes to the earth (the family's witchy cottage becomes its cave for the winter), the eagle flies high, soaring above and seeking out its prey with its piercing vision. Rose Red, who is so earthy and wild, finds her true mate in one who can rise above, fly high, and see all possibilities from that faraway perspective. Thus, she shows that while she may have a free spirit, she can also consider carefully all perspectives and make decisions based on higher reasoning.

Rose's mate is of the air, while Snow's is of the earth – a beautiful balancing for both of their energies.

The Ungrateful Dwarf

I WONDERED, WHILE TELLING MY VERSION OF this tale, just why the dwarf is so very angry and bitter. Why would he be so furious at the girls? I don't have an answer – apart from his fury at his beloved beard being snipped away! It's a mystery, but I like to contemplate his story. Perhaps he is the last of his kind, and with his loneliness and isolation has come great sorrow – which, in time, has turned into corrosive bitterness. I think the treasure was stolen by the prince's ancestors, from the tombs of the shining ones – and so the dwarf feels justified in stealing it himself. Perhaps his paranoia about the jewels has made him lose his mind.

Regardless of his reasons, the dwarf in our tale possesses great magicks, for he was able to turn the princes into a bear and an eagle. But did turning them exhaust him? Did it bring him close to losing the last of his powers?

I'm sure our bad-tempered dwarf has a story, and a long and fascinating one, at that. One thing is for sure, though: his anger at the girls for their three rescues and his willingness to sacrifice them to the bear to save himself leads directly to his death. Still, I like to imagine that by dying he may return to the earth, where he can perhaps be restored and return once again – with a different story to tell in his next lifetime.

THE POWER OF THE BEARD

IN THIS STORY, THE GIRLS RESCUE THE BAD-tempered dwarf three times – that magickal number again! And every time, to save him, they must cut off a portion of his beard – which is where, I suspect, much of this dwarf's power resides. Thus, the forest, with its wild cunning, has seen to it that the little man's beard grows smaller and smaller, until, finally, he is destroyed.

Dwarves are often depicted as having long, full beards, which grow with their years, often going uncut their entire long lives. Tolkien says, in the *War of the Jewels*, *No Man or Elf has ever seen a beardless Dwarf – unless he were shaven in mockery, and would then be more likely to die of shame ...*

This may provide a clue to our ungrateful dwarf's horror at being freed in this way. Perhaps it seems to him that the girls have found a way to humiliate him and rob him of his power. I don't believe they have this intention at all – but their ignorance of dwarves and their protocols, along with their compassionate desire to help the little man, create of him their implacable enemy.

BY EARTH, BY WATER, BY AIR

I LIKE TO THINK THAT THE ELEMENTS AND the forest, itself, are trying to tell us that the dwarf has misused his powers in some way, for three important elements turn on him during the course of the story. In the girls' first encounter with the dwarf, he is caught fast by a tree – the element of earth has held on to him, perhaps to stop him doing further harm. Next, they find him trapped by his own fishing line – thus, the element of water turns against him, too. Thirdly, the eagle is taking him up into the sky – and the element of the air is also brought in.

Where, you might ask, is the element of fire? In the old Celtic system, there were three elements worked with – often referred to as land, sky, and sea, or earth, air, and water. Fire was considered a very different element. Is that because we humans can make fire? No-one can truly say, but we can see that the girls help free the dwarf from these three elements – thus, they undergo three elemental initiations in this tale.

THE FATE OF THE JEWELS

AFTER HIS DEATH, SOME OF THE JEWELS retrieved from the dwarf's hoard were returned to magickal crowns and sceptres; others were offered to the faeries, to the tree, and to the waters; and finally, one is returned to the earth with the little man's body – with magickal restrictions placed

upon its future use! With this act, the girls are returning to the earth what has been taken.

This reminds me, too, of many spiritual people's obsession with crystals, which are beautiful and sacred – but which are also mined from the earth, and often in harmful, harsh ways. It can be helpful to remind ourselves that, even when working with crystal magick, we must be mindful of giving back to the source, the earth, which gives to us all. Without her blessings, we cannot survive or thrive.

The Wisdom of Snow White and Rose Red

THIS IS AN UNUSUAL TALE, AS BOTH THE heroines have an unshakable friend and ally in the other. Most faerytale heroes and heroines are abandoned and alone – but these girls and their bond is central to the story. It's given much more focus than their bond with the princes, and is an ode to the power of female friendship.

But what if we have no such bond in our lives? I like to think the story asks us to consider being compassionate, still – to help even when there is no apparent reward for doing so (as there is no gratitude from the dwarf!). The family's hospitality and willingness to share – to give to each other, to the bear, to the forest, and even to the faeries – has its own reward, that of a contentment that comes from being in tune with the world, rather than grasping to take all that it has. In these ways, *Snow White and Rose Red* is a story of generosity, of compassion, of solidarity and loyalty, of hospitality and sharing. The love stories within the tale seem to spring from these qualities. Perhaps the tale is sharing with us that true relationships are built upon that foundation.

It is a delightful tale, and it lightens my heart to think of that happy, all-female family, a little priestess-hood deep in the forest, at peace with each other and with nature, wise and free and blessed.

RAPUNZEL

ONCE, THERE WAS A MAN AND WOMAN

who lived in a sweet little farmhouse far away in the countryside. They had few neighbours, and their nearest was a very old woman who lived in a tumbledown thatched cottage. She had the most wonderful garden, which went right to the border of the couple's little farmyard. Her flowers grew highest, her trees shone with life, and the birds, with whom she shared the fruits, flocked to her orchard.

The man and the woman loved to sit and gaze at the old woman's garden, which all the creatures enjoyed. But stare was all they could do – for while she was friendly to all the animals of the land and the birds of the sky, all the winged and furred ones, she could not abide people.

The man and the woman were very happy together, and loved each other dearly and truly. They had a little goat, and chickens, a cat to keep away the mice, and four fine dogs, but their world did not feel complete. They wanted very much to have a child, and although they had been married for near nine years, no child had come to make them whole.

One day, after the woman had milked the goat and tidied the cottage and swept the yard, she found herself dreaming of the child she longed to have … and at that very moment, a little bird flew into their neighbour's garden and sat upon a tree just above a sea of beautiful, slender herbs, whose tall stems were the softest green, with a little purple flower springing from each side of the stalk.

The woman stared at the perfect green of the rapunzel herbs – how they vibrated with energy. *If only*, she said to herself, *I could eat a little of those greens. I am sure, then, I would draw in the child I know is around me.*

She rubbed her flat belly gently and felt her hunger grow for that green and purple herb.

A whole field of rapunzel, almost, she thought to herself. *Surely, she of the cottage wouldn't mind if I had just a little?*

Just as she'd had the thought, the little bird flew from the tree, dove into the rapunzel patch, and plucked a few of the shining green strands from the earth. It gathered them up in its sweet little beak, flew over to the woman, and dropped them at her feet.

"Thank you, sweet bird," she said, surprised.

She took the herbs into her cottage, and when she had her soup that lunchtime, she sprinkled the green herb atop it and savoured its peppery goodness.

Sure enough, within days, she found she was carrying a babe.

The couple's happiness was so deep and so strong, they felt nothing could shake their world. But with every day, the strange hunger the wife had for the rapunzel plant grew and grew, and soon the little bird could barely keep up with her desire for the green herb that flourished in the old woman's garden. Within a moon, the bird had to fly back and forth from the witch's garden to the woman almost without pause, just to bring the woman the herb she craved.

She ate and she ate, then she craved and she ate again. Nothing could satisfy her hunger, until one day, when the bird was too tired to fly, she strode into the old woman's garden and fell to her knees, pulling one of the remaining plants from the warm summer earth with her bare hands and devouring it.

It was there that the old woman found her.

You see, the old woman was a sorceress, and all of her herbs were magickal. It was forbidden for humans to eat of them, and so she struck the mother with her cane.

"What are you doing here? You have dared to eat from my garden? You have destroyed my rapunzel patch!" she cried in anger.

"I craved it so – do not strike me! I am with child," the mother said, shrinking back from the blows.

"I will do more than strike you. I will cast forth your babe," the old sorceress said, her voice dark with bitterness.

"No. There must be a way," pleaded the mother.

"Stupid woman! You do not even apologise for your theft! For this offence I will have your life and the babe's," the crone shot out, her eyes red with fury.

And the mother screamed.

At that moment, her husband, hearing the screams, ran into the old woman's garden. "No," he said with courage. "You cannot take her, old woman."

"I will take something," the sorceress snapped back. "I will have that babe, then, when she is born. You know it is a girl, yes?" she said, her eyes cunning and bright. "You shall give her to me."

"No," wailed the mother.

"It's that, or death," the sorceress snarled.

"We can have more children," whispered the husband. "The deal is done," he said, his voice anguished. He lifted his wife and took her into the shelter of his arms.

"She shall be named Rapunzel," called the old woman after them, as he carried his wife away. "For that which you stole from me, I shall now steal from you."

And, indeed, when this babe was born, the old woman crept in the very first night, while the parents slept, and took the babe from the cradle before they awoke.

The sorceress then abandoned her garden, for now she had a child to tend to, to play with,

to care for. She had been lonely and had hated humans for so long, to have one of her own was a strange delight. She dressed the babe, she fed her, and in time she taught her. But when she noticed people admiring the child and the hopeless agony of her neighbours, she knew she would move.

"Everyone covets what's mine," she muttered. "The garden, the plants, and the fruits from the orchard. But they shall not have my Rapunzel."

She took the child far away, carrying her in her arms to a high, tall tower the sorceress knew was abandoned. About the tower were fine herbs and plants, which she began to tend, and in time, she removed the lovely child further and further from the world, until, finally, the little girl never left the tower, and gazed out from it through eyes that grew larger, and clearer, and sweeter with each passing day.

But it was her hair that was the marvel.

The witch never cut a single hair on that child's head – not from birth. And what hair it was. Golden and long and strong as a vine. For the witch fed Rapunzel all the good things of the earth, and she was a blooming, healthful child.

In time, she became a young woman, and her wondrous hair grew and grew.

Seeing her beauty blossoming, the old witch grew fearful. *If someone should see her, they would want her*, she thought.

She imagined blighting the girl's beauty, to ward off others, but she did not want to deny herself the pleasure of Rapunzel's face.

Then, she knew the answer ... and slowly, with her magick, she took away the tower steps, and its doors, and all the floors in the tower, except the one that held Rapunzel's room, right at the very top. All vanished, as though they had never existed. And amidst the herbs about the tower, she began to grow the thorniest of trees and plants, knowing none would dare approach this fierce garden.

***

WITHIN THAT TOWER, RAPUNZEL BLOOMED, though she was pale without the sun. Every morning, when the day dawned, the old sorceress left the tower room she shared with Rapunzel and scoured the countryside for the herbs and stones she needed for her potions.

How did she leave this tower, you ask? This tower that had no ladder, no vines, no stairs – did she fly?

No. For Rapunzel's hair had grown so exceedingly long that it reached from the very top of the tower to cover the plants on the ground below. And so, each day, the old woman would say:

"Rapunzel, Rapunzel, let down your hair!"

And Rapunzel, making a game of it, would take her great, shining braid and fling it out the window – it was good she was so strong and well, for her hair was heavy, near as weighty as spun gold.

Some days, when the old woman was gone, the girl would lean out the tower window and turn her face to the sky to feel the sun's warmth upon her face, the dance of the air upon her skin. She would sing to the sky, opening her heart, and that would leave her feeling better, for sometimes sorrow gathered within her.

Why is it, she thought, *that I am never with my mother* – for so she thought the old woman – *on her foraging? I would love to visit the forest for myself and see the plants growing within the woods. To smell them, to have the sun on my whole body! To dance with moss underfoot.*

These were her humble dreams.

One night, when the old woman returned, after they ate their soup – of wild rapunzel – and chewed the bread and devoured their berries and honey, Rapunzel took the bowls, and set them in a bucket of rainwater, and turned to the old woman.

"What is the forest like, Mother? Is it green, and fresh, and sweet?"

"Ah, it is my beauty," said the old woman, picking up a brush as Rapunzel unbraided her hair.

"It is as sweet as freedom," the old woman added as she began to brush the girl's hair. "It is a land of faery folk and wild things, all still and lovely, of flowers so rare none have seen them but me, and trees older than the books I've left you." She chuckled, for she had humour, this old woman, dry as a bone though it was.

Rapunzel read, and sang, and played a harp the old woman had found in the forest and brought up with her. She helped with the herbs and stirred the cauldron within which they were brewed. But the old woman's words had fed her hunger to be in the world, rather than apart from it.

She recorded every potion in a book, for she was taught her letters, and sometimes, in the long days in the tower, she experimented, and little explosions would litter the floor with ash and dragon's blood and frankincense. She would wipe her lovely face and begin again. So, she sang, and she wrote, and she danced, too, all in the small, walled circle that had become her entire world.

One day, while mixing the potions, she added salt to the brew, and a huge *boom!* scattered the birds that often gathered at her window. She coughed and gasped for air and put out the flames in the cauldron with the water the old woman had left for her.

But the boom from her cauldron had been heard. Sometimes, travellers nearby thought they heard a faery song coming from the old tower, but this great noise echoed through the trees, until it reached the young ears of a fine prince, riding in the woods, far from the tower.

He turned his horse in the direction of the sound, finally tying his steed to an old oak and making his way by foot through the tangles of the dense woods. Then, he saw the tower rising above the ancient trees, and he beheld a girl, young, with a beautiful voice, leaning out the tower window, singing to the sky – and coughing just a wee bit, too.

He pushed his way through the forest of thorns and herbs the sorceress had created and found himself at the bottom of the tower. But he did not call out to the girl. He just listened to her song, gazing up at her beauty. And then, as the sun was close to setting, he heard the old woman making her way through the trees, grumbling about this and that, and he stepped back, melting into the gathering darkness and watched as the crone stepped forward, a woven basket heavy upon her back.

"Rapunzel," she cried. "Rapunzel, Rapunzel! Let down your hair!"

And he watched as a golden waterfall of a braid fell from the tower and reached all the way to the ground.

The old women shoved her pointed boot into the braid, just as if it was the strongest rope, and he watched as she climbed the girl's hair, swinging a little, side to side, agile and strong for a woman of her age. (That's what years of walking in the woods will do for you.)

He left the tower, returned to his horse, and rode back to his castle. He thought and thought, and then he slept, and his dreams were full of a voice like a silver bell and hair of gold, falling from a tower. And in his dream, he said

RAPUNZEL

the words, and he climbed that hair. And when he reached the tower, he found her.

That night, Rapunzel, also had a dream, the strangest dream. In it, someone – not the old woman – was climbing her hair to the tower. But Rapunzel could not see their face.

***

THE NEXT DAY, THE PRINCE SET OFF BEFORE dawn. He made his way through the woods, and walked his horse for the last part of the journey. He tied his steed to a slender birch, and crept closer, hiding, sheltered by the old oaks and hawthorns and ash, and watched as dawn turned the world to rose gold.

As the sun rose a little higher, he heard a voice – *Hers*, he thought, a bird of rapture flying across his heart; then he heard another voice, more pepper and salt. *That's the old woman,* he thought, and he felt fear.

The shining tresses fell, sparkling in the light, and the old woman wound her way down the rope of Rapunzel's hair. Once she reached the ground, she turned, as if sniffing the sir, suspicious and frowning, but the forest seemed to close about him for a second, shielding him.

He watched. The girl sang. She talked to herself awhile, of magickal things, of herbs and birds and song.

And then she talked of a dream, where a stranger had come to the tower and called out her name, and she had, she confided to the birds, her voice drifting down, let down her hair, and the stranger had climbed to her tower room, and she was so happy, she said. It was a dream. But it felt so real.

"Rapunzel, Rapunzel, let down your hair," he whispered, gathering courage.

"Louder," he commanded himself. "She dreamt of me. 'Tis meant to be."

"Rapunzel, Rapunzel! Let down your hair," he said, stronger.

Until, finally, he stepped into the light of day and called out, with all the strength in his young body, "Rapunzel, Rapunzel, let down your hair!"

She stopped.

She looked down. And as if in the very same dream she'd dreamt that last night, she let down her hair.

He thrust his boot into the golden mass, although it seemed a sin. It was so strong, yet so soft to the touch, he noticed. And he began to climb.

***

EVERY DAY, FOR THREE MOONS, THIS TOOK place. The old king was disturbed, as the prince was no longer spending time at the castle, but roaming the forest, instead. Some said he was bewitched by a faery. But none knew truly where the prince went.

And, still, the old woman was no wiser.

The prince and Rapunzel spoke of many things and fell, as young people with pure hearts do, deeply in love. They did all the things young people in love do, and to be together was bliss.

Until one day, they fell asleep, just as the sun was readying to lower in the sky and the old woman was making her way homewards through the woods.

"Rapunzel, Rapunzel! Let down your hair," she cried, and the two awoke from their deep sleep, their lovers' rest, nested within each other's arms.

"Let her climb," the prince said. "Let us

talk – let us find a way to have you leave this tower," he said. He had begged Rapunzel to come with him, again and again, before this, but she had not wanted to leave the old woman all alone. She knew she was the woman's only solace.

"She will not allow that," said Rapunzel, now. "She is darkness – with me she can be good, but she will end you, if she knows."

So, he slipped into the shadows beneath the bed, and the old one climbed, and when she entered, Rapunzel calmly asked her of her day, and tried her best not to glance over to where her love had hidden himself.

"Mother," she said. "Are you not tired after such a long day? Here, let me mix you a draft to help you sleep. Tonight, let's rest early – the long days take their toll, I see."

"I'm too busy – too much to do," said the old one, who would never admit to feeling anything other than perfectly all right.

"Come, now. You do so much. Let me, this night, prepare the potions. You know I can. And here – drink this. See what you think," said the girl.

The old woman smiled, showing three teeth like tombstones for triplets, and drank the draft as cheerily as someone of her disposition could. She lay back on the little bed that was hers with a raspy sigh, and fell instantly into a deep sleep, sprinkled with beautiful dreams.

She twitched a little, but when she settled into snoring, Rapunzel said, as low as could be, "Come out, now, my love."

They kissed, and the prince climbed down her golden hair into the night, and they were safe to spend another day together.

The next morning, the witch arose, as always, and climbed down the hair of Rapunzel, but instead of venturing into the woods, she stayed

close by. She'd noticed the girl was different. More colour in her cheeks. Like a woman awakened from the enchantment of the girl she had been.

And she was nothing if not a very suspicious and very wise old woman. So, she hovered beneath the tower, making herself busy amongst the healing mosses and red amaranth, with its sweet green flowers, glancing up every now and again.

And then, he came.

He called.

He climbed.

And the old sorceress saw the girl's betrayal.

She waited beneath the tower, her anger growing around her heart like thorns.

And when the prince began his climb down that evening, the sorceress stepped out and screamed a great and terrible curse, raising her sickle-shaped boline in the air like a cruel moon, the herb knife glittering in the setting sun like a spell.

"Fall, fall, you false creature – your love will blind you, now!"

And the prince fell from way up high, and was caught in a cradle of thorns that reached for him, and his eyes were blinded by their savage cuts, and all the world for him went to dark.

He awoke a long way away, but where, he knew not. He stumbled, broken, through an endless night, and could not even cry, for his eyes could no longer shed tears. His heart was torn, his love was gone, and all the world was cold and black, and joy was forever lost to him.

***

WHEN THE PRINCE FELL, THE WITCH CAUGHT Rapunzel's hair before the girl could pull it back up. The woman climbed and climbed, and when she clambered in the window, the girl stepped forward to meet her gaze.

Why is she not afraid? the old woman wondered.

"You betrayed me," she accused the bold girl. "I gave you everything. I gave you my knowledge, and shelter, and food, and safety. You were without any need, and you took it all gladly. Never could the world hurt you."

"But you could hurt me, Mother. You kept me chained within this tower. Now I must go."

"Go, then," screamed the witch. "But first, you shall give me your hair."

And she took the sickle knife, the boline with which she cut the herbs, and in one dreadful slash, she cut off Rapunzel's hair. She tied the rope of hair to the window, and dragged the girl to its sill. "I could fling you down and break you into pieces," she snarled.

"Is that what you did to my love?" asked Rapunzel, winter in her voice.

And the witch said, "Yes. And worse still. You shall not find him, you foolish girl." And she took Rapunzel in her strong old arms and climbed the girl down her own hair, dragged her into the forest, and flung her by the banks of a stream.

"Survive, if you can," said the old one, "without all I gave you. You are alone, and no-one loves you, not even your own mother who gave you to me. I loved you, I alone, but now no-one ever shall care for you again." And the old sorceress turned, ranting and raving. As she made her way through the forest, the very trees shrank from her spite and bitterness.

There Rapunzel sat, upon a log, feeling for the first time the terrible blessing of freedom, with all the sorrowful clarity of knowing the old woman was not her mother. But after a while, she shook off the shock and began to gather herbs to make a little dinner.

In the days that followed, she wound a trail through the forest, searching hopelessly for her love. She took comfort in all the small creatures around her – the birds sang songs to her, and in time, she found a little abandoned cottage, with a hearth, and a stove, and a cauldron. She gathered blueberries, catsfoot, and wood ear mushrooms, and found nuts and blackberries and good roots to eat, and she made do. She found peace and a fair amount of joy in moving about. Just washing in the stream that ran outside her cottage door made her quietly happy.

But her longing for her love did not cease.

One morning, she was singing with the birds. They would sing one line, and she would reply. Then she would begin a new line, and they would follow her lead. When she looked up, she saw a man standing right at the edge of the glade in which her home nestled.

He was wild and tangled, covered in vines, almost a thing of the woods. He wore ragged clothes that once had been fine, and where his eyes should have been was a piece of cloth. He walked forward, graceful, though he could not see.

"My love," he said, and she ran to greet him.

"My love, my love," she cried. "You are blinded."

"I cannot see you," he said, his hands reaching for her. "But I heard your voice."

"All will be well," she cried. "We are together again."

"I am not who I was," he said, sadly.

"I am not who I was," she said.

And she held him while he shuddered

with sobs, and placed his face in her lap.

"Let me see," she said, as she unwound the bandage from his poor, unsighted eyes. "I can make a healing poultice for you."

"I know your skill," he said gratefully. "But no poultice can cure these wounds."

She did not gasp or make a sound when the terrible wounds were revealed. But her beautiful eyes filled with tears. They rolled down her face, and very slowly, two great, heavy drops fell into her prince's poor, blind eyes.

And he blinked.

And he blinked.

And he began to see before him the beautiful face he thought he'd lost, and as each great tear fell, more of his sight returned, until there she was, the forest light soft and sweet around her, her face a flower amidst the halo of short golden hair, and he reached for her.

"Your hair," he breathed, touching the dandelion crown of her head.

"Your eyes," she said, kissing them again and again.

And they held each other, and laughed.

In time, the prince returned to his kingdom, and so did Rapunzel. And she told her strange story to the king. He was a wise man, and he sent out messengers across the land to find out more about the girl, and in time, they came to a sweet little farmhouse, bordered by a great wild witch's garden, and within they found her own true parents.

And they came to the castle for the wedding, and, in time, she began to know them.

And they were happy, ever after, indeed. Children came, and long years went.

And never did they see that witch again.

DISCOVER THE MAGICK OF RAPUNZEL

"RAPUNZEL, RAPUNZEL! Let down your hair!"

A golden waterfall fell from the tower and reached all the way to the ground.

The old woman shoved her pointed boot into the braid, and she climbed, swinging a little, side to side, agile for a woman of her age.

(That's what years of walking in the woods will do for you.)

History of this Tale

I'VE ALWAYS LOVED THE luscious imagery and tactility of the *Rapunzel* tale. When I first read it, I was captivated by the extreme length of her hair, I dreaded the sharp prick of the thorns that grew in the forest, and I shivered at the thought of being kept in that lonely tower, so far away, so cruel and enchanting.

I also relished the herbal magick aspect of the tale, and so I hope I've successfully brought the wondrous rapunzel herb, with its lavender bells, right into the heart of the story. But most of all, I loved the sense that Rapunzel's tears are healing. In a world that still insists upon viewing tears as weak, there is so much strength in this story where the heroine's tears have restorative powers when shed with love and compassion.

BEFORE THE STORY WE ARE FAMILIAR WITH first appeared, there was an old Persian folktale from the 11th century about a princess in a tower who lets down her night-coloured hair so her lover can climb up and reach her. And Saint Barbara, who was walled up inside a tower by her cruel father, finds an echo in *Rapunzel*, too. But the origin of the story we know best is the French version – the "parsley" version – written by Charlotte-Rose de Caumont, in 1694. With shifting European borders, this French version found its way into German territory, where its parsley-inspired heroine, *Parsinelle*, morphed into the Rapunzel we know now. That version was first published in the German language in 1812. (There is also a related tale, Italian in origin, first published in 1634.)

I like to think, though, that the deepest heart of *Rapunzel* lies in the ancient Celtic legends of female seers, known as "walas", or "veledas". These solar oracles took up residence within towers built high enough for them to connect with the rays of morning light and divine messages from the sun – which they did, well before any of the folk living closer to the ground had the chance to.

The rays of the sun were symbolised by the seers' extraordinarily long hair, tumbling from the towers. So, within the *Rapunzel* story lies this idea of an oracle of the sun, a bringer of light, who must first learn the secrets of the dark forest before breaking the forest's spell in order to bring light and fecundity back into the world.

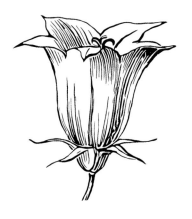

HEALING AND MAGICKAL HERBS

I WANTED THE FOREST IN THE STORY TO FEEL very alive for readers, and so I included a level of detail about the flora of the forest that I had not encountered within other versions of the story. The plants are central to the whole tale, for without the witch's herb garden (no trespassing!), our heroine with the longest hair that ever was, would never have been born at all.

The most prominent herb in the story is, of course, Rapunzel's namesake. But in the French versions of the tale, Rapunzel, herself, is named Parsinelle, after parsley – so this herbal theme runs through all the versions of the tale. The strange thing about naming the heroine Parsinelle, or *Persinette*, is that parsley was once used as an early herbal aborticant – a form of birth control meant to prevent unwanted pregnancies. Yet, the German versions of the stories have the girl named for the rapunzel herb, which, as a self-fertilising herb, has quite different properties – properties which allow the mother within my version of the tale to become pregnant. So, perhaps the herb itself impregnates the woman, rather than her husband's seed?

The rapunzel herb is also known as rampion and as evening primrose oil, which today is sold in health food stores to ease pre-menstrual syndrome and regulate hormones. Interesting that Rapunzel's mother was drawn to the very herb that, in modern times, has been used to help with women's fertility cycles!

Of course, a witch's herbal garden, a kind of magickal apothecary, ought to be sacred, and trespassing in a wise woman's garden is never a good idea. At first, Rapunzel's mother has the help of the birds to bring her the herb she craves, but as her pregnancy develops, she craves so much that she exhausts her winged helpers, bringing that relationship into imbalance.

Rapunzel really is the most exquisite plant. It is delicate, edible, and medicinal – and is also associated with faeries, due to its lavender-coloured, bell-shaped blossoms, so there is an element of otherworldly healing attached to the herb. It's associated with balance between the human and faery worlds, natural gifts, loyalty, wise women, and visions of the otherworld! An old Italian folktale features a rapunzel plant, that, when pulled from the ground, reveals a faery stairway that opens to the crystal caves beneath the surface of the land.

Who would not want a little of the magick of *Rapunzel* in their world?

The Maiden in the Tower

The tower in the story is all that remains of a ruin, a forgotten part of a lost world. And as it is almost impossible to reach, it is the perfect place to lock away – or, as the witch believes, "protect" – Rapunzel from the outside world. It is the witch's fortress, and it keeps her "child" away from all except those who are willing to pass a great test to find her, as the prince does. Initially the tower is surrounded at its base by herbs and flowers – wisdom and learning, medicine and healing. But over time, as the witch wishes to keep all away from Rapunzel, she begins to draw to her the thorned ones of the forest, and a bramble-hedge of hawthorns (which, in the Celtic Ogham system of trees, is said to establish borders) surrounds the tower, preventing others from ever reaching Rapunzel. The tower in this tale does not fall, like the Tower card in Tarot, signifying an ending to a great power or an abrupt shattering of the status quo in the life of the reader. This tower has a more subtle fate, after Rapunzel finds her freedom – I like to think it would be completely consumed by the wild, so it can never be used cruelly again.

The Maiden, the Crone, and the Lost Mother

This is one of several examples of a tale where the mother – the true mother – is absent, and the crone (the witch) brings up the maiden. This theme shows up again and again in the tales, as if motherhood itself was so precarious the stories are invoked to show us we must be prepared to lose that love at some point, in order to grow and mature ourselves.

Terrestrial Potions Made in a Celestial World

I love the idea that Rapunzel helps to make the witch's potions. It gives her a connection to the earth, which she cannot reach, locked away as she is. So, the magick of the deep earth and the promise that she too can one day walk amidst the bounty of the forest is hinted at in the presence of the herbs she comes to know in her room in the sky.

Witches' potions are, of course, powerful things – the right blend of herb and root, stone and flower can create a potent concoction that is sometimes drunk, sometimes bathed in. A potion is a watery thing – like tears themselves – and the tears that Rapunzel has within her are the base of the most powerful magickal potion she will ever bring to birth.

If you decide to make a potion, do be sure to use ingredients that are safe to be ingested (if the potion is to be drunk) and safe for use on your skin (if it is to be used for anointing or blessing). Many herbs cannot be ingested, nor can their oils be applied neat, directly to the skin.

Of course, witches' magickal potions are the precursors of most modern medicines. Within them is held much ancient wisdom, and to create them is to reconnect with that long line of witches or wizards who may belong somewhere within your own particular human faerytale of ancestry and entanglements with the divine.

The Magick of Long Hair

Long, flowing hair has many magickal attributes. We have already learned that Rapunzel's hair connects her to ancient Celtic sun oracles. But there is a thread running through every culture about the power of our hair. To some cultures, hair is seen as an extension of the nervous system, alive and sensitive, able to react before the rest of the body to threats or wonders. I believe hair is an extremely sensitive organ, not dead, yet not quite alive – infinitely subtle, it is almost like antennae, or a feeler, or a cat's whisker.

The hair on the head is connected to the crown chakra, and thus to our power for sovereignty. The absence of hair can show humility and openness. A head can be shaved as an act of devotion or rebirthing, recreating childhood within us, a tie to when we were newborn, when, as we grow into awareness and experience, our hair grows, and attached to it are all of our experiences and memories. Yet a head may also be shaved as an act of punishment and humiliation.

For some, their hair is a very real source of sixth-sensory abilities. During the Vietnam War in the 1960s, for example, reports emerged of Choctaw and Navajo men being recruited specifically for their uncanny ability to move through enemy lines undetected. They were said to have "outstanding, almost supernatural tracking abilities". Yet, their officers were surprised at the men's inability to duplicate in the field the results they had showed at home.

Older recruits explained that, after receiving their required military haircuts, they could no longer "sense" their enemies, and could no longer read the signs about them. One report claimed that tests went on to show that of these Native American recruits, those with long hair out-performed recruits who had the military haircut. The scouts had, in truth, lost a vital part of their sixth-sensory ability, along with their hair.

And in various spells, hair is used as a kind of personal signature – a way of being recognised by the deities. A small portion of hair can be burned in a cauldron, or contained within a locket, or buried to support the very real connection of the spell's energy to the spellcaster. It is one reason that those who gather hair to use in spells without the person's consent are not acting, I feel, ethically. This was done to me once, and it is the act of a person with serious boundary issues.

Rapunzel's hair is her strength and her

vitality, her connection to the sun and to the earth. It is a golden ladder that marries the heavens and the earth, the celestial and the terrestrial. And, for an added touch of enchantment, her glorious hair is braided, which in itself is a magickal act. Braids are a variation of the Celtic knot, which shows the interconnectivity of all things and creates a strong bond between parts. Braids use three strands, so the power of three becomes woven into the hair. Often, I have braided my hair with one word for each strand – so love, insight, and strength may be my words for a day. Or, if we are weaving the hair of a child, for example, we may wish to weave in three qualities we would like our child to have as they go about their day.

Making Magick: Rapunzel's Magickal Braid Spell

Recreate a little of the magick of Rapunzel with this simple, but very effective, hair charm. Take a section of your hair, divide it into three, and begin to braid it. As you cross each strand of hair, you are binding good fortune, love, delight, wisdom, protection – all the good things you wish for – into your hair, into your energy field, and into your emotional and physical bodies.

This is also a way to work with a spell called the Witch's Ladder, a traditional knotwork spell. Here are the words, which you may wish to adapt and rework to best suit your intent and the beings you are working with. Enjoy! Have fun, and feel the sense of protection and extra magick this gives you!

By knot of one, the spell's begun
By knot of two, my spell is true
By knot of three, blessed be
By knot of four, the open door
By knot of five, the spell's alive
By knot of six, this spell we fix
By knot of seven, earth as is heaven.

Seal it off with a pretty hair band or tie, adorn it with tiny bells, a feather, or a shell, or simply leave it natural and simple – whatever you feel is best! As you tie the hair off, bind it three times, each time saying, *As I do will, so mote it be!*

The Healing Power of Tears

There is a potency to tears that moves us, draws out what lies right in the centre of us. When we see pure tears shed, we know we are witnessing a sublimely human act, one which can reflect a huge variety of moods and purposes. There are tears shed for joy and for fear, tears of pain, of grief, and of empathy, too. Each of these types of tears contains vast amount of chemicals – when we cry we are simultaneously connecting

and releasing, allowing ourselves, for a moment, to fall into the softest part of ourselves.

Rapunzel weeps when she is confronted by the image of her love, blinded, his eyes unable to weep even for himself. So, she weeps for him, and into him, almost like a watery kiss of life, and restores his sight and brings back his own ability to weep, and be emotional, too. Thus, Rapunzel, like her namesake herb, brings about clarity and emotional balance through the release and sharing of feelings, the core of our tender humanity.

Men's tears and women's tears are viewed differently, and there are strict protocols around appropriate places to cry within our cultures. But we are changing – we see more men weep, today, and we mistrust those who are not moved by life's poignancies. The tears we once held back, dammed within, we are now able to release, and as we do this, culturally, our ability to feel and to see is also being restored to us. When we move beyond the need to shame anyone for the tears they shed, we may move into a new and more compassionate stage of our human evolution.

The Wisdom of Rapunzel

I think this tale shares with us that within every strand of hair there is a little life force. But within tears there is *power*. If this version of the story can make people feel better about their emotions, make them feel that their tears could even be healing, that would be wonderful. Embrace your emotions! Know that you are magickal, right to the tips of your fingers. Know

that if you dare to show the world how you truly feel, if you embrace your tears as much as you do your smiles and your laughter, you will become stronger than you could ever have imagined.

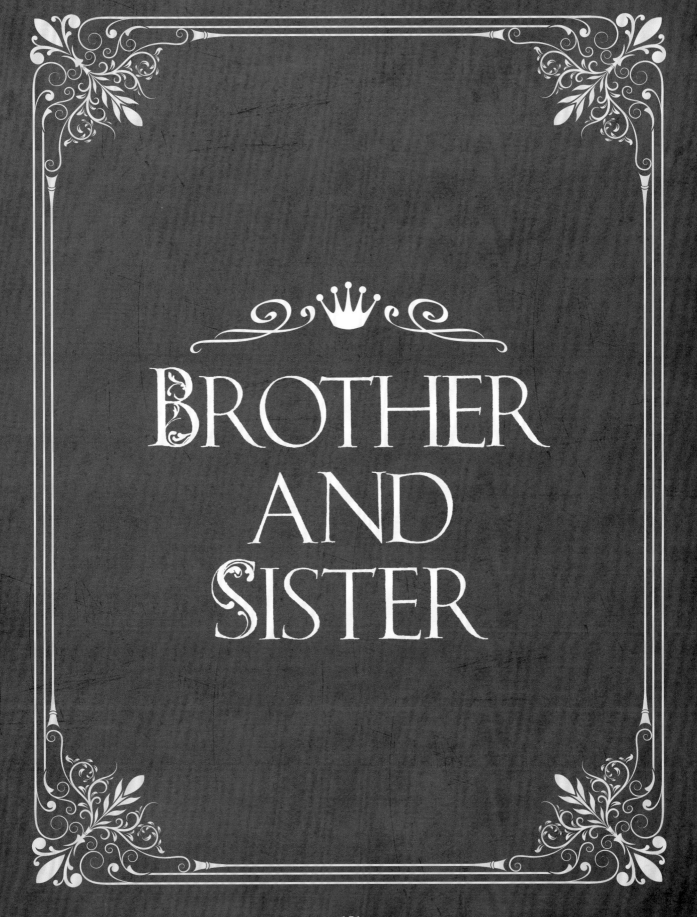

Brother and Sister

BROTHER

WHEN CHILDREN SEE ME, AND THEY ASK whether I did something bad – as if I look like this as punishment for something – I just let them look and take in my strangeness. In time, they will decide for themselves whether I am living with a blessing or a curse. And I wonder what they would say if they knew who made me thus. But that is the end of the story. The beginning is long ago, and it is where we must start.

From before we were born, Sister and I did everything together. We shared each breath in the underwater of our mother's womb. Once we emerged from the dark water into the heavy world of the air, we were devoted to each other. And later, in our suffering, we protected each other. Sister threw herself over me when fists rained down, and I took the kicks aimed at her. I looked after her, and she tended my wounds until they scarred. And we loved one another. Despite it all, we never turned on each other. I think it is because of this that neither of us became warped with hate and bitterness.

And perhaps we still believed Father would awaken from her dark enchantment and protect us from our cruel stepmother, who cared only for her own daughter.

But one day, tired of hunger, and of counting the scars, cuts, and bruises on our skin, the last tendril of hope that Father would save us from our torment, died. Out of sight and hearing of our callous stepmother and her daughter, I murmured, "Sister, we have nothing to eat but scraps from her table. Nothing but harsh words and insults from her lips. And she beats us both. If we stay, she might kill us."

"I can feel my spirit dying," whispered my sister.

"Let us leave," I urged, "and place ourselves in the hands of our wits and of fate."

Ensuring she was not seen, Sister slipped into Stepmother's room, the one she shared with our father. Sister went to a great chest and looked a little while, before taking out a long, fine golden chain.

"Mother's?" I asked.

"Mine," she replied, looping it about her white neck.

I took her hand, and we began to walk away from the house. We walked and we walked ... stony roads pushed into our feet and cut open our soles, wheat fields gave way to us as we waded through the golden crops, and soft sweet meadows of flower-sprinkled green filled our senses with hope. But that hope soon faded. Rain began to fall, and when it grew heavy, my sister began to cry like the clouds, saying whichever god looked over us, be they old god or new, they were weeping at our fate.

Finally, we entered a vast, dark forest. We were so drenched, so worn with sorrow, and so empty in our hearts and stomachs, we could not walk another step. We helped each other into a great oak tree, and we slept in its strong arms, beneath the full cover of its leaves.

We rested in those broad branches till dawn's song woke us. The previous day's rain had vanished, and our hunger was terrible. Still, we were used to hunger, but the cutting thirst was harder to bear. When I swallowed, my throat was like stone. We climbed down, thanked the tree, and squeezed what sap we could from the wild onions that circled the base of the oak – but it was not enough. Sister chewed on their stalks calmly, but my fortitude began to fray. I yearned for a deep spring by which to quench my dreadful thirst. We walked deeper into the forest

in silence, until the sun's rays forced their way through the foliage so far above our heads.

"Sister," I said at last. "I have a terrible thirst. I think I can hear a little stream. We must stop, and we will drink."

Sister

I had already felt the dryness of his throat, and the headache beating at his brow was echoed in mine. I always felt what he felt and knew what he needed before he voiced it. And I knew he would drink as soon as we came to the spring.

My need for cool, clean water was as deep as his, but my ears were keener. I could hear the spring, and I could also hear its song. I knew our path was cursed, and this spring would change whoever drank from it.

I could still hear our true mother teaching us, "We become that from which we drink." It was her way of telling us to be careful to whom we listened, learned from, and believed – and I believed this spring when it said it was enchanted. It was flowing with the curse of the false mother we fled from.

We couldn't help but stumble upon the spring, as it barred our way. It shone with light as it ran over the smooth clean stones and spoke to me in the way the world had always spoken to me. I could feel, hear, and know what others say they do not. And so, the spring sang to me – and I heeded it.

"Don't," I cautioned my brother. Pulling him back from the edge of the stream, I urged him to listen.

"I cannot; my head is pounding," he said,

his raw, thin voice an agony of thirst.

"Listen," I whispered, touching his ears with my hands.

Then he heard its song: *Whoever drinks from me will become a tiger. Whoever drinks from me will become a tiger.*

"Don't drink, my brother. You will change into something that will destroy us both. She has cursed this spring. We must endure and go on, or we will become what we drink from."

He trembled in fury, but he had heard, and we moved on.

BROTHER

WE WALKED FARTHER INTO THE FOREST. Though the summer was fierce, I knew the springs in those old woods still ran, and I would drink before nightfall. So, I listened to my sister, heard the spring, and was glad I did not drink in its curse. I would never want to harm her.

We walked wearily on. Tree branches are not as conducive to sleep as you might think, and going without food and drink is not as easy as it seems in tales like this. As we walked, I grew strange in my thoughts. My mind fevered for any sound, scent, or sight of fresh water. At last, we came to another spring. It ran less strong than the first, but it was just as enticing. The water was clean and good, and I waded in, filled my cupped hands and bent my head to drink.

SISTER

I SLAPPED THE WATER OUT OF HIS HANDS, and he howled with frustration. All I wanted was to drink and drink and drink, to ease the fire in my throat. But I knew I must fight. And he must, too. I took his hand and pulled him away from the stream.

"Brother, listen," I said.

"I can't hear it," he barked. His thirst raged, clouding his love for me.

"You can," I insisted, and touched his forehead.

And then he heard with his mind what the body would not admit: *Whoever drinks from me will become a wolf. Whoever drinks from me will become a wolf.*

He came back to himself, but I could see the madness of thirst was taking its toll. We trudged on, for there was nothing else to do.

"Brother, can you not see? She cursed the first spring – a tiger you would have become. But at the second, you would have become a wolf. She is growing weaker, I know it."

"Her magick could go on forever, but my body cannot," he protested. "What is next? Am I to become a hare? a fish? a tadpole? a worm? Perhaps it is better to be a wolf than to be eaten by the birds."

"If you give in to this, we will be lost to ourselves and each other forever," I said softly.

I knew our stepmother. Her way was to hit hard and strong. She would spend herself in her fury. We had become adept at knowing her limits … at knowing how much more we had to endure before she could muster the energy to raise her fists no more.

"Dear Brother, her magic is waning. She has but one more try left in her, and then, if we

hold on, we will be beyond her twisted ways. We will be free."

However, my brother could barely hear me. He was desperate for a drink.

Brother

The third spring claimed me. I ran on longer legs than hers, threw myself into the water, opened my mouth, and drank. I turned to see her weeping by the side of the stream.

"Don't!" I heard her beg me. "Brother don't – you will change."

But I had already succumbed to the spring's curse. When I clambered from the water, it was on four legs, and the forest was alive with scents and sounds. She wrapped her arms around my long, strong neck and wept. Bone-thin legs wobbled beneath my white-and-gold-furred body. My reflection in the stream was that of a small deer.

I drank some more water, for it tasted good, and the harm was already done. I ate some grass, and still she wept. Finally, I went to her and lay my head upon her lap. That seemed to help, and we slept a while.

When she woke, I could see she needed food and water – and for me to be strong. I gazed deeply into her eyes and felt her quick breath, her human smell, her strange, slow clumsiness. Yet, I loved her and wanted only to be near her.

She sat up slowly, putting two weak arms about me. "My brother," she said. "My sweet, I shall never leave you."

She reached about her throat for the golden necklace she had taken from the chest in our stepmother's room. It had once belonged to our true mother, and it was as strong and fine as she had been. My sister looped it about my neck, then plaited a leash of strong reeds. "Come now, sweetling," she murmured, holding the leash. "We need to find a home."

I would have walked with her without that gentle cord.

We journeyed onwards through the forest, and in time we came to a clearing with a well and a small house, as tiny as could be. Sweet wild herbs grew all about its wattle-and-daub walls. Sister stumbled to the well and pulled up a pail, and I could smell that water's goodness! She drank until not a drop was left in the bucket.

When Sister pushed open the old wooden door, years of dust and cobwebs caught in our throats. We blinked in the dimness of the room. She put her hands on her hips and looked about. No window, no chair ... but a fireplace, a bucket. She made a small, sure sound in her throat, like someone who knew exactly what to do. She went to the meadow beyond and gathered wild garlic, pretty yarrow, tender lamb's lettuce, and dandelion flowers with their bright heads and raggedy leaves. The willows around the well were hung with ragged strips of cloth. Sister bent down and tore a strip from the bottom of her dress, then held it tenderly to her heart, her lips moving in silent supplication to this pagan place. She kissed the cloth, and tied it around and about a strong branch filled with green life and promise, and knotted it three times, to bind whatever spell she was casting. She stood back and nodded, satisfied, then went to work scraping the bark from a willow tree, all the while begging its pardon, so she could make a potion to help us heal.

I watched her forage wild greens from beneath the weeping willows, their soft green branches trailing to the ground, shading me and the emerald clover that grew beneath their protective circle. I ate, enjoying the novel feeling of pulling my food straight from the ground, while Sister gathered me fresh grass – though it tasted strange from her hands. She lit a fire in the hearth and boiled a little water for a tea made of thyme. Restored, she found a young oak with bright, hard acorns and pounded them with a rock on a broad, flat stone. Then she mixed that rough flour with the well-water, sprinkled in her herbs, and baked that bread in the coals. Finally, she dampened the coals with water from the well, gentling the fire so it would burn less bright while we slept. Then Sister sang a little charm of protection over us both, and we grew drowsy with our full bellies. I nestled into her, she wrapped her arms about me, and on that first night in the forest, we slept deeper than we ever had before.

Sister

You could say we grew up in that forest. At times, we were still hungry, but we were not lonely. We were companions. At first, I spoke to Brother every day, but as we grew older, he became more of a deer, and I more of a human, and we no longer needed words. With every season's turn, Brother fit into his skin with greater ease. When his antlers came in, the change was more definite, though, and he could barely fit into the room we called home. Still, we slept within each other's warmth each night. He ate the clover, and I the wild herbs, acorn bread, and berries. Three summers later, I was strong and sun-gilded, he was lean and proud, and we ventured farther and farther from our clearing each day.

That worried me. I knew I must roam to find food, but he was restless for more than the life we had. I don't know what we thought would happen – I didn't give tomorrows much heed at all. I was busy finding food, storing what I could for winter, checking that the well was thriving and clear, weaving rough garments, and learning the calls of the birds of the forest. Each day, I knew the woods and myself a little better. I knew the cycles of the moon, the plants of the forest, and how to trap a fish. The solitude was a fine thing to me. I did not miss my father, and was glad to be free of my stepmother and the others who had turned their faces and conscience from our troubles. Brother and I shared the peace and quiet of our clearing in the woods, and it was as charmed as it could be. We were together. We were safe.

Brother

She was without another human. I was without any creatures like me. We were of our own kind. We survived hard winters. More than that, we thrived. She was clever and found ways to live where others would have surrendered to the wilderness.

One spring day, though, I sensed them, long before we heard the hooves of their horses. When the great call of a terrible horn tore through the forest, its sound urged me to run and run and outrun those who followed. But, wide-eyed, she cooed and calmed me, as she covered the fire, stilled the smoke, led me inside our home, and closed the door. She shook, and I trembled, until the beat of hooves and horn were long stilled.

SISTER

I SAW HIS DESIRE AT ONCE. IT WAS LIKE THE impulse that drew him to the spring, which he had resisted two times, but not the third. Now, I knew his urge would build with each call of the horn. The sound of that horn invoked a force as old as blood. I could feel his instinct shoot through him – to run, to fly before them, and to draw the danger away from me. He could have done it too ... so fleet was he, so brilliant and swift were his movements. And when the hunt returned a second time, he began to strike at the door with his antlers. I held him back with our mother's golden chain as best I could, but he reared in the agony of being so refused. His blood rushed with the heat of the chase, and he wanted it – the danger, the test, the near-death of it.

Oh, he pleaded, *let me go and join the hunt. I cannot stand it any longer.*

When thrice they came, I said, "If you must go, you must, but you hear me, little brother. You come back to me this night. I will not be left alone in these woods. When you hear these words, 'return, return, return,' you will come back to me."

It was an incantation I created in my own unlearned way, and all at once I felt I was a witch in the forest. I opened the door, and he turned once so that his great, brown eyes gazed into mine, and then he exploded with lightning speed into the wild green world of the woods.

His strength, poise, and grandeur were apparent. I heard them scream their anger at missing the antlers and the rare coat of white and gold that would be such a prize to them. They might miss today, but the draw of such a rare and splendid creature would be powerful. Now it had

begun, the hunt would not abate.

I did not light the fire, but paced outside, listening, feeling, and trembling for his safety. Suddenly, the birds of the forest fell silent, and I called out to him in the emptiness, "Return, return, return."

Maybe I should have summoned him sooner.

I heard later that he stood still in their path and looked at the hunters, as if he wanted to speak to them. Perhaps, for a moment, he was dazed by the memory of who he had been. It was then that an arrow found his leg – but they did not bring him down. He fought off the dogs with his antlers and vanished into the bracken, as only wild things can. When the hunt was abandoned for that day, and the men returned to wherever it is they go to rest from killing, my brother, the stag, came back to me.

I led him by the golden chain back into the cottage and gazed about the clearing. Brother was sure he had been followed, and I thought I sensed a human presence, too. Seeing nothing, though, I closed the door on the forest, on the hunt, and made him a bed of fresh rushes and tended his hurt. The fire I made at dusk was low and cautious. I needed heat to nurse the wound.

Then, in the gloom of the evening, through the smoke of my fire, I saw a man.

I stood and screamed a banshee yell, and lifted my fist to the sky. Although I had not spoken a word in anger for so very many years, my tongue called down all manner of horrors upon him. The man fled, shaking and snapping the saplings in his haste. I went back in and spent the night half asleep, not knowing when they would come once more.

THE KING

THE HUNTSMAN TOLD ME THE GOLDEN STAG had fled to a cottage in the forest, where a young woman had hugged him, taken him in, and closed the door. The huntsman swore they had spoken. He said that when she came out later, she screamed dreadful spells down upon him.

"A witch, sire," he said, terrified. "She may have cursed us all."

I did not believe the young woman to be a witch – I had heard too many men use that word when coming across a woman they did not understand. But his words intrigued me, so I decided to find the mysterious stag, myself.

The next day, I saw him ... with his great brown eyes, his fine white-and-gold hide, and his antlers, silver-white in the soft morning light. He had a poultice on his wounded leg and a fine golden chain about his neck. The hunters had seen that flash of gold the day before, and some thought him a faerie beast. The man who fired the wounding arrow was convinced he had shot a White Hart and could not be consoled. There was already talk that the woman was its keeper, and that he, perhaps all of us, would be cursed.

I stood before the stag in awe. He knew me, and I knew him. For all that I was a man, and he was a beast, he seemed to know I wished to make amends for his wound. He turned, and I followed him straight to the cottage the huntsman had spoken of. There, in the garden, was a wild girl of gold, white, and blue. Her pale hair coiled in and out of itself in great loops. Her wide eyes were the colour of the sky. Her skin was golden brown. She was a beauty, pretty as a wildflower, strong as owl's claws – and I stared, struck dumb by her presence.

She ran to the stag, and though I could not hear the words she crooned to him, I felt the whole wild world become gentle at her voice and with her touch. I stepped forward softly, so as not to startle her. She stared at the bow in my hands, and stepped between me and the stag.

"What do you want with us?" the strange girl asked. Her voice was harsh and lovely.

I could not answer, for my throat was tight with longing. I loved her before I knew her. The tender way she had spoken to him would be the tender way I would keep her. If I could keep one as wild as her.

I put my bow down at her feet.

"A drink of water," I said. "I have a terrible thirst."

She led me in and quenched my thirst.

From then, I visited them for a year and a day, during which time I kept my men at a distance. I gathered herbs and hunted fish with her, and I earned her trust. When I told her who I was, she did not flinch. Perhaps she'd always known.

On the last day, I came to her with two ribbons as red as her mouth, and wound one around her wrist and mine. She did the same in return with the other. I kissed her and asked them both – stag and girl – to return with me, and again, she did not flinch, but said, "And what shall become of us?"

"We shall be a family. Will you be my queen?"

"Yes," she said. "I'll miss this place, but I am gladder to go with you."

BROTHER

THEY WERE MARRIED BEFORE ALL THE PEOPLE in a great church. I went in by her side, walked with her to the man who was king – and then, she was queen. We all lived in the palace grounds. She grew her plants, tended the sick, and taught others the skills she'd learned in the forest. Before long, her belly grew and grew, and we knew a babe would be born. I was protected and cared for, but ran wild as often as I could. Orders were given for none to harm me. All obeyed, for nobody wanted to kill the queen's brother.

When the babe was born, though, and it seemed we could not be happier, cruelty came to find us. People like *her* cannot bear another's good fortune. They either need to make it their own or ruin it altogether. She'd hoped I'd devoured my sister as a tiger or wolf, so when she heard about the new queen and her deer companion, she was consumed with a desire for vengeance. I was in the woods with the king when she encroached on our happiness once more.

SISTER

I WAS A NEW MOTHER, and although my happiness was great, I was weary. Sleep was rare, and when it came, it was broken. I chose a good woman to nurse my babe. He was in her care, and I had taken to bed, when a woman both strange and familiar entered the room.

"Come, Queen," she said, "'tis time to bathe."

I felt drowsy and weaker than I had since our babe was born. She helped me to the great tub. A blazing fire raged in the hearth. The room was suffocating, closer than a hand over my mouth.

"It will draw any sickness out of you," said the woman, as I was lowered into the bath.

She threw a handful of herbs on the fire and left the room. Slowly, my eyes closed, and I slid beneath the water and slept in its embrace. Within minutes, my spirit rose and floated out of my body, hovering there. It was only then that I saw the woman was our stepmother. How foolish humans, no matter how magickal, can be.

"Quick," she said, shoving into the room a younger woman I knew to be her daughter. Stepmother stripped the girl, dressed her in my clothes, and pushed her into my bed. Then she drew the curtains over the windows and made the room as dim as a cave in winter.

Whenever someone came close, Stepmother told them I had been taken with a fierce headache and must be left to rest. Beneath the cover of night, she and her daughter buried my body amidst the healing herbs and plants of my own garden.

Having been told that I must be left alone to the wise woman after childbirth, my king let me be. He left, as kings must do, to meet with his chieftains. Our son was in the care of the nurse. That nurse sat, nodding her head in a half dream as she watched over my child. When it came midnight, I gathered all my strength and power, and my spirit entered that room, going straight through the door as though it were a cobweb. I stood over my son's cradle, and I knew by the look on the nurse's face that she had seen me.

I worked my mouth in spirit, and a laboured echo emerged from my spectral self, *"How is my child? How is my stag? Two more times I shall come, then never again."*

I stroked my son's face, taking in his thistledown hair and the soft freshness of his full,

rosy cheeks. I swore that he would never know hunger or springs too enchanted to drink from. Then I left without another word, lest its solidity break whatever spell allowed me this spirit form. The next morning, the nurse asked the guards whether they had seen me – or any soul – come into the nursery. They had not.

I was weak and floated somewhere between mist and the Summerlands. But the knowledge of my boy, my brother, and my king drew me back into that strange strength, and after two days, I knitted together the shards of my spirit, entered the room, and again spoke to the good nurse, who now knew this was no dream, *"How is my child? How is my deer? I shall come once more, then never again."*

The nurse trembled and asked the guards to tell her the moment the king returned. And I waited.

The next time I entered, my husband, the king, was at the side of our child. His fine hand rested on my brother's back. He saw me and began to weep.

"How is our child, beloved? How is my brother? I come this last time, then never again."

My husband leapt forward, as if to embrace me, but his arms ran through me like I was water.

"You are my true, dearest love," he said.

"I am," and in saying so, I was.

In that moment, when I was truly seen, those parts of me that were buried beneath the healing herbs were revived and reformed. Life poured back into me as spirit and flesh became one, and I was returned to the life that had been stolen. My king and I embraced. Our child cried. My brother danced a little and bowed his antlers to me. And, we were together again.

BROTHER

MY SISTER, THE QUEEN, TOLD US WHAT HAD taken place. Our false mother had cursed us twice by water. Once, by the stream that took from me my human form. Twice, by the drowning of my sister. The king vowed there would not be a third time. The two imposters were brought before the king, denying all, until my sister stepped forward, alive and full of health, with her babe in her arms.

Our stepmother and stepsister took flight, and disappeared into the woods. Not long after, a great storm rose up. First came the rain, then a mighty wind arose, pulling dark clouds across the sky to spear the earth with their silver lightning. A fire raged in the storm's path for a night and a day. I cannot be sure, but I think our cruel stepmother must have perished in those flames, for after that storm, I was returned to myself. I quivered and shook, and became again a man – tall, strong, lean, and bright, but upon my head there remained a strange kind of crown. For all my days hence, I have worn the antlers.

We lived, all of us, well and full of love, each for the other, until the end of our very long lives. And it is up to you to decide whether this crown of antlers is a blessing or a curse.

YOU COULD SAY we grew up in that forest. At times, we were hungry, but we were not lonely. At first, I spoke to Brother every day, but as we grew older, he became more of a deer, and I more of a human, and we no longer needed words.

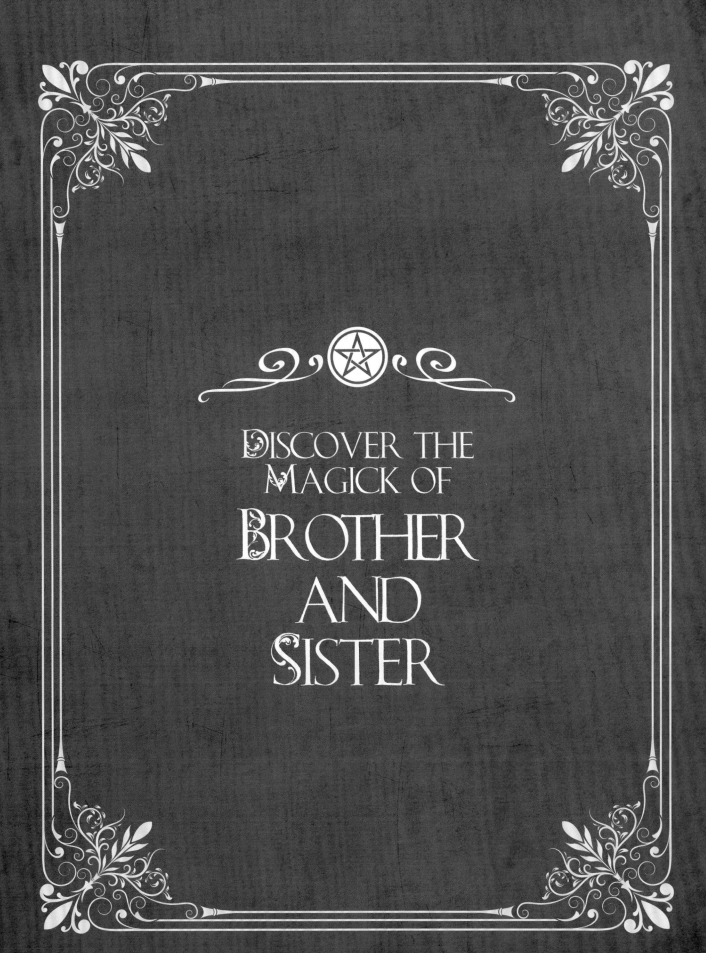

DISCOVER THE
MAGICK OF
BROTHER
AND
SISTER

HISTORY OF THIS TALE

THE FIRST RECORD OF *BROTHER AND SISTER* is an Italian story, *Ninnillo and Nennella*, from 1634. There are also versions from Germany, Africa, Russia, India, and the Balkans. I have given this version a Celtic feel, but it is not located in an actual "land" – it is a faerytale, after all. In fact, I see all these tales taking place in a mythic space that could be anywhere, at any time in history. What is most important is the resonance of the story and the truths and mysteries within it, which seem to have a universal appeal.

THE NUMBER THREE

THREE IS A VERY MAGICKAL NUMBER. OFTEN, three times *is* the charm. In other words, when things take place in groups of three, we know enchantment is at work.

Within this tale, three streams must be crossed, and it is the third to which Brother succumbs. When Sister must somehow call him back from the hunt, she cries out, "return, return, return!" – like an incantation, which it is. And, towards the end of the tale, Sister must visit her family in her spirit form three times before she

I FIRST CAME ACROSS Brother and Sister while exploring an old edition of the Brothers Grimm. I fell in love with the boy and the girl who are so devoted to each other, despite the cruelty they've endured. There is so much magick to the story – such as the cursed streams speaking to the girl, perhaps telepathically; the shapeshifting from human boy to young roe; and the queen returning from beyond the veil to physical life. I wanted to emphasise the siblings' courage, their wildcrafting, and survival skills, and show a little of how the healing power of nature works upon these lovely children as they grow up in the forest and break the curse of their younger years.

It felt right to let these characters have their own voice, so the tale is told from the perspective of Brother, Sister, and, momentarily, the king. The voiceless ones within this version are the children's father, stepmother, and stepsister – but no doubt, they too have their stories.

can reconjure physical life and be reunited with those she loves.

There are echoes of the holy nature of three in Christianity's Trinity – but also within much older forms of pagan belief. For instance, we have the Triple Goddess in the form of Hecate (Greek), Brigid (Irish), Cerridwen (Welsh). In modern paganism, many subscribe to the Law of the Threefold Return, the belief that whatever energy the spellcaster sends out will return to them with three times the spell's original power. When a spell is completed, it is often customary to say, "By the power of three by three, as I do will, so mote it be!"

In *Brother and Sister*, the stepmother's curse on the two siblings may have invoked that law, as she perishes by natural forces. The storm – with its rain (water), wind (air), and lightning (fire), and the resulting conflagration – suggests these three elements of nature turned against her, returning her power threefold to its source, thus restoring some kind of balance to the world of the tale.

DEER, STAGS, AND THE ANTLERED CROWN

WITHIN THIS STORY, BROTHER TRANSFORMS not into a tiger, the curse of the first stream; nor into a wolf, the curse of the second; but submits to the curse of the third stream and becomes a deer, a young roebuck. As a creature of the forest, Brother retains some humanity, but over time, his nature becomes wilder, and he increasingly sees the world through the eyes of a deer, an animal long considered magickal.

Once the stepmother is vanquished, the spell which transformed Brother is very nearly completely broken. Only his antlers and his memories remain to remind him of his time spent as roebuck and as stag, perhaps to signify that a part of him will always be wild and free.

In many cultures, deer symbolise gentleness, alertness, sensitivity, and intuition. While young, they are fleet and will find ways to hide and stay safe. As mature stags, they are symbolic of great strength and nobility, and a willingness to do battle. Stags were associated with Druids, who were said to be able to shapeshift from human form into that of their animal counterparts – often a stag. Myth has it that Amergin, a legendary Irish Druid, could transform into a red stag. The same is said for Taliesin, the greatest bard of all time.

The stag was often called the "king of the forest", and was associated with the Celtic God Cernunnos, a powerful, virile lord of the wildwoods. Cernunnos was depicted as a human man, with a crown of antlers upon his head. The Horned Man is an archetypal pagan god with Celtic origins, much like Cernunnos. The

marriage of the Horned Man with the Goddess helps the land to be renewed at Beltane, the festival of fertility celebrated by the Celts on the last evening of April and the first day of May.

There's also an echo of Buddhism within this tale, by way of the association of deer to the site of the Buddha's first teachings. Thus, as one of the quests of the Buddhist is to find peace and leave behind the pain of human existence, to "walk the path of the deer" is to pursue an end to suffering.

The White Hart

WHEN ONE OF THE KING'S HUNTSMEN STRIKES Brother, the man is terrified that he may have struck a White Hart, a legendary white stag with magickal powers, which is said to dwell at the heart of the forest. And he had good cause for his fear, as maiming or killing the White Hart – which was a little like a unicorn and was the purest of all faerie beings – would incur a great curse.

Even to see the White Hart was a sign you had gone beyond the human world to a land of bewitching strangeness. This is true in the case of

Brother and Sister, who live for many years beyond civilisation's reach.

A Year and a Day and Sacred Timing

TRADITIONALLY, IT TAKES A YEAR AND DAY to be taught the very basics of magick. The year and a day covers both all the lunar cycles and the solar cycle. I wanted the king to come to Sister so he could learn from her, earn her trust, and, in a way, be initiated into her world before she left to become queen in his world.

A year and a day is also the time a traditional handfasting remains valid. Those bound in the Old Ways were free to depart the union after that time, if they so wished, or to enter into a more lasting arrangement if that suited both parties. I like that, despite being king, and therefore having many duties, the monarch made Sister a priority for the length of time a handfasted couple would be together. That way, I think he earned her trust – elsewise, why would she leave a happy, peaceful life to re-enter the world of humanity?

THE WISDOM OF TREES

LIKE THE STAG, THE ROYAL OAK TREE IS ALSO often called "king of the forest". The magickal properties of this tree include longevity, endurance, recovery, and nobility. Oak is renowned for being able to withstand calamity, and was often used for doors, due to its strength, and its protective powers – which would safeguard your entire home. Traditionally, oaks also govern entrances, so these mighty trees are the ones to allow you in or create a barrier.

Oak's acorns make a rough kind of flour when they are ground, and this was baked into a rustic bread by those who had few resources other than those offered up by the forest.

For me, the oak offers a hint of the transformation of Sister from abused child, to girl of the forest, to queen. When Brother and Sister take refuge in the oak, we sense the forest has let them in and taken them up into its arms. The oak is present at the cottage, again a sign they will be protected. While oak's presence is a harbinger of Brother and Sister's destiny, it also alludes to their courage and resilience. Despite their troubles, they are as enduring as the mightiest of oaks.

Another tree, willow, features in this story. Willow's medicinal powers are well known. It is from willow bark that we glean salicylic acid used for modern-day aspirin. Willow also speaks

of emotional challenges, impulses, and huge leaps forward. It is a tree of enchantment, dreams, harmony, intuition, and gentle powers. I wanted Sister to come to understand the trees surrounding the cottage she and Brother live in for so many years. She has an instinctive understanding of the ways of the wilderness and the healing qualities of plants, all of which enables both Brother and Sister to survive. Her ability to recognise what the willow can offer heals their pained bodies, as well as the emotional ache caused by the cruelties of the past.

HERBS AND WILDCRAFTING

THE WILD ONIONS THE CHILDREN FIND AFTER leaving their abusive home, do grow in the forest and are edible. Sister forages by the cottage and in the forest, and the herbs and other plants she finds are often sought after by wildcrafters.

Before you eat a single wild thing, though, be sure you know exactly what it is you are putting in your mouth! The children's hunger meant they had little choice. If you choose to wildcraft, I hope you check your harvest very carefully with a reputable source before feasting on the foods of the forest.

MAKING MAGICK: BROTHER AND SISTER CLOUTIE CHARMS

YOU MAY HAVE WONDERED ABOUT THE PIECES of cloth hanging from the willow trees around the well. These were cloutie charms, perhaps wound about the willow's slender branches by a wise woman or healer working old magicks deep in the forest, long before the children arrived. Cloutie charms are a traditional way of asking trees for healing or for wishes to be granted. They are still found bound to trees by the ancient wells and sacred sites of Great Britain and in the northwest of France.

If, like the cloutie charms in our story, you work with willow, you could ask for flexibility, hydration, emotional stability, harmony, the ease of suffering, or an end to migraines and headaches. For other wishes, research the symbology or observe the characteristics of the trees near you, and choose one accordingly.

To make your own cloutie charm, you will need:
• A piece of fabric or ribbon
• A healthy tree or plant (preferably in your own pot or garden)
• An offering, which can be a crystal, some water, or a little of your time spent helping other trees or supporting environmental groups who focus on trees, for example

Take your cloth or ribbon in your hands, and as you hold it, envision what you would like to bring into the world. For healing, visualise yourself well, whole, and healed, and allow that strong conviction to pour into the ribbon. Take your ribbon to the tree.

Approach the tree you wish to work with respectfully, and when you sense the very edge of the tree's auric field, introduce yourself. This can be done with words or with energy. Once you have made this connection, move closer, still actively connecting, and if it feels right, put your hand on the tree's trunk. Now, ask the tree for permission to do this work together. Wait until you feel a sense of warm, friendly energy. This is a sign of agreement from the tree. When you feel consent has been granted, tie the fabric to a part of the tree that seems to be growing well. Spend a few moments making your wish or feeling the tree begin its magickal healing work.

Thank the tree and leave your offering – or let the tree know you will be supporting other trees as a way of honouring their gifts to humanity. Say farewell, and be sure to visit the tree and your cloutie charm from time to time.

THE WISDOM OF BROTHER AND SISTER

I'M SO MOVED BY THIS STORY, AND I OFTEN wonder just why. It might be that in it, when Brother changes so substantially that he is not even human anymore, Sister's faithfulness endures. I think there is a wisdom to this loyalty. Because, in life, we will all change. Sometimes we change because of circumstances. And when sad and tragic things happen, and these events alter us, it helps to know that we will still be loved – that even if we seem quite different than who we once

were, those who truly care for us will still be able to recognise us because some core quality of our soul remains. Similarly, when Sister's life and place are taken, once she is seen, truly seen, by one who loves her, she can come back to life. Perhaps, then, no matter how changed we may be, when we are seen, understood, and recognised, we, like Sister, can return to life, too.

But even prior to Sister becoming queen, Brother and Sister have created a good life for themselves, away from the suffering they endured. I find a sense of satisfaction in their having built that unconventional and independent life first, before the offer of another new life, filled with promise, arrives through their encounter with the king. If they had just been simply rescued, their choices would not have the same resonance.

In the end, perhaps a very large part of this story's beauty and intelligence is that it offers us all hope. Hope that we can recover and recreate ourselves. And that even if we bear the scars – or the antlers – all our lives, we can make a life of meaning, deep affection, and purpose.

BEAUTY AND THE BEAST

THERE WAS ONCE A GIRL WHO WAS BORN during a very rare event. The Wolf Moon arose during the winter solstice, and there she was, a child of light, born at the darkest time, the coldest time, shining and silver as the full moon that glowed so brightly above her. She was the seventh child, and her mother had been weakened by her birth, so her father gave her into the care of her eldest sister.

Her sisters (for there were three other girls) and her brothers (for there were three of those, too), all doted on her, and perhaps because she grew up amidst so much love, she became beautiful. And perhaps because all her brothers and sisters had different interests, and were clever and quick as any teachers, she became gifted. She learned to dance at the very same time she learned to walk; she learned to sing as she learned to talk; and, as soon as she could heft it, she drew a sword alongside her youngest brother, and was fierce in their mock battles – telling her brothers and sisters she wished for a test to prove her courage.

Their father, who was a wealthy man, a spice trader, was proud that his children were so skilled. Not only did he provide them with tutors of every sort, he created for them a library filled with books, brought back from every country to which his travels took him.

And to her father's great pleasure, his youngest child adored, above all, those very books. Within their pages, she learned of all manner of things, seen and unseen, and of the wider spaces that lay beyond their grand house, their stables with their fine horses, and their garden with its flowers and trees from all over the world.

Their mother, too, took especial joy in the fourth of her daughters, wondering at how, of four girls, one seemed so bright a spirit that her life could not help but be full of the unexpected and the adventurous. She noticed all the ways that shaped her youngest's difference. The other children went straight to bed after dinner, but the girl, whom everyone called Mab (for she had been born at solstice, after all), stayed up late at night, reading under the light of the moon. The other girls had begged for dresses, and dolls, and carriages to push them in, but Mab wore her clothes till they were torn and muddied, and she neglected her dolls, their carriages lying on their sides, still and silent. Instead, she would be found in the stables, brushing down the horses, whispering secrets into their manes.

Her mother watched as Mab spent hours stalking the small wild creatures that would find their way into the gardens. She would leap and snarl, jump and hop and scratch her nose, her pretty head tilted to one side, then the other, in imitation of the movements of the small, wild ones. And after finally persuading a rabbit to take grass from her hand, Mab never ate meat again, just pushing it to one side on her plate and focusing on nuts and seeds and fruits and the deep, wholesome vegetables that she filled her bowl with.

She climbed trees, and within their branches she would devour her beloved books, and at night, she would make pronouncements at the table, eager to share what she had learned of that day – about the length of a ship's mast, the proper way to harvest almonds, the reason dogs howled, and many other strange things.

Her sisters found her amusing, and her brothers ruffled her hair, thinking one day she'd change and be more like other girls. But her mother knew she wouldn't. She sensed some kind of destiny at work within this seventh child.

And, though vastly weakened from childbed, she laughed with delight at this young girl, a sword by her side, wings at her feet, larks in her voice – and, especially, she was proud of the child's quick mind, her piercing curiosity, and her hunger to explore the pages of every book in the library. *She is*, Mab's mother thought, *a strange blend of the studious and the untamed.*

"Be sure, though, my wild little love," said the mother one night, "to remember that there is a difference between knowledge and wisdom." They were alone, for the girl loved to steal a moment with her mother and have her brush her long hair, while she gazed into her mother's small mirror.

Mab nodded, although she could not imagine what the difference would be. To know things was important, and through books she could gain knowledge about everything, from the oceans to the stars to the histories of peoples who had come before.

This love of the word, the mother knew, was good. Books could teach and inspire. But she also knew what her child would most need later in life could not be found in books – for she felt Mab was created for adventure, and to discover, and to go further than others dared to go. So, she understood that her daughter could read her way to knowledge – but wisdom walks a different path. Mab must find a way to understand and connect, to have insight and perception, and this, her mother knew, could only be created by one's own experience, not by the words of another.

Yet, she must try.

So, she showed her child how pretty she was, as they gazed into that small mirror surrounded with golden roses, bright, enamelled leaves, and gleaming silver thorns.

Then, "Daughter," she said softly to her seventh child, "you are beautiful. But what we see here, within this looking glass, is not all of who we are. It is a reflection of what we appear to be. Remember. There is a world within every one of us as vast as the world that lies out there."

Mab's eyes widened in wonder. She was so small – it seemed she could not hold anything as large and important as the world within her humble boundaries. She looked to her mother, a question in her glance.

"Look into the mirror, darling," instructed her mother.

Mab stared at her reflection, frowning, trying to see what her mother must see.

"That is just the surface of a deep, deep lake. You must remember to let your gaze drop far beneath to find the essence of yourself."

***

MAB GREW MORE AND MORE BEAUTIFUL AS the seasons passed, but she barely noticed. She was too concerned with learning, with discovering the difference between knowing things and understanding them. She had taken her mother's words to heart, but she still could not help but think that all she needed to know, she could learn from books.

But she tried. She stared at herself in the mirror some nights, not noticing her lovely features or her fine eyes, nor her glossy hair or rose red cheeks. She was busy trying to see below the surface – still in search of the essence of herself. She would sigh, and wonder if she would ever be able to go deeper, to be wiser, as her mother wished her to be.

Mab may have dismissed her beauty, but others were beginning to notice. Young men would seek out the trader's youngest daughter, but she could not take their attentions seriously. They all seemed to think she was interested in their clothes, or how much money they would come into, or how many other girls sought their attention. She could not see anything beneath

their surface – and, so, many disgruntled young men walked away from her, wondering why they found a girl so bookish and strange so attractive.

Some might imagine that being so lovely would inspire Mab to vanity, but her brothers and sisters – who each had their unique gifts, and were thus free from jealousy – took the edge off any pride she could have developed. There was teasing, and plenty of pushing and shoving, but, all in all, for such a scramble of boys and girls, their lives were filled with love and laughter.

At night, the family would gather round and listen to the father speak of traders and wars at sea and the ways in which he was able to break a blockade to bring through the precious cargo. They were so very loved and comfortable, that they barely understood the risks he took to bring them such plenty. Indeed, it never seemed there could come a time when they would want.

Not even Mab (who, inspired by his tales, would hurry to find a book after each dinner table adventure and read long into the night, her mind hungry to know, to learn, to discover more and more and more) could imagine such a thing.

But the wheel turns for us all, and the family's blessings one day began to reverse. For a great war broke out in another land, which meant the spices that were their fortune had been sunk along with their father's ships, and all their hopes lay at the bottom of the cold, dark sea.

And so, there came upon them a bleak time. But the trader was a pragmatic man, who had thought often of what he would do if this day arrived, planning as best as he could for it. Now, he directed that everything that could be, was sold – gowns and hair combs, furniture and paintings, fabrics and curtains, and all else that was not necessary for the simplest of lives.

Mab, who by now was nearing her first

flowering, offered to sell her favourite books, but her father insisted she take them. "We each can take one thing we prize. Then all else can go. But these," he said, gesturing to the library's shelves, "these are treasures we must keep."

So, the books were packed with care, and each of the family gathered up a pair of slippers or a treasured dress, a mirror or a shining sword. They kept one carriage and four good horses and – bidding farewell to the dancing master, the tutors, and the butler – made their way out into the woods, where stood another house that would become their home. (And where all the goodwill of the years that came before would now be put to the test.)

For Mab, this move was a delight. She wandered the woods, finding flowers she had only read about and trees she had only studied – and some of the animals she had only seen in illustrations were now hers to speak to and spend time with. She did not let go of her books, but, somehow, the knowledge within them began to entwine with the lessons to be found in the world about her.

Her mother noticed her youngest child seemed to now be growing as wise as she had previously been knowledgeable. She saw that the girl was growing even wilder, too, her hair unbrushed, her feet bare, her shoulders golden in the sun, but she knew that this was part of her daughter's destiny, to become a woman who was free and clever, never to be tamed, or held back by the conventions others seemed to hold so dear. Mab, she knew, was meant for some great adventure so all this was good.

The other children, though, did not adapt so well. They began to fight amongst themselves, the brothers feeling cramped in the small house filled with books they never read, the sisters disliking the roughness of woods and meadows, their civilised hearts pained at all they had lost. And Mab's happiness was no balm. Instead, her sisters began to feel resentful at the youngest's satisfaction with her lot. For Mab's part, she could not bear their petty glances of dislike when she sang, or their insistence that she be sad at their newly-impoverished state. So, she spent more and more time on her own, feeling her soul grow open with the expanse of the sky and finding delight in the wild and unwalked paths all about her. This seventh child also experienced a quiet contentment when she and her mother whispered wishes into the mirror.

Meanwhile, her brothers were restless, and the eldest talked of leaving for a larger town to reclaim the family's fortunes, while the two younger boys began to work the small parcel of land around the house, hoping to grow strong crops. But her father wept at night, thinking of the men who had gone down with the ships, their bodies red and gold with the spices that now lay beneath the sea.

As time passed, their mother grew even more frail, and one night, after she and Mab had brushed their hair and whispered prayers into the mirror, she pressed the looking glass into the girl's hands and told her to go, saying she was tired. And when the moon rose full, Mab's mother slipped between the worlds and stayed there for seven days – until one night when the moon was dark, a cold wind blew throughout the house, and when it left, it took her soul with it.

The family buried their mother in the garden, and piled the grave with rocks to stop the small animals finding her. And from then, Mab took her books to her mother's grave each day and read there out loud. "I will be wise," she said to her mother. "I will not just *know* things. I will understand them, too. See," she said, smiling through tears, "I listened to you, Mother."

***

After all the seasons had taken their turn in the great wheel, a rider arrived at their door and handed to the trader a parchment with a seal from a land far away. A single ship of his had slipped through the blockades and the storms and the smugglers, and had made it to port. The children all laughed and hugged, and the trader was most glad that, once more, he could visit those wild, warm places, where the spices grew, that sang to his soul, and perhaps, in time, take his sons and his daughters. The three older girls brightened, and began to speak in whispers about dresses and dances and suitors they might once again hope for. But Mab grew sad.

"You have to go, Father," she said.

"Of course, Mab," he replied. "You know that. I have to see what has survived the journey home, be sure the men are paid, and see what state the ship is in. You could come with us, if you wish." He nodded towards her brothers, who were already saddling the horses. (He did not invite her sisters along.)

"But I need to stay," she said, remembering her mother, and the woods, and the pathways, and the ways she would become wise. *I cannot*, she thought, *become wise in the town.*

"One day I will come, Father. But not now."

"Stay then," he said, kissing the top of her head.

"What would you have me bring you?" he then asked each of the girls.

His three older daughters asked for dresses and jewels, and for him to learn all he could about the eligible young men they'd met long ago, and discover if those gentlemen remembered them, the trader's pretty, learned, talented daughters.

"And you, Mab?" he asked. He smiled, for she always managed to surprise him. And she did not disappoint him.

"A rose," she said. "A little rose bush, which I can plant here, with Mother. I miss their perfume, and I am sure she does, too."

***

And so, his daughters' wishes in his mind, the trader rode with his sons to the port town, where they found the ship in the harbour, beaten, bedraggled, and torn from its adventures – and discovered, as well, the men who had made the passage in a poor way, indeed. The trader sought out a healer who could help the men, and gave that wise woman the last of his coin to coax the sailors back to health in her home.

Then, from the recovered ship, he took the barrels of fine, rare spices to the markets, and he and his sons stood in the sun for days, haggling, until a good price was fetched. With that money, he bought seed for the land, and a dress for each girl, a mirror and jewels, fresh horses for his sons, and repairs for the coach. He asked his sons to stay in the town with what remained of the money and seek out a shipbuilder to begin the task of creating his small fleet once again.

And with the dresses and the seed, and the bonnets and the jewels, he began the journey home. But the weather soon turned foul and dark, the skies opened, and the rain drove him to find shelter. He found a turning into a fine road, a great one, with strange statues lining the path, and he followed it, barely able to see through the rain. Then, through the great trees glistening in the moon's light, he saw a flickering yellow glow in the

distance, high, oh, so high. As he drew closer, the trees opened up to reveal a chateau, with gables and turrets, and he saw that the flicker was that of candles shining from the chateau's windows.

His exhausted horse, head bowed beneath the pelting rain, followed his nose to a stable, where the trader, sliding from his mount, found hay and fresh water. Unsaddling the horse and leaving him to the warmth of the stall, he shook off his sodden cloak and stumbled to the door. The entrance to this strange chateau was immense, intricately carved with shapes from another world, part human, part animal, but the trader had seen many stranger things in foreign lands. He knocked, his fists leaving damp marks upon the great door. When there was no answer, he knocked again, with all his strength. But there was still no response. Finally, his hunger and the need for shelter drove him to break with all the laws of courtesy.

He pushed open the door and found his way to a great hall, where a fire burned brightly, and a long cedar table was laid with good food and bread. A hot leek pie, a warm loaf of bread sprinkled with rosemary and garlic, a plate of ripe figs and soft white cheese made his mouth water. He ate the pie where he stood, wiped his mouth, then took the bread and the cheese and figs to the fire. He sunk into an extravagance of a chair, larger than any built for a man, and piled high with cushions. He poured golden, fragrant wine from a heavy jug into a goblet, and slowly he felt his travelling clothes dry. Soon, his stiff limbs began to relax with the heat and dance of the fire. And finally, his head sank to his chest, and there, before the flames, he slept, warm and full and content, in this strange place, with not, it seemed, a soul about.

The trader awoke the next day to find the great logs of the fire just black and crimson coals – but a fresh suit of fine clothes lay by his side, and strong beer, purple grapes, and creamy milk were set fresh upon the table. He drank deep, ate everything before him, and felt better than he could recall having felt in years. He was unsure of whether he should wear the clothes set before him – they seemed so fine, and he had already received so much mysterious generosity. But then the comfort and the beauty of the garments seduced him, and he dressed quickly, feeling uneasy at the silence and at his eerie sense of being observed.

He made ready to leave, and wound his way back to the stables, where he found his horse groomed, well-fed, and watered, with a warm, dark rug upon his back, and his saddle and bridle oiled and hung upon a brightly polished hook.

Then, seeking the road by which they'd come, he walked his horse through great gardens, which had been obscured by the horrors of the storm the night before, and there he noticed a tiny, intricate garden house, filled with roses of all colours.

Remembering Mab's desire for a rose bush, one to plant beside her mother's grave, he entered the garden house and began to dig at the earth beneath one fragrant rose, covered with an abundance of blooms, and radiating the most powerful fragrance. Just as he unearthed the rose that flowered so abundantly, the ground began to shake …

As he turned, the earth falling from the roots of the rosebush, the sky darkened and he beheld the most glorious and beastly creature he had ever seen. He was tall, taller than a man should be, and broader of shoulder than any man could be. He was richly dressed in blues like that of the seas in which the coral grew, and his golden hair flowed over a stiff brocade collar. His eyes were immense, his lashes and brows thick and splendid. Indeed, he had all manner of handsome features, but all were somehow wrong – one eye golden, and one eye blue, like sapphires, pupils shaped like a crescent moon, and two tusks pointing from his lips. From what might be called the creature's hands curled claws, long, and sharp, and dangerous.

The trader shook, his knees went to water, and he fell to the ground and covered his head with his hands, still clutching the rose he knew would cost his life.

And then a voice like a storm tore through his soul and hammered at his ears, as the great creature, splendid and dreadful, said, "You have taken what is most precious to me."

The trader kept still, saying nothing, hoping he could halt the relentless trembling that rattled his body, while that voice, which could tear through forest, crack earth, and raise a great wave, continued. "You shall die for this cursed ingratitude. I shall show you how I repay such insults."

The trader gathered his courage and stared into the great Beast's huge gold and sapphire eyes. "My lord, forgive me. I have taken what was not mine. Tell me how I can make amends for this insult to your generosity."

The Beast snarled and began to clap together his two great paws. "The prettiest speech anyone I've had executed has ever made."

"Lord," the trader said, forcing himself to his feet. "I have children. Three boys and four daughters, and this – this was a gift for the youngest of them. I meant no harm, although I did wrong."

There was a long silence.

Then, "You can take the rose," said the Beast, his voice low and full of threat. "But you must return by the time the moon is full to be my captive. And if you do not, all whom you hold dear will die."

There was something in the way he said it, something in all that had taken place since the trader had entered into the Beast's enchanted world that made him certain the Beast had every intention of keeping his dreadful promise. "My lord? For a rose – a mistake – you would take my freedom?"

"A very considerable mistake, trader," said the great Beast. "For now, I must have what is clearly the greatest treasure you possess. I will have your liberty."

At this, the trader's sadness fell like a lead cloak over him.

"Be certain you return, sir," added the Beast. "Or the grief you feel will seem a little thing compared to what I shall visit upon your world."

With nothing to bargain for his freedom, the trader mounted his horse and bade farewell to the Beast.

Through the forest he wound, and the world's beauty seemed to taunt him.

Just before nightfall, he was at his home, and he could see Mab coming in from the meadows as he approached. She ran to him, and he slid from the saddle, and they held each other tight.

"The storm last night," she said. "I could not sleep." And when she saw her father's grim face, she stepped back. "What is it?"

"Here, my love," he said. "Take this rose and plant it now."

She held the little rosebush, and her eyes grew wide at its blossoms. She closed her eyes, took a deep breath in, and inhaled their sweet, full scent. She breathed out, full of contentment, and her smile broke her father's heart.

"I have books for you, too, my dear. But go now, and let me speak with the others."

She took the rose to her mother's grave, and dug into the rain-softened earth till she'd formed a bed for its roots. As she lowered it into the earth, she whispered to her mother.

"I am learning mother. I am learning the difference between knowing and understanding. I recalled our garden, and I imagined over and over the smell of these flowers. I read and read of the perfume of these blossoms, but never could I recapture the delight of breathing in their essence. I think this is what you wanted me to discover – that there is a joy in my being and coming alive to the world around me, to know it, and to see beneath its surface. To have experiences of my own, not merely to read of others and their adventures. You knew I would not be satisfied …

You are now beneath this surface, Mother, and I know you are no longer here in the same way that you once were. A book may tell me of where you could be – heaven, I would say. But I know you best here, Mother, in this space that holds all of what you once were, still helping me with what I shall be."

She plucked three roses, one for each of her sisters, so they could share in the pleasure the flowers offered, and then Mab stood under the bare night sky, lit with cold stars, brushed the dirt from her dress, blew a kiss to her mother.

She paused there, staying another moment beneath the stars, reluctant to leave and break the spell of peace and connection that fell all about her, a cloak in the darkness.

When she returned to the house, her cheeks flushed with the chill of the approaching evening, she found that though the room was filled with her brothers and her sisters, it was silent and tense. Warily, Mab took the roses she had picked and placed them in a vase and put them on the table.

"What," she demanded, "is the matter? You all stopped speaking the moment I entered."

"Get those things out of here," suddenly screamed her eldest sister, dashing the roses to the ground.

Mab cried out, and her father stood. "Stop this! It was not her fault."

"She asked for a rose. You wanted the very best for her, as you always have." The sister turned to Mab, her face red with fury, blotched with tears. "Father took that rosebush from a great and cruel lord. To repay the debt, he must return and give up his liberty. It is the end of our family – all for your roses, all for you to grow your sweet flowers."

"Is this true?" Mab asked. When she saw her father's face, she had her answer.

"I will leave within a week," he said. "That Beast is no ordinary creature, and there is a kind of magick at work in the world of his chateau."

"Can we visit you?" Mab asked, her lips trembling.

"I doubt it," he said, voice heavy with grief.

"Will you ever be free to leave?" she asked, one great tear sliding down her cheek.

"I think not, my daughter," he replied.

***

THE NEXT WEEK WAS SPENT PREPARING.

As Mab watched the moon swelling a little more night after night, her heart grew stronger with fury. And after their father's last night with his children, she walked outside and stood by the roses, stood by her mother, and spoke out loud as the broad face of the moon rose in the sky.

"This is my rose, and it is my burden to

bear," she said to the moon. "Give me courage. Let me do what is right." She thought for a long time, and finally, in the silence of the night, came her answer.

Returning to the house, she took a sword from the great hall, where it was hung over the fireplace, and she took three books from the library. She paused before leaving the room filled with shelf upon shelf of bound volumes, wishing she could take them all with her. *I will have to find the knowledge within*, she told herself firmly, stilling the quick sharp pain that rose up inside her at the thought of this loss – and she smiled a little sadly to herself, for she knew her mother would have named that "knowledge within" as "wisdom".

She quietly continued her preparations, brushing a tear or two away as she packed bread, and a cloak, and a hood, and some dresses, and a pair of good solid shoes. Then she lifted her mother's little mirror and stared at her face, surrounded by the roses and the thorns, wondering whether she was saving her father or breaking his heart.

She stilled her hands, which trembled, and wrote a brief, brave note, and left it on the table, under the vase with the roses.

Mab walked, quiet and sure, to the stables, and saddled her favourite horse. "I should not take you," she whispered to the white mare, who had the grand name of Lady of Mists. "But it is better I steal you away than to do the smaller good and stay."

She swung onto Lady, and into the silver night they trotted, until they reached the wide, white road her father had described.

"This is the way, my Misty, my Lady," she said, soothing the horse, who was growing fretful and nervous. Her voice steadied her steed, and she began the long journey down the carriageway towards the chateau. It was a lonely path, and the sense of something strange being afoot arose with every click of her faithful horse's hooves.

By the light of the full moon, she could see that roses adorned the banners hanging sadly from the towers, and Mab shook her head.

"For a rosebush, we gave ourselves away, my Misty," she said. "Come now ... onwards into this next adventure, darling girl."

And so, they stepped beneath a great stone archway, and Mab dismounted. She led Misty to a stable, where she found fresh water and sweet-smelling hay. Unsaddling the horse, she hugged her tight. "Now, my Lady," she whispered. "I go on alone for a time."

Making her way to the chateau, she paused, captivated, before the great entrance, and her white fingers traced the peculiar shapes carved upon the door, teasing out the parts that were human, the parts that were wild. She had read of such things, but never had she seen anything of its like, and her eyes widened, and, for a moment, she forgot to breathe.

She raised her hand and rapped upon the door, each knock sounding dull and small in comparison to the size of the place she sought to enter.

When there was no answer, she knocked again, hard and fierce. There was still no response, so she leant upon the great door, and it yawned open.

She walked into the hall, her right hand tight around the hilt of the sword beneath her cloak. There was not a soul present. But, just as her father had described, a great warming fire raged in the enormous hearth, and all manner of luxurious foods were upon the table, along with a flagon of the finest, sweetest chocolate, warm and seductive. Mab narrowed her eyes and looked

around. "I suppose," she said out loud, "you will watch me awhile, before you come and speak with me. So, I may as well introduce myself."

She put down her traveller's bag, and threw off her cloak, and walked about the hall, with far more confidence than she felt.

"I am Mab, and it was my father whom you sentenced to a kind of beautiful imprisonment in this fine place. He did not break his word, though. You must know this. This was my decision."

A tremor in the darkness hinted at her host's presence, and she turned in the direction she sensed him.

She waited, peering about her, trying to see where the lord of this place could be. But not a sound came in reply.

"I am here to offer myself in his place," she continued. "If you accept my proposition, you are not to harm my father, not in any way, nor any of my brothers or sisters."

Her words echoed about the great hall. She swallowed, fighting back the fear that urged her to run, to find Misty, to saddle her up and ride her home, to hide from this fate that she had chosen for herself. She shook her head and stamped her foot a little, bringing herself back to herself, to her choice.

Again, from the corner of her eye, she saw a movement, like the shifting of a great shadow. *He is coming closer*, she thought, pleased and frightened, all at once.

"I must thank you, great Beast," she said, careful to keep her voice from shaking, "for this generosity. Such plenty I see before me! But I will not eat alone. I will see you, sir. I would know with whom I will share my life."

Still, there was not a sound except that of her own voice resounding off the thick stone walls.

"Perhaps you are shy, sir," she said lightly. "I have time. I can be patient. And I have a wonderful story to read."

She pulled out one of the books from her satchel that lay upon the floor. The book groaned open as she placed it on the sumptuously set table.

"The Illustrious Travels of Sebastian the Adventurer," she declared, and stopped, sensing the creature she could not see was readying to move. She focused again on the page before her, and she began to read out loud the story she had loved so well for so long, her fine voice ringing off the walls. And as she read, the Beast came closer and closer ... until she became aware of his immense shadow, cast against the wall by the flickering flames.

She watched that shadow, tracking his every movement. He moved closer and closer, until, at last, he settled his massive frame into a chair at the head of the table. She did not falter, although her voice shook a little when she saw his thick, curved talons, his tusks that were sharp as carving knives, and the shoulders so broad he blocked out the fireplace. She heard his breath being drawn like a saw across stone, and he sat back in the huge chair, a king of beasts on his throne – and she read and read, until her voice grew thin with fatigue.

Noticing, he reached over, and took the great flagon. He poured the chocolate, gleaming darkly in the light into a goblet, and passed it to her.

She drank it, feeling its warmth and its sweetness. Then she cleared her throat. "Thank you, sir."

"My lady Mab," he said, "thank you for your story. But you grow tired. Come. There is a room prepared for you, with curtains thicker than sunlight. You can sleep."

She stood and swayed, and gripped the side of the table, battling a wave of fatigue, like an undertow.

"You are considerate, sir."

He stood, powerful and dreadful, and she felt her heart sink.

"Would you leave the book for me?" he asked her. "I would like to finish the story."

She relaxed a little, feeling that if he read books, he might not be as dreadful as he seemed. "Of course," she replied, with a tiny flicker of delight.

Then he led her to a room, high, high up, and as she climbed the stairs behind him, the hallways lit by candles, and watched the door to her chamber swing open by itself, she thought, *I must remember to ask about that.* And as she sank into the huge feather bed that was to be hers, from this day forth, she thought, *I must remember to ask about everything here ...* And then she slept, without a dream at all, a little like the death before a new life begins.

***

THE DAYS BEGAN TO FOLD, ONE INTO THE other. Mab rode Lady around the gardens, and visited the roses and the trees – and was sure she saw strange creatures darting in and out of the old oaks about the centre of what was a wooded garden.

The Beast would ride out with her, and they would talk. Or he would persuade her to talk. And she did. She shared her love of plants and animals and told him of the stories she had read and of the lands she would have loved most to see, had her life been different.

"Your father has seen many places, my lady," said the Beast.

"Indeed, sir. If ever I could see but half of what he had seen ... That is why books are my great friends. My father brought them back for us. I would wait for his return, and pounce upon each great work, eating it up with my eyes!"

The Beast laughed, a low rumbling sound, like thunder in the distance.

"I can sit at the foot of the sages of Persia," she continued. "Dance within a crystal hall, read the books of the lost library of Alexandria, and see the seven mountains of Olympus. Books are the worlds, and they take me away from ..." Mab hesitated.

"From here?"

"From here. From there. Perhaps most of all from the small world of myself. They show me what I need to learn – what I can seek out ... what I could have discovered," she said, her voice sad with the realisation that this chateau was her home.

The Beast said nothing.

The next morning, there was a large, old, golden book at the dining table. Mab spent the day reading it in the gardens by the rose bushes, and when the sun set, she carried it inside the great chateau and continued reading by the fire.

The moon was full, and she was spilling over with energy, and so she read through the night, unable to stop, enthralled as much by the beauty of the book in her hands as the wisdom within its thick, aged pages, which held stories of the deeds of great men and women, as such histories always do. But this book went deeper, Mab realised, as she read. It explored what lay beneath the surface. It went to the very core of these heroes and heroines. Their hearts and souls were examined – and it was as if she could see her mother smiling as she turned the pages.

This is what my mother meant, thought Mab. *This is edging towards the understanding. In*

my hands, I am holding wisdom. I am holding true treasure. And a small seed began to grow within her – a seed of happiness, of a strange and unusual kind. *This life is not one I would have chosen. And I am not free. But I am not unhappy. So, what is this?*

She went to the great window and looked out at a moon so full it reminded her of the stories she had been told about her birthing night. *We don't know what our destiny is,* she thought. *But this ... this is a remarkable life. Perhaps as strange a country is this, as any my father has travelled to.*

And as she gazed down at the silver light glancing off the trees, she saw the Beast below, and stepped back. He was a huge shadow against the moonlit trees, and he had in his claws a small, limp creature – a rabbit, or a hare, perhaps – and he was devouring its carcass, his relish evident. And even in that moonlight, Mab could see the lifeblood flowing from the creature. It was like an awful, ancient ritual, and as he gorged and fed, she began to weep, and that tiny seed of hope shrivelled within her.

Perhaps, she thought, *that will be my fate.* And anger, bright and true, sparked within her. Even knowing she should not, she called out.

"Stop it! Stop it, Beast. That creature is helpless!"

He turned and looked up at Mab. His face was bloodied, and his tusks gleamed white and scarlet, and she fell back in shock that the promise in her life was vanishing into horror.

The next day, she placed the book he had given her back upon the table of the great hall, and she took Lady out earlier than usual for their ride. She went to the gardens, looking for traces of the evening's terrors, but where she had seen blood falling, flowers were growing, and she sank to her knees in wonder. Doors that opened, servants who were invisible, a beast for a lord, and

flowers instead of a corpse? Nothing made sense. It was a puzzle.

But this, she knew, was a mystery that could be resolved with wisdom and knowledge. She went to the roses, and spoke with her mother for a while, and then returned to the chateau.

When she passed through the great hall, she saw that the book she'd left upon the table was gone, and in its place was a key and a folded note, on the face of which was written: *Enter, if you will, and see the ancient sights of the lands of our ancestors.*

Mab unfolded the note and found a map of the chateau and a small, hand-inked line that showed her the way to one of the many rooms she had not yet seen. The handwriting was beautiful – strong and curving and fine, clear but full of flourishes.

Dramatic, she thought, with a frown. Nonetheless, she followed the map to the room, and came to a great door, higher than five men. The door shook and shimmered, as she approached, and words and runes and sigils danced beneath its woods, like living tattoos written in sap. The door was a part of a great tree, its roots snaking across the floor and stretching down into the ground.

"How is it I have not seen this place," she wondered out loud.

"You have not been shown the way to this place," answered a voice ... and she saw within the wood a face emerging, then another ...

"We are the authors of the books within," the faces said. "We are the keepers of the door. And welcome, lady, for this room is now yours to explore."

"It is?" she asked, unsure what to make of this magick.

"Indeed, we welcome you to the lost library," said many voices at once.

Then, the faces receded and the doors swung open, and Mab stepped into a land of wonder – seeming to awaken hours later, drunk with the beauty and the knowledge and all the moments of magick that lay within a realm of books that spoke and lived and asked to be read.

But soon her thoughts turned back to the Beast. "You could not *want* to do what I saw you do," she said to herself. (Mab was given to speaking out loud, so often was she alone these days.) "There must be a way to stop it. And it may be inside this library."

No sooner had she had this thought, then she found a book on the shelves titled *Enchantments*. Taking it from the library with her, she read and read, as the moon waned – learning from it that some beings were shapeshifters, and that moonlight altered them, and that curses worked under moonlight were especially effective. This led her to think of the natural world, of how plants bloom only to be harvested and eaten. Of how the wolf hunts and takes the small ones. Of how all that rises, falls. Of how all that lives in some way takes life.

What was the hare's death feeding? she wondered.

Yet, she did not wish for the Beast to attack and destroy, as she had seen him do. But she now knew that the fact that this destruction had taken place under the full moon was important.

Finally, after days of reading *Enchantments* and other books, of visiting and revisiting the library, Mab knew that, somehow, she could help him see that his role could be to protect, to defend. That he could use his great force and power to help – and she met once again the Beast.

He turned from her as she approached. "I know, lady, you have seen me and all that I am, and you cannot help but be repelled. I, too,

am repelled. But no matter how repulsive, how disgusting I find myself, each full moon sees me devouring innocents, feasting on their flesh, and with ... with delight. It feeds me. Their death feeds my soul. And my soul therefore is cursed." His huge shoulders hunched over.

She came behind him and reached out a hand.

"Ride with me tomorrow morning," she said. "Let's speak of other things. For the whole world is full of horrors, and many things must die in order for others to live."

"But I am a beast," he roared, his arms swinging out – and with one claw, he struck the book from beneath her arm, so that it fell to the stone floor.

Mab scowled and thrust out her chin. She would not back away.

"I am sorry," he said. "I cannot be what I am not. I am a beast. I will stay far from you."

"Then I will be alone here," she protested. "I need to speak, and to share, and to ... to be seen and heard and be known. I will *not* be alone here."

"You are better alone," he insisted, and left her standing there.

***

For days, Mab saw nothing of the Beast – there were no talks, no rides, no sharing. But, there were food and books upon the table. And, oddly, music began to play when she walked among the roses, and jugs began to pour themselves, and every door she approached – not just the door to her bedroom – swung open. Candles lit themselves without a match being struck; the fire erupted into life at sunset; and when she walked upon the floor she began to feel light of foot ....

But, despite all these wonders, she found

that, although she had seen the Beast's true nature – had heard his roar and seen blood on his claws – she missed him. She *missed* him.

Hidden away in her room one night, Mab stared into her mother's mirror, thinking of how everyone she loved, she missed. She missed the Beast. She missed her sisters and her brothers and the garden. She had Lady of the Mists with her, it was true, but having her horse from home seemed to make all the other missing worse. She missed her father so much it hurt.

And most of all she missed her mother. She would have told Mab how to see into her own soul and understand what strange transformation was taking place there. She would have known the name of the pain within her heart.

But even as she stared at her tear-stained face in the little mirror, her mother's face began to swim into view.

"What enchantment is this?" she cried. "I am tired of illusions. I want life."

"I am your mother," said the face in the mirror. "I am here from the underneath, to tell you of what takes place in the world outside this world."

Seeing that it was really her mother come to comfort her, Mab wiped the tears from her face and smiled, lips opening like petals parting. "Is it good news, Mother?" she asked. "How fares my father?"

"Your father is not well, Mab. He fears for you. He suffers, knowing what you did for him, and he wishes only to take this curse from you – this curse that has grown to be a blessing. Let him know, Mab. Tell him. Tell your father you've found a strange happiness. Let him know you have found love."

"Love?" she cried. "No, it is not love, Mother!"

"You are feeling the sharp pain of love, my daughter. Now, talk to the Beast. And tell him you must see your family. For if he lets you go, you will know his heart is yours."

The next morning, she sat at the great table, and called out for him.

"Lord? Beast?"

There was no answer.

"Sir, I must go. I must see my father, he is not well. I have news for him, too. About ..." She paused, unwilling to say more into the silence. "I know you are listening. I know you understand. I know I do not need to say more. I must go. I will go, Sir Beast."

"Go," he said, his voice soft and full of shadows.

"But I will come back," she called out, taking her sword.

"I will, sir. I will return. We have a bond, you and I. We are not done."

"Return ... before the last petal falls from my rose," he whispered.

And she ran to the stables and swung onto Lady, and she rode.

***

HOME IS NEVER HOME, NOT ONCE WE HAVE found that the place our soul belongs is elsewhere. A part of us is always left, and either we grow, or we die a little when we leave. When she came home, Mab knew it was no longer hers.

She spoke with her father for days on end, telling him of her strange feelings, and her father grew distressed, and protested, saying it was not possible.

And he asked, "Who will care for me, my child? Only you loved this home."

"Come back with me, Father."

"To that dreadful place? To that prison?" He shook his head, as if to dislodge the memories of the night he spent in the chateau. "If only I had never knocked upon that door. Would that there had been no storm, no rose bush – would that your mother was still here!"

She held him, quiet and still, murmuring words of comfort.

"Father, you have wandered and discovered, and you have taught me, too, to know adventure. In books, I found it. And now I have found it in life."

"Are you enchanted, then? Are you mad? He is a beast."

"He is," she said. "But then, so are all of us, father."

"You cannot return. It will not be safe. A ship came back to me, my child. I am wealthy again. Your sisters are married to rich men, and your brothers have made their fortunes. We could travel. Or you could stay here, build another house, create a great library, full of wisdom, and share that knowledge with the world."

"That is wonderful, Father. I'm happy for my sisters, and I thank you for your offer. Once it would have been all I could dream of. But I have changed, and I will return."

"Child, there may be nothing to return to …"

"What are you telling me, Father?" Mab asked, very quiet and still, the way we hold ourselves just before a terrible blow is delivered.

"After you left us, we went to work. I could not rest, knowing you had taken my place. So, we raised more money, child, and I hired mercenaries, men who kill for a living – they can be found, if you know where to look, at any port."

"But there's no need, Father. I am returning, and you can come with me, too – to

see that what I am saying is the truth."

"I was clever, my child. I could not send them, knowing you were there, knowing what kind of men they were. But when you arrived here, I immediately sent word to the ports – and the mercenaries set out to the chateau the morning after your arrival. Your Beast may already have been slaughtered."

"We have to stop this," she said. "We have to."

Leaving her father no time to protest, Mab ordered Misty and her father's horse saddled, and called to him to join her, to return with her to the place that began it all. They set off at a gallop, riding as hard as their mounts would permit … but as they neared the chateau, Mab saw that the rose banners were torn, and the garden was burning, and the walls had been broken by stones flung from great, unkind machines – and then her gaze fell upon the Beast, who was stretched out upon the ground, his massive clawed paws tied and twisted behind his back. He lay helpless within the garden, a book flung beside him, his huge, different-coloured eyes, with their crescent moon pupils, staring at the last rose within the garden.

Flinging herself from Lady, Mab reached for the bleeding Beast, whose fine clothes were shredded about his vast body, which was cracked open. And, somehow, for all that she was small and he was immense, she turned him over, and crooned to him, and held his great head upon her lap, while his blood flowed down her white gown and red roses grown from his life's blood bloomed upon her breast – and she smiled at him.

"Do not leave me, Beast," she whispered, her voice tender, teasing, pleading. "I wish to ride with you, talk with you, adventure with you. You shall read me stories. No! We shall make stories. We could leave this place together and journey

the world."

He did not move, did not seem to hear – although she thought she could feel him listening.

"I care for you, your vast heart and brooding dread. You are kind and generous and honest, and I want you, only you, as my companion in this life."

At this, the Beast's eyes opened, and two great tears stained ruby with his dying blood fell, and she cried to see them.

"You are strong," she told him. "Come back to me." And she opened her heart and the words came out. "I love you, Beast. Only you. Come back to me."

As she sobbed, her father looked on, his heart breaking to see his dearest child lose her love and grow up and leave him, all in the one moment.

Mab's tears abated, but she stayed, holding the Beast in her arms until dark came, so sure she was that his strength could not be overcome by death. And when he saw she would not leave her love, her father brought her the food from their bags and the wine from his pouch to strengthen her.

Finally, exhausted, she lay down next to the Beast's body and she slept in his lifeless arms.

That night, when that full moon rose, there began a stirring in the garden. Little mice came forth, one by one, and began to scurry over the fallen Beast's great body. Mab woke and slapped at them, crying out. "Leave him, leave him. Stop it, stop it, you must not ..." Then she realised that each little mouse was carrying a rose, one after another – a yellow rose and a red and a white and a violet, until he and she were almost covered in roses.

And as the moon rose higher and higher, there bloomed all about the Beast the strangest glow. The silver of the moon outlined his fierce

profile and those cruel tusks ... and then the light that shone around him began to shimmer and whirl, and his skin gave off small sparks and, little by little, as if she was watching a flower grow in the fastest time, she saw the Beast begin to change.

Now, his jaw did not jut so, and his brow was less ridged. Soon, his tusks drew back and became shining white teeth, covered by lips that were strong and well cut. His form changed until it was that of a powerful, broad-shouldered, well-made man. His talons receded into nails, and his torn clothes were suddenly too large for that form.

Mab stepped back, amazed and frightened, and her father stood, astounded.

And the Beast awoke with a gasp that a man held underwater or buried alive underground might give when first he breathes again the sweet rushing air.

***

You know well that they had great rites, then, this enchanted lord and his lady, the beauty born at the full Wolf Moon, the one whose love broke a terrible curse.

You know, too, that they did not find their answers in books (although they loved them well all of their days together). Instead, they set sail, as soon as they could. They went to the tombs of Egypt. They sat at the feet of sages in Persia. And they searched for the lost books of Alexandria.

And they both knew that within us all there is savagery, and death, and claws. But that we are flowers, too.

And their love took them to the halls of ecstasy, and they drank the mead of the gods, and they found their greatest bliss, and their best selves, within each other's understanding and embrace. And they found wisdom, and love, and

wonder eternal.

As you can too.

For within you is Beauty. Within you is Beast.

Which will you be, reader, when next the moon is full?

AGAIN, from the corner of her eye, she saw a movement, like the shifting of a great shadow. *He is coming closer*, she thought.

"I would see you, sir," she said, careful to keep her voice from shaking.

Still, there was not a sound, except that of her own voice echoing off the thick stone walls.

Discover the
Magick of
Beauty and
the Beast

HISTORY OF THIS TALE

Before I went to school, I could read. This was due in no small part to my mother, who no doubt grew tired of me trailing about after her with various books shoved under my arm, one in particular held out open at a story I longed for her to read to me. Again. And again. And again. So, my mother taught me my letters, and how they represented sounds, and how these came together to make words – and then, oh, what magick was available to me! Books were my friends, my companions, my teachers –even my saviours in some respects. And I read, and I read, and I read. And I learned that books are conduits to other worlds. We can travel and experience, learn and imagine, and books can teach us what it is to be wise – not just what it is to know things. So, this tale, with its bookworm heroine, spoke to me.

I also love that the Beast is so magnificent, and so masculine, and perhaps an example of the wounded god – a kind of thwarted masculinity, unable to love himself. He appears to be a monster, and he therefore behaves like one, at times. Even so, he is able to love another, despite feeling unworthy of having that love returned.

So is the magick of this tale not so much that he transforms into a man, but that love blossoms between two beings, even while one is considered a monster? I like to think the tale asks us to look beneath what people *appear* to be – because when we do so, we can sometimes discover wonderful things.

I think *Beauty and the Beast* has story relatives in Giovanni Frencesco Straparola's *The Pig King*, and perhaps even in *The Frog Prince*, as retold by the Brothers Grimm. But the true roots of this tale may lie within the myth of Cupid (or Eros) and Psyche, in which Psyche marries an unknown bridegroom and is forbidden to look upon him. It is inferred by her sisters, who are jealous at her happiness, that her groom must be a monster – but in truth she is married to the god of love.

The faerytale retold here, however, owes much to two Frenchwomen – one of whom is Gabrielle-Suzanne Barbot de Villeneuve, whose version was published in 1740, and the other is Jeanne-Marie Leprince de Beaumont, who reworked Barbot de Villeneuve's version in 1756.

The original French tales have interesting differences. Villeneuve's added the Beast's personal history to the tale, letting us in on his childhood

and the reason he is the way he is (an evil faery, a curse), while other versions make the story of the Beast recede well into the background. Others, still, like the Disney version, give him a castle of marvellous servants, who are also under the same curse, and thus longing for love to break the evil enchantment within which they are all trapped. But the version most often referenced today – apart from the Disney reworking – is Beaumont's, which is very pared back, and offers the barest minimum about the Beast.

In my own retelling, both Beauty (Mab) and the Beast emerge from imprisonment into freedom and become explorers of the world – and their relationship, I imagine, remains robust, pioneering, and passionate! And, despite being so busy adventuring in faraway lands, I am sure they both retain their love of reading!

THE WOLF MOON

IN THE NORTHERN HEMISPHERE, THE MOON throughout January is often called the Wolf Moon. It is called so because this is often the time of the most extreme cold, when the world is barren and covered in snow, when the wolves howl, perhaps pleading with the moon to let the sun return. In the story, I shifted this moon to December, loving the feeling of a Wolf Moon rising right at the moment of the solstice.

Many cultures name each of the full moons of the year. It can be worth naming them for yourself, according to the seasons and the way nature manifests herself where you live. When we do this, we are anchored more firmly into our own relationship with the land, the plants, the animals, and the seasons that turn again and again. It creates a true knowledge – wisdom, even – of our own region, and its unique characteristics. This brings us back into connection with the natural world, without which, we can float, ungrounded, not having the true relationship with the earth that all humans need and so few have.

WINTER SOLSTICE AND BLESSED BIRTHS

THE SOLSTICE IS THE PAGAN FESTIVAL OF THE rebirth of the light, or the sun, and is celebrated between December 19-23 each year in the northern hemisphere, while in the southern hemisphere, it takes place between June 19-23.

It is the time when the light each day begins to lengthen, and the dark begins to fall back, giving way to warmth and sunlight, and with these, hope and growth and new life. It is a renewal of all that brings light and life. This is considered a very auspicious time to be born – so Mab's birth is a time of celebration, for many reasons.

She shares her birthday with a "child of light", known as the Mabon (see more, below), and with King Arthur, for according to legend he, too, was born at this solstice, which is therefore sometimes called "Alban Arthur". And, of course, Christianity claimed this solstice and its pre-existing rites for the birth of Jesus, the son of God – a rather clear inversion of the birth of the sun god.

Some say the goddess herself gives birth to the sun's new light at this time, and in many pagan traditions, candles are lit to help the goddess, to offer her strength, and to support the light of the child.

MABON, THUS MAB

IN MOST OF THE VERSIONS OF 'BEAUTY AND the Beast', the titular Beauty is called Belle, or even Beauty. I changed this up a little – for our heroine is born during a Wolf Moon, at winter solstice. In Celtic tradition, a child of light is born at the winter solstice, and the name given to this child is, in many neo-pagan traditions, "the Mabon". The name Mab also is a less-than-subtle reference to Queen Mab, a faery queen of great power, who seeks to keep the Old Ways alive, and is a kind of living magickal library of all the oldest traditions and lores, rites, and rituals. Confusingly (stay with me!), Mabon is also the name of the autumnal equinox, so our heroine, Mab's, name has another layer of meaning, that of a time of balance, preparation, intelligence, and survival.

Perhaps calling her Beauty would have been more sensible – after all, it is the tradition. But if this child was born at such a magickal time,

and if she has the power to break such a great spell, perhaps, just for this time, it is right to break with tradition and give her a name as magickal as the journey she takes. For what is most significant about our Mab is not her beauty. It is her fine character, her compassion, her intelligence, her quest for wisdom, her courage, her sacrifice, and her love of learning and adventure that make her such a compelling heroine. This is not to deny the power of her beauty, for she is very beautiful – but her beauty is not the characteristic that makes her most worthy of great love and adventure. I wanted to shift the focus a little, from that physical aspect to her character.

THE SEVENTH CHILD

SEVENTH CHILDREN HAVE LONG BEEN thought of as special, as possessing peculiar and uncanny powers that other children may not have. This belief may have arisen from obvious associations with longevity and fertility, as well as the special qualities of the number seven. As seven is a faery number, perhaps the gifts of the seventh son or daughter are from the faery themselves? (And perhaps, we all have these skills and talents, and seventh sons or daughters – or sons and daughters of seventh sons or daughters – have these same skills, just amplified.)

Seventh sons or daughters were especially sought out throughout medieval times for their gifts. In 1579, Thomas Lupton, in *A Thousand Notable Things*, wrote about a seventh son who could heal the "king's evil" – a sinister euphemism

for the painful swelling of the lymph glands that is a symptom of tuberculosis. This is associated with the fact that many kings would touch victims of this disease in large public blessings, and it was widely believed for centuries that the touch of the king (or queen) could cure. That gift of healing with a touch was believed to belong not just to kings and queens, but to seventh sons and seventh daughters, too. It was considered to be a supernatural power, and one which would cure suffering and break the curses that brought about all kinds of illness.

Of course, Mab is just a seventh child, not, strictly speaking, a seventh daughter. But she, I feel, has some of those gifts – for, with the gift of her love, comes the breaking of a curse and the lifting of a kind of physical prison for the Beast, within which, he is doomed to be feared, to inspire only disgust, and to never be loved.

This reminds us that human touch, when given with consent, love, compassion, and sensitivity is a healing gift. And there are some individuals whose gift of touch, whose exquisite ability to know how and where to lay their hands upon another, brings about healing. We all need both to touch and to be touched. It is a part of what makes us human. With the return of loving touch, the Beast's humanity can override his animal instincts, and he can return to himself.

Do Not Break the Laws of Hospitality

In *Beauty and the Beast*, we see an example of a law of hospitality being broken. It may seem a petty transgression – to steal a rose bush – but breaking a law is breaking a law. It is just the kind of moment that makes the Beast's precarious mask of civility slip, and gives his rage and resentment an opportunity to be unleashed.

Ancient cultures had strict protocols around the behaviours of hosts and guests – and breaking these laws resulted in terrible misfortune. It was essential to always offer hospitality, even to the humble traveller, as it was thought that gods often travelled in disguise, testing humans. An encounter with such a god could lead to great rewards – or terrible punishment if they were turned away and scorned. And it was considered the bare minimum of courtesy to offer guests welcome, then food and a bath, and to refrain from any questions until the guest had rested. In return, the guest must take nothing from the abode, be grateful and courteous, and do their best to not be a burden or take advantage of the generosity given.

While the customs of generosity and courtesy being shown to guests date from prehistory, ancient protocols became formalised under laws such as the Greek law of Xenia and the Celtic Brehon laws, in which a mutual relationship between guest and host was deemed a kind of sacred contract. These laws were codified and considered an extension of personal honour in the Celtic, Nordic, and Germanic systems. To treat a guest well was to bring good fortune upon yourself, as this passage from *Havamal* – said to

be the words of Odin himself – shows:

I advise you, Loddfafnir,
To take advice;
You would benefit, if you took it;
Good will come to you, if you accept it:
Do not scorn a guest,
Nor drive him away from your gates;
Treat the homeless well.

Although the giving of impressive gifts was often a part of the ritual of honouring guests – and particularly the exchange of weapons and items that were ritually significant, such as cauldrons, garments, jewels – even the humblest people could keep the most basic of these rites and expect favour from others and from the gods.

Perhaps, then, with the taking of the rose bush, the merchant is obligated to give a gift in return – either his own companionship or that of his daughter.

Chocolate:
A Way to Open the Heart

CHOCOLATE HAS LONG BEEN A CEREMONIAL drink, and was considered a sacred elixir over 4,000 years ago in the central Americas. It was worked with as a medicine in Olmec, Mayan, and Aztec societies, and it's only today that Westerners are awakening to its powerful qualities in cacao ceremonies.

One of the active ingredients within chocolate is theobromine – "the food of the gods" – which stimulates the release of dopamine within our bodies, lowers blood pressure, widens blood vessels, and stimulates the heart. Thus, imbibing or devouring chocolate creates the same chemical and biological chain of events as falling in love. When the Beast includes hot chocolate as one of his offerings to Mab, he is already asking her to open her heart to him and to what may come.

A Lost Library Found

WITHIN THIS TALE IS A PLACE WHERE enchanted books dwell – perhaps even books that are yet to be written live beyond its magickal door. I feel this library is a kind of subtle ancestor of the lost libraries of Alexandria and, as such, an antidote to all the losses of all the books, both those our heroine had to leave behind and all the wisdom we've abandoned throughout history, even destroyed and burned. I love that within this "prison", where she is at liberty to come and go, but which she cannot leave, Mab finds an intoxicating freedom of the mind.

That she can read at all is a kind of miracle – yet it is within the first tellings of this tale that we find her love for books, which is remarkable. Today, we take it for granted that women in Western cultures are literate. But in the 1700s, when this tale was written, women's literacy was still low – perhaps around thirty-two per cent – and it was limited almost exclusively to wealthy women whose families allowed them to learn to read, and who had the means to have their daughters educated, for sons were always educated first.

MAKING MAGICK:
BEAUTY AND THE BEAST AND THE
ENCHANTED LIBRARY

ONE OF THE MOST HEART-WARMING ASPECTS of *Beauty and the Beast* is the way this tale highlights just how vital books can be to an imaginative and wondrous life.

If you would like to create a little of the magick of books within your own life, you could begin by creating your own fantastical library, like the one found in the Beast's chateau. And one of the first books you could add to it could be one you create yourself – a traditional esoteric book called a *Book of Shadows and Light*.

A Book of Shadows and Light is traditionally kept by witches and wise ones, healers and wizards, and it holds within its pages spells herb lore, phases of the moon, your own secret wonderings and wishes, and so much more!

To keep one, you will simply need a blank-paged book. They are often decorated quite beautifully by their owner, or you can purchase one. I have created one you could use for yourself, full of beautiful images and many magickal secrets to inspire you. Whatever kind you choose, you can record your own ideas, thoughts, and discoveries, the meaning of your dreams, and any potions you may create.

Books of Shadows and Light, grimoires, or Books of Shadows are a witches' tradition, a personal spellbook passed down through either blood families of witches or the alternate family within a coven. They are precious and intensely personal.

Once these books were kept secret – because to be discovered to be a witch, or to have ancient knowledge and the ability to use it, was a very dangerous thing. Today, we have a great deal more freedom to celebrate and share our magick.

You can keep your own Book of Shadows and Light very private, or in time you could share it with another, just as the Beast shares his magickal library with Mab. Once, we passed them on at the end of our lives – now, we tend to be much more open, and open the pages to those who have a sincere calling to the Craft.

If you decide to keep a Book of Shadows and Light, you may even wish to cast a magickal circle about it, before you begin to write in it, as I like to do. The circle is a world between the worlds, a place of sanctuary and pure, sparkling energy, within which will be held safe while you do your magickal writing.

To cast it, holding the book in your left hand, stand up, and take a deep breath in. Draw the breath up, and, as you do, see energy being drawn up from deep within the earth. When you feel it really gathering within you, extend your right arm and feel the energy being sent out from your right hand.

Point your index finger and, beginning in the direction of the east, move deosil (sunwise or clockwise in the northern hemisphere, anti-clockwise in the southern hemisphere), and say out loud:

I cast this circle by
The Earth that is the page,
The Air that is your word,
The Fire that ignites the spirit,
And the Waters that are the emotions.
The Circle is cast about my magickal book,
to protect and inspire,
to explore and enquire.
So mote it be!

You end where you began, in the east, having come full circle, so to speak!

After you have finished writing in your Book of Shadows and Light, you simply turn in the opposite direction, starting again in the east, and say:

I give thanks for all that has flowed through me
Into your pages this day (or night!).
This circle is now closed, but never is it broken.
Blessed be.

You could have a special box you keep your Book of Shadows and Light within, or it may simply reside with the other books of wonder within your magickal library. Happy magickal reading to you!

The Wisdom of Beauty and the Beast

I TRULY ADORE THIS TALE. IT SHOWS US THAT even when we are outcast, alone, and orphaned by circumstance, our salvation can be found within books. It shows us that knowing things is not the same as understanding them, and that wisdom is not about facts – it is about seeing into the heart of another being and knowing who they are. It asks us, as Mab's mother asks of her youngest daughter, to go beneath the surface, beneath appearances, to truly reflect on who and what we are, rather than what we appear to be.

The tale says that our beauty is not what is most valuable about us. Mab is learned, curious, defiant, and compassionate – her beauty may be the most conspicuous of her qualities, but it is her*self* that is most valuable and rich. She is a heroine who shows courage and who dreams big. She is willing to sacrifice herself, but she is no damsel in distress – there is a liberty to her actions, where she chooses, again and again, what will happen next.

The tale also shares with us that our connection with another can lie within our conversations and the stories we have in common. We can bond through heart and mind – relationships of substance include ideas, exploration, companionship, and like-mindedness, as well as great differences.

Beauty and the Beast tells us that if we have the courage to move beyond the boundaries of home, enter enchanted castles, and open books of wisdom, we may also be rewarded with the freedom to explore the world with a true soulmate by our side. I hope that a little of this tale's deep and lovely wisdom works its way into your life, along with the gifts of great companionship, immense understanding, being valued beyond your appearance, and, of course, the loyal and enchanted companionship of books.

CINDERELLA

ONCE THERE WAS A BEAUTIFUL WOMAN who loved her husband and their young daughter, Ellorah. The woman's little family was bright with joy and strong in conviction, and goodness was their hearts' creed. Together they helped each other to be the best people they could ever be. They lived in a fine home, with a bustling housekeeper and a wise gardener – and a deep, old well. When her husband was away making their fortune, that beautiful woman loved to sit by the old well whispering to it and speaking to the trees, just as she had done when she was a child.

And all in their world was peaceful and happy.

But after one very long, very cold winter, the woman was never quite well again. Even though the summer was glorious, and the autumn a golden song, it became clear to all who loved her that she was dying. When she felt her time was near, she called her daughter to her, and they took their seats at the well, where they were accustomed to spending some time each day, exploring their thoughts, sharing a mother's secrets, asking a daughter's questions.

"Ellorah," she whispered, once her daughter had ceased to sob, knowing now her mother would soon leave. "Be kind, be brave, and know how very loved you are."

When Ellorah's mother died, she was put to rest in the earth in the garden, near the well, and a copper beech tree was planted over her grave. Each day, Ellorah would go to the grave, tend to the beech tree, and talk to her mother. And sometimes, yes, 'tis true, she wept into the earth, for she missed her mother so.

Snow fell, and the little tree's roots spiralled into the earth. When spring came the beech tree budded and grew taller, and the girl did, too.

When the snow melted into spring a third time, the girl had a stepmother, for her father, whose hair had turned silver when Ellorah's mother died, believed he had found happiness again.

The stepmother had two daughters, Hylda and Haduwig. Ellorah's father thought the girls would be great company for his daughter, as he saw how she pined for her mother. But the stepsisters were so different in character to Ellorah's, that she wondered how they had come to be the people they were. Her stepsisters seemed to take no pleasure in each other, but constantly fought and quarrelled, except when they sided together to torment Ellorah. (Of course, they took care not to show their cruelty when her father was around.) Ellorah's stepmother seemed kind enough, but she was very proud. She gloried in her position as the head of the house, the queen of their home.

All of this left Ellorah feeling strange and unsettled, but she held on to the comfort of her father's love, her mother's gardens, and the beech tree that marked her mother's grave. She sat by the well, and spoke her dreams out loud to the mice and the birds and the trees as her mother had taught her – and in these ways, the strangeness of her inherited family did not harm her too much.

Soon, though, it came time for her father to leave on business once again, and Ellorah's heart felt heavy. Before he had even saddled his horse, she began to count the days until he would be home with her once more. On the morning of his departure, he asked each of the girls what they wanted him to bring back for them.

"Oh, lace, do bring me back the finest lace," cried Haduwig.

Hylda pushed her younger sibling aside and hugged her stepfather tight. "Bring me back the finest earrings, oh, do, beloved Father," she begged.

"And what of you, my dearest Ellorah," he asked his daughter tenderly.

"Dear Father," she whispered, as he drew her into his arms, "bring me back the first branch that brushes against your hat when you turn homewards." Like her mother, she loved the garden, and adored all kinds of trees, especially ones that grew in faraway places.

He laughed and agreed, and smiled into her eyes. And she turned away, quickly, not wanting him to see the tears that had welled up in her eyes. His promise to bring her home something special did little to still the pain that rose up within her at the anticipation of her loneliness. Ellorah longed to keep her father close. She felt strange amongst these new people, who quarrelled, compared, judged, and hurt each other. She spent the days following her father's departure walking the gardens, scattering grain for the birds and the mice, whispering to the well, and tending the memory of her mother beneath the beech tree. "Soon," she would tell herself, "soon he will be home."

Only, her father did not come home. On his journey, he had a bad fall from his horse, from which he could not recover. When the news came, it came with the branch of a silver birch tree. The branch was heavy with catkins, and when it was handed to her, Ellorah took it and planted it next to her mother's beech tree – her tears falling into the earth once more.

The stepmother was furious. "How shall we provide for ourselves," she demanded of Ellorah. "Your father has left us, and we are ruined. All for that stupid branch!"

Soon, the gardener was dismissed, and the housekeeper followed, after, leaving Ellorah tasked with keeping the house and the animals, and tending to the needs of her stepmother and her stepsisters. Her day began before first light. In the pre-dawn darkness, she would sweep the ashes from the fireplace, go to the woodpile, and set the kindling and fresh logs in the kitchen hearth. She loved beckoning the fire to life, adding her breath to the sparks, and watching the flames take hold. Each morning, she stared into the flames, savouring those golden moments of peace before the first ring of the bell summoned her from reverie to servitude. Then, she sombrely prepared and served breakfast, her face smudged with salt and ash, while her stepsisters laughed and called her names, trying them out one by one, until one stuck. *Cinderella.*

Each day, Cinderella fetched water, cleaned windows, scrubbed floors, and cared for the animals, whom she had always loved. She brushed the long, pretty hair of her stepsisters, mended their stockings, and walked into town to fetch their favourite foods or a bow they'd taken a fancy to.

She made the meals, tasty and fine as could be. She stretched the ingredients as far as she could, but once the others ate, there was little left for her. When she asked for a little more, she was told, "You already eat too much. We cannot afford to house *and* feed you. Perhaps if you try a little harder, more can be found for you."

When she was packed up from her room and sent to the attic, she made a little straw bed on which to sleep and befriended her new roommates: some white mice and a fine rat. And each day, she would steal away to the copper beech and the silver birch and tell her parents of her sadness. She would hear her mother's voice whisper through the branches, reminding her, *Be kind, be brave, and know how very loved you are.* And so Cinderella would square her fragile shoulders, straighten her spine, and go back to work.

The stepmother was very ambitious for her own daughters. They were no longer just pretty girls, but had become blossoming young women, and if she could but hide their spiteful natures from suitors for long enough, there was every chance they could make good marriages before the estate ran dry. An attractive woman, herself, the stepmother held hope that she, too, might still make a grand marriage to a wealthy man if she set her mind to it. She was determined and strong willed, and it seemed she would get her way.

It was Cinderella who was given the task of making them all beautiful. She styled their hair, wove flowers into their locks, and suggested which necklace to wear with which dress for each social occasion, for she had an eye for such things. The stepsisters were cruel, though, and mocked her suggestions, even while taking them on. They punished her smallest oversight, but when she did something well, they were jealous and nasty.

While Cinderella worked hard to beautify her mistresses, she too was growing up. Unlike her stepsisters', her own beauty was effortless – although they told her otherwise. In fact, she was never allowed to see her reflection in a looking glass, should she see for herself how lovely she was becoming.

With no new clothes, Cinderella's old dresses were falling to rags. She mended them herself, with a stitch here and a patch here, and as smudged by ashes and as hard worked as she was, she still outshone her stepsisters and

stepmother. Her radiance shone right through the house, warming it, just as the fire brightened her mornings. For, despite all else, it was still her cherished home.

Thus, while others would have fallen into bitterness and despair at the treatment she received, Cinderella's soul stayed sweet. By the beech tree, by the birch tree, in the hallways, by the firelight, she remembered her mother's words, *Be kind, be brave, and know how very loved you are.*

One day, when Cinderella was in the marketplace, she noticed the town crier had gathered a crowd about him. "Hear ye, hear ye," he bellowed. She stopped, smiling at his puffed-out chest. And then he made an incredible announcement.

"At the next full moon," he cried, "three weeks from this day, there shall be a great ball in the castle. Every maiden in this realm is to attend, be she highborn or low, be she wealthy or wanting, and from you all, your prince shall choose his queen."

Every maiden? wondered Cinderella. She cared not about being a princess, but oh, to dance again! To dance as she had once twirled with her father, to wear a dress, to see the castle, to laugh and to lose herself in the music! Ah, what joy!

She hurried home to find the news had already been received. The house was in a frenzy, with drawers, wardrobes, and jewellery boxes being ransacked for the best and brightest adornments.

"Stop!" ordered the stepmother in her most commanding voice. All stilled immediately, each stepsister scowling at the other. "You have just three weeks to become the kind of young woman a prince would choose to marry."

They simpered and nodded. They found themselves extremely appealing – how could anyone resist either of them?

"You shall have the finest jewels, gowns, and carriage we can manage. And we can manage quite a deal," the stepmother said. And she stared at Cinderella, who knew she would be asked to double her efforts to make Hylda and Haduwig beautiful enough to capture the eye of the prince.

And so Cinderella was put straight to work, creating special potions and brews for her stepsisters' hair and complexions. In a few short days, their skin glowed. In a week, their cheeks were pink as peaches and their lips as red as cherries. In two weeks, their hair glimmered like diamonds.

When the stepsisters' gowns came back from the dressmakers, they tried them on and squealed with delight at their own magnificence. They marvelled even at the buttons, each a crystal the size of a thumbnail – amethyst for Hylda, citrine for Haduwig. They tied and retied the wide bows of lavender and yellow silk that would encircle their throats, before growing frustrated at the knots and the tangles they'd created and calling for Cinderella to come help tie them elegantly, for she had quick and clever fingers. They squealed at the lace, dyed to match, foaming from beneath their wide satin sleeves, and at the cascade of ruffles at the base of each dress.

And they tried on their dancing slippers – of lavender and yellow, striped and stack-heeled to lend the girls height and grace. And each sister silently assessed the other's charms, vowing that she alone would catch the eye and win the heart of the prince.

Finally, the day of the ball arrived. Gowns were fitted, faces were painted, powdered,

hair was curled, and sweet jasmine was dabbed behind ears. When all was done, Cinderella's stepmother gasped, for her daughters did look splendid. The stepmother looked very fine, too, with peacock feathers, and bows the colour of the first leaves in spring, and emeralds aglitter at her white throat. Cinderella, seeing the woman's satisfaction, wiped her brow and turned her attention to herself for the first time in what seemed like forever.

Quietly, she took herself to the well, where she washed, carefully pouring rosemary water through her hair, rinsing away the tell-tale signs of hard work and of the cinders that were her namesake. For a moment, it seemed like her mother was there with her again, both of them by the well, wondering out loud at the mysteries of the world. A small, secret smile made her sad eyes sparkle. She felt comforted, yet light with freedom, like a bird who has escaped its cage.

In an ancient cupboard in her attic, Cinderella dug beneath layers of cast-offs from her sisters and the rags she carefully washed each week, to find a very, very old dress she had hidden there. The dress, a precious keepsake that had belonged to her mother, was blue, and simple, and so soft and pretty that when she put it on, she spun about, delighting in its loveliness. Then she slid her feet into her mother's dancing slippers and came down the stairs.

Stunned, her stepmother gasped, her emerald eyes widening in disbelief, for she had forgotten how lovely her stepdaughter could be. Then, recovering, she addressed Cinderella with disdain and amusement. "And where do you think you are going?"

"The invitation was extended to every maiden in the land. I am a maiden. I am invited," Cinderella said simply. "And so, I will go."

"You can't go," said Hylda, with a curt little nod that shook her pretty red curls.

"You are our servant," said Haduwig, pursing her plump pink lips. "What are you thinking?"

"I heard the crier's call," said Cinderella, her voice growing firmer. "It was for *every* maiden, high or lowborn. Rich or penniless. I know I am invited. I can go. The king himself has said so."

Her stepmother was aghast. As simply dressed as she was, Cinderella's beauty far exceeded that of her own daughters. They had this one chance to capture the prince's attention. Cinderella would ruin everything! "Get back upstairs, take off that dress, and get back to work," she snapped.

"I've finished everything," Cinderella said softly. "And you all look beautiful."

Enraged, her stepmother strode forward and in one fierce movement tore Cinderella's dress from shoulder to waist.

Cinderella cried out.

Hylda tittered at seeing another take her mother's anger, for she feared her, too – more than she loved her, truth be told.

Even Haduwig looked sad for the briefest of moments.

But quickly, the three woman composed themselves, and then, in a whirl of feathers, laughter, and jasmine, they sallied forth, leaving Cinderella behind.

Alone, she gathered the remnants of her mother's dress about her and climbed the stairs, where she gazed out a window and, as their laughter and bickering faded away, she watched the carriage carrying her stepmother and stepsisters follow the road toward the castle. It was just one of many carriages, horses, and wagons taking maidens to the ball that night.

They would all be dancing. Every maiden, but her.

Cinderella's small face grew pale with despair. She did not feel good, nor brave, nor loved. She suspected the world of being a bitterly cruel and awful joke – and she knew it was so when she heard the catch of a mousetrap and a distressed squeak.

Releasing the little creature, she popped it on her shoulder and slipped out to visit the beech tree and the silver birch. She curled up in the roots of the trees, as if they were the arms of her mother and father, and sobbed into the earth. It had been so long since she had received a single kind word or one soft touch, and she longed to feel her mother's hand on her cheek, longed for her father to arrive home from his distant voyage. But they were both dead. Indeed, all hope was dead.

But then ...

"Ah-hem," she heard, a little way off. "Ah-hem-hem. AH-HEM!"

Cinderella wiped her face and leapt to her feet. "Hello?" she said into the night, a little embarrassed to have been caught crying so hard.

"Here I am, dear," said a voice laced with years and wisdom. "Here, a little further. Here, by the well."

Cinderella moved toward the voice, and there by the side of the well sat a very, very old woman.

"I wanted to get myself a drink of this sweet water, but I lack the strength. Can you help me?" she asked.

Cinderella was puzzled. She wondered who this old woman was and how she came to be in the garden, but she saved her questions. Instead, she pulled the bucket up from the well, filled the ladle, and put it to the old woman's parched lips, holding it there while the woman drank deep.

"More?" asked Cinderella. She'd known hunger, but she had never lacked water. And the woman must have been quite parched, as her face seemed to soften and grow younger as she drank the water. Again, Cinderella dipped the ladle, and again the strange old woman drank her fill. This time, Cinderella stepped back. The woman was changing before her eyes!

"One more ladleful, my dear," she said in a voice as soft as song. "Then I shall be quite myself once more."

Cinderella trembled as she again dipped the ladle into the bucket, but it was with wonder, not fear. This time the woman took the dipper in her own hands and drank, drank, drank all the water down.

"Ah," the no-longer old woman cried happily, "that is better!" And it was! The water had poured new life into the woman's being – it had even revived her gown. She now stood before Cinderella, sparkling, ageless, beautiful.

Cinderella was struck silent. Had despair, loss, and cruelty sent her mad?

"Not madness, my sweet girl," said the woman, as if hearing Cinderella's thoughts. "Magick is afoot, tonight. I am a guardian, my dear. A protector, a wise one ..." She paused at the sight of Cinderella's puzzled face.

"I'm here, dear child, because I loved your mother. She was the closest thing to a human friend I ever had. I've been watching you from down under the earth, and while I would usually just send you a little extra energy, tonight your tears quite broke my heart."

"My mother?" asked Cinderella, now wondering if it was the woman who was mad.

"Oh, yes, my dear. She's not strictly here,

but thanks to that beech tree, your mother is ... well ... everywhere. And she tells me you want to go to a ball, and then I saw you sobbing, and so I've come to see what I can do." The woman smiled merrily at the thought of being useful.

"Oh – are you a faery godmother?" Cinderella asked.

"A faery godmother? I wonder? Faeries would not use a word like 'godmother'. Old god? New god? Their god? Our god? The 'god' word is a troublesome one, have no doubt about it. Perhaps I am, as your mother sent me; that is the simple truth of it." The faery's voice sounded a little sad as she remembered her friend. But after a pause, she shook her head, as if breaking the spell of the past.

"Now, let me see ..."

The faery godmother tilted her head to one side and carefully considered Cinderella – who was now beginning to smile. *If I am quite mad,* the girl thought, *it is much nicer and far more fun than being miserable.*

"First things, first," said the faery godmother, matter-of-factly. "It's getting late, and most people are arriving ... so let's work on the transport."

Will I grow wings? wondered Cinderella.

"No, silly," answered the faery godmother, who could read minds, as all faeries can. "We must be practical." She frowned, very prettily too, and gazed about the garden. "That great golden pumpkin – let's have that."

Practical indeed! Cinderella restrained a giggle as she skipped over and picked up the pumpkin. She sat it on the ground next to her strange new friend thinking, *Whatever next?*

"Why, a coachman of course," answered the faery, and a little lizard, who had been peering at the curious goings on, slithered over.

To Cinderella's eyes, he seemed to be grinning.

All at once, the little mouse, who had been perched on Cinderella's shoulder all this time, stirred and squeaked excitedly. To her astonishment, the faery godmother responded to him by name.

"That *is* a good idea, Tomkins," said the faery, approvingly. "Call to your friends."

Six mice were soon gathered in the garden. "Lovely. That will be perfect," said the faery, contentedly.

"One more," sang the faery godmother, and a fine fat rat popped out of a flowerpot and lumbered over.

"What gorgeous creatures you are," cooed the magickal being, and all the animals preened, adoring the attention.

Cinderella laughed out loud, then stopped, startled. She hadn't laughed for so very long. What a beautiful feeling!

"Well, that is your transportation taken care of," nodded the faery godmother.

Oh, thought Cinderella, looking at the pumpkin, the lizard, the mice, and the rat. *She is no doubt magickal, but she's as mad as I am.*

"Is that so, sweet one?" said the faery godmother, her red lips twitching with mirth. "Everything can change."

And with that, she waved her wand gracefully, once, twice, three times ... and sparks of light flowed from the wand into the pumpkin, the lizard, the mice, and the rat. And indeed, each one of them did change, until they were quite unlike themselves – but, remarkably, somehow the same. The pumpkin became an exquisite golden carriage; the lizard, an elegant footman dressed in vibrant greens; and the mice, six glorious, white horses. The portly coachman, golden reins in his hands, was the rat! Seeing

Cinderella's admiring glance, he twinkled, and his wide smile revealed two rather long front teeth!

"Let this madness be truth," Cinderella declared. "You are all pure magick!"

"Not 'madness', dear. Magick!" laughed the faery godmother. Then, looking serious, she said, "Now, this," she said, touching the dress lightly with a gentle hand, "this I remember! It is lovely – a shame about the rip ... but may I just make a few changes, to make it more yours?" And before Cinderella could finish nodding, the back of her gown grew into a graceful long train, while the front of her gown stitched itself together, and where once there had been a great tear, diamonds and pearls sparkled on the bodice. And finally, the faded blue silk deepened until it glowed like the sea in the morning light.

"And now, your hair." Another wave of the wand beckoned two little songbirds, who each gathered up a golden strand of Cinderella's hair within their beak. And as her faery godmother chanted, "Kind, brave, beloved. Kind, brave, beloved," they darted in and out, weaving two delicate braids that showed off the beauty of Cinderella's face.

When the birds were done, the rest of Cinderella's abundant locks fell free, all the way down to her waist, now iridescent with the tiny diamonds and pearls that were sprinkled throughout. There was just a little sparkle on her cheekbones, a mother's kiss glowing on each cheek, and a touch of dew upon her lips.

Cinderella gazed down at herself, raising her arms in wonder. "Ah, yes," said the faery godmother, "those arms cannot be bare." And just like that, gloves of pale blue silk slipped up Cinderella's hands and wrists all the way to her elbows.

"And, now," the faery godmother said, approvingly, "you are ready." But this was quickly followed by, "Oh, dear! Those will never do!" For she had caught sight of Cinderella's shoes. "I know they are hers," she said softly. "But this is your night, and she would want you to take what she's given you – all of it – and make it quite your own."

Cinderella nodded, feeling all the old love – and the joy she'd pushed down for so long threatened to rise up and spill over. She swallowed, and her eyes shone with unshed tears. The faery godmother saw, and knew, but only continued kindly. "Your feet are so pretty ... Let's see, something clear and crystalline, I think." The magickal wand danced through the air, and a pair of slippers spun from glass poured over the girl's tiny feet. The slippers sparkled and shone, and Cinderella could barely feel them, as she stepped gingerly forward, for they were as weightless and free as moonlight.

"Ellorah, you are utterly beautiful. You were your mother's darling, your father's joy, and I am proud to be your faery godmother."

"Thank you," Ellorah replied, her breath catching, so moved was she to hear her own name once again.

"Go now. Enjoy every moment. But this magick can only last so long. On the twelfth chime of midnight, all will return to what it was ... all except those glass slippers. Those, I think, are thoroughly yours, my dear." And with one last burst of magick, the faery made sure the slippers would remain here on the earthly plane forever.

Ellorah smiled. It had been so long since she had had anything new – anything of her own at all. To have this – what was her mother's keepsake become somehow her own perfect ballgown – was like a memory returned

and become a promise. Her hands trembled, and the gratitude she felt inspired one unshed tear to overflow and spill down her cheek.

"Go now," whispered her wonderfully magickal protectress, drying the tear with a touch of her hand. "Dance, smile, laugh … and who knows, Ellorah? You may even fall in love."

And so she said farewell, stepped into her golden carriage and was whisked away. She may not have had wings, but she felt like she was flying. As the carriage rolled toward the castle, she gazed in wonder at the countryside passing swiftly by her. There were lanterns in the trees, and sleepy songbirds formed the most beautiful choir. She could hear an orchestra in the distance, and when they crossed the drawbridge, her heart began to pound. She quietened herself, telling herself, over and over, "I am brave. I am kind. I am loved." When she did this, she kept the excitement, but the fear faded just enough for her to breathe properly once again.

The castle was ablaze with the light of a thousand candles. A long, long staircase led to the entrance. Ellorah was helped from the carriage by her elegant footman, and as she descended, she smiled and dipped her head in thanks. Then she patted Tomkins, who shivered with delight.

"Oh, I wish you could come! Will you wait for me here, please?" she said gently to all of the animals who were part of the magick. None could speak, but all smiled at her with warm, happy eyes, and each gave a little nod.

"Then enjoy yourselves, dear friends," she said and turned to climb the stairs.

Before she entered the great ballroom, a footman asked, "What is your name, Princess? How should I announce you?"

She hardly knew how to answer. Was she Cinderella? Or was she Ellorah? Or was she some new creature, spun of magick and memories? With no ready response, she simply curtseyed, smiled, and was soon staring out onto a ballroom filled with what seemed like hundreds upon hundreds of swirling couples. Everyone was dressed in their richest finery. Milkmaids danced alongside countesses, and all were lovely in the candlelight. She smiled at the sight, then let her eyelids close as she swayed and hummed with the orchestra until the beautiful music stopped. When she opened her eyes, there was a young man standing right before her.

"Lady," he said, his voice deep and rich with kindness and humour. "Would you do me the honour of this dance?"

She nodded, nervous and uncertain, flooded with a giddy delight. *What can it matter?* she wondered, as she took his arm and shyly smiled into his eyes. *This is a dream – and soon I will wake up. I'll enjoy it as if it is real.* The room stilled as all eyes watched the couple make their way down the great staircase. As they took the floor, whispers began to ripple through the crowd.

"Who is she?"

"How enchanting she is!"

"That dress – what can it be made from?"

In the candlelight, Ellorah looked otherworldly. Her dress was an ocean flowing around her as she took her place on the dancefloor. Her hair, her eyes, her lips, her shoes all caught the light of the candles and reflected their warmth. She curtseyed, he bowed, and they began to dance. It had been many moons since she had danced, but her feet – or was it her glass slippers? – knew every step. Her grace and loveliness delighted the young man, who danced with her again, and again, and again.

In time, Hylda and Haduwig were invited

onto the dance floor. They ignored their partners to fling envious glances over their powdered shoulders at their stepsister, whom they did not recognise.

"She *is* lovely," sighed the younger sister.

"That she is," said her partner, whose enthusiasm was rewarded with a sharp tap from Haduwig's fan.

So, the night went on, and Ellorah and her young man danced. After many hours of waltzing, promenading, twirling, and dipping, the young man found his voice and asked, "May I get you a glass of wine?"

"Oh, yes, please," Ellorah replied. "I quite forgot my thirst. You must be parched, too," she added.

He smiled and led her from the dance floor, and a servant soon appeared, offering exquisite refreshments. The two drank wine from golden goblets and smiled shyly at each other.

"Beautiful lady …" he began.

But one of the king's advisors interrupted them. "Prince!" the man said. And yes, the young man was, of course, the prince. "We wish you to meet the princess of …"

"A moment more," the prince replied. "I am with this young lady."

Ellorah, though, took a step back. "Prince?" she asked, startled.

"I am," he said, "but not now." Seeing her confusion, he explained, "Tonight, I am simply a man, you are a woman, and we dance."

And so they returned to the dance floor, and the music lifted them, until it seemed the orchestra was playing just for the two of them.

As they danced past her stepmother and stepsisters, Ellorah smiled to herself, seeing they did not know her, even though she spent every day with them.

For the stepmother's part, she had quickly realised her efforts to gain the prince's interest in either Haduwig or Hylda had been in vain, and had set about finding other available, wealthy men for her daughters – and perhaps for herself.

Meanwhile, as Ellorah whirled in the prince's arms, she wondered, *What if he doesn't recognise me, when I am just myself? I am not this sparkling girl with whom he dances. I am just Cinderella, and this cannot last.*

But her mother's words echoed, *You are kind. You are brave. You are beloved.*

And everything can change. This last phrase came in the knowing, mirthful voice of her faery godmother.

"What sadness has passed over your face?" the prince asked, with concern. "Come, tell me."

"This ball is a world away from my own life, Prince," she said. "I will be sad to see it end."

"But it need never end," he said.

At that exact moment, the great castle clock began to chime midnight. She stared at it, astonished at how the time had passed.

"Is it midnight, already? I must go. Goodbye. Goodbye. It was just wonderful!" she said, and she turned and fled.

The crowd parted to let the beautiful young woman through, and within moments she was leaving the enchantment of the castle. But she dashed so quickly down the stairs toward her carriage that one of her glass slippers sprang free from her foot. She turned to reclaim it, but saw the prince and his men coming after her – and her stepmother was not far behind!

So, leaving the slipper gleaming on the stair, she ran to the carriage, leapt in, and the mouse-horses took off at a gallop. As they

pounded down the carriageway, Ellorah prayed to her faery godmother and all the good creatures in the wide world that the magick would hold long enough for them to get safely away.

It seemed that time had slowed – the clock still chimed, but as they raced along, the magick began to slip. Ellorah's gown transformed stitch by stitch, until it was her mother's torn dress that hung from her shoulders. Her hair fell loose about her face. The beautiful white horses began to get smaller and smaller, as did her carriage, until at last she tumbled forth and found herself sitting on the road beside a pumpkin, a little bumped and bruised.

She stared back along the long avenue toward the castle and knew the ball would continue without her. Tomkins soon found her shoulder, and she scooped up the other mice, the rat, and the humble lizard into the fold of her dress. Then she smiled. "At least this one night was perfect," she confided to her accomplices, and began the lengthy journey home, singing a little as she walked. And she held the single glass slipper close, as if clutching this night to her heart. This treasure, this gift, vouched for her memories. Without it she would already be thinking it was but a dream.

***

When she crept up the stairs that night, she put her single glass slipper safely away in the same place she'd kept her mother's dress. And she slept with the music of the dances she'd shared with a prince playing in her mind. She dreamed of his face, of his gentleness, and of belonging in a world she'd never thought she would again enter.

The next day, she was up early to coax warmth into the hearth and stare just a little longer than usual into the flames – only to find that the kingdom was up early, too, and abuzz with talk of the ball. And no place more so than in her own home.

Over breakfast, her stepsisters and stepmother dissected the evening, easing their disappointment in not making a good match by describing in detail the wonders of the castle in earshot of the one maiden they imagined had not had the pleasure to see it herself. Their conversation kept circling back to the mysterious lady who had enchanted the prince.

"Did you see her dress?"

"Oh, *I* did not like it," pronounced the stepmother.

"Oh, I though it beauti—," began Haduwig, but Hylda silenced her with a sharp look.

"It was an awful dress," the elder sister snapped. "Simply hideous."

"Indeed," sniffed the stepmother. "Your garments were far superior. The prince was simply caught by her ... charms. I didn't realise he would be so easily caught in a witch's snare."

Cinderella smothered a giggle, and kept at her work. Every now and again, she did a little dance, and once she was even caught by Haduwig, but she put her finger to her lips, and they both smiled. Something had changed in the night. Perhaps the dancing had done all three of the girls more good than they knew.

Then, at noon, there was more news from the castle.

"The prince has made a declaration!" panted Haduwig as she fell in the door, her face flushed with excitement. "He is searching the entire kingdom for *her*!"

"What if she doesn't want to be found?"

asked Cinderella.

"What?" scoffed Hylda.

"Well, what if she … what if she wants to stay hidden? What if it was for just one night?"

"You ignorant girl," scoffed her stepmother. "You are just a sad, lowly cinder maid, good for nothing but stitching up our stockings – and you're stupid, too! Do not speak of matters you know nothing about."

Her stepmother's insults couldn't reach Cinderella's heart, though. Her prince was searching for her, and she couldn't help but feel happy. But if he found her … would he want her?

She was clearing the noontime meal and giving Tomkins a little piece of cheese when the hubbub began in the front rooms.

"He is coming here, today!" her stepmother shrieked. "Quick! Get into your gowns, daughters. Cinderella! Cinderella! Brush their hair, wash their faces, make them shine, you silly girl! We have another chance to win the prince!"

When the handsome prince arrived at the house with a team of advisors – one of whom looked quite disgusted at this mission – Cinderella ran to her room, smoothed her hair back, checked her reflection in a teapot, and stood at the top of the stairs, holding her head up high. From here, she could watch the foray, keep out of her stepmother's way, and decide what to do. Her stepsisters were in the front room, Haduwig hopping from one foot to another in excitement, Hylda elbowing her sister in the ribs to calm her down.

"The lady whose foot this shoe belongs to shall be the prince's bride," announced an elderly footman.

"That is, if the lady agrees," added the prince, frowning a little.

Oh, good, thought Cinderella.

"I am sure one of my beautiful daughters shall fit the shoe," announced her stepmother. "I think you may have shared a dance or two."

How silly, thought Cinderella. *Surely, he remembers who he danced with.*

Still, Hylda thrust her foot forward for the glass slipper. The footman tried it one way, then another, as the girl grunted and pushed, her eyes watering at the effort. But no matter what she did, the slipper would not allow her foot to enter.

Cinderella watched her stepmother's face turn beet red with rage.

"It does not fit," announced the advisor. "It is not your fault, lady," he said, with courtesy to Hylda. "It is a very, erm, *particular* kind of shoe."

"Perhaps my foot has swollen with all the dancing," pleaded Hylda.

"Could she try it again in a few days?" the stepmother asked the prince – but he just looked solemn and shook his head.

"The other sister?" asked the servant, elegantly sidestepping the stepmother.

Haduwig put her foot forward, but while her foot was rather lovely, it was much, much too long to fit the glass slipper.

"Haduwig is a growing girl," wheedled the stepmother. "Every day she sprouts more and more!"

But again, the prince shook his head. Then he asked, "Are there any other maidens here to try on the slipper?"

"There is no-one else," said the stepmother, in a very definite tone of voice.

"There is Cinder—" started Haduwig, before Hylda clapped a hand over her sister's mouth.

But not before the prince was alerted. "If there is another, bring her forward, now," he commanded.

"There is only a stupid halfwit of a serving girl, my prince," said the stepmother dismissively.

"Bring her forward," repeated the prince, in a voice that would have no answer but yes.

It was at this moment, having seen his fairness, that Cinderella knew what she would do. She walked slowly down the stairs, and he recognised her immediately.

"It's you?"

"It is."

"Will you try the shoe, my lady?" asked the prince.

"Yes," she said, nodding in return. She pinched the back of her hand, hoping this was not a dream. *It must be real, else I'd feel nothing.* She felt her heart beating so strongly she thought everyone in the room must hear it. *It must be real, else my heart would not be pounding so.* She straightened her back. She pushed back her shoulders. She took a deep breath and stepped forward to her fate, whatever it would be.

The footman gestured graciously to the chair, and Ellorah sat down and extended her pretty foot, which poured effortlessly into the magick slipper. Then she took the slipper's mate from her pocket and handed it to the prince, who got down on one knee and placed it on her other foot. At that moment, light seemed to pour into the room, and the two of them smiled deeply into each other's eyes.

"It *is* you," he said.

"And it is you," she answered.

"What is your name?" he asked.

"Ellorah," she replied. "And yours?"

"Freiderik," he said, and he took her hand. "Will you come with me?"

She said, simply, "I will."

And together, they left the home.

Ellorah's stepmother raged for three full days. She beat Haduwig and would not speak to Hylda. Finally, the sisters left their mother and went to the castle to speak to Princess Ellorah. She forgave them, found them good, fine work to do, and they grew to become better people. The stepmother, though, was never seen again. Some say she vanished into the forest, wailing and beating her hands against her head.

In time, Prince Freiderik and Princess Ellorah took their children to the place where the beech tree grew and the silver birch reached up to the sky, and to the well where the faery godmother had appeared. They introduced their little ones to the sweet mice and clever lizards darting about in the garden.

And the faery godmother smiled, for faeries like nothing better than an ending where one who is kind, brave, and beloved, comes to realise how everything can change in the blink of an eye, in the wave of a wand, and the sparkle of a single glass slipper.

SHE CURLED UP in the roots of the trees, as if
they were the arms of her mother and father, and sobbed
into the earth. It had been so long since she had received
a single kind word or one soft touch. But her parents
were dead. Indeed, all hope was dead.

But then …

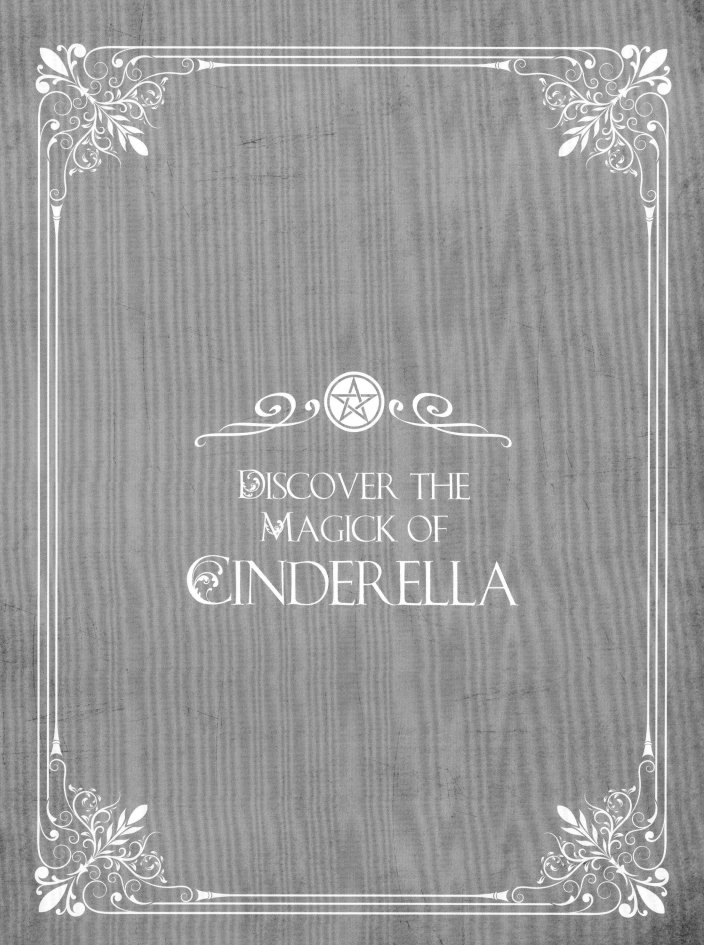

DISCOVER THE
MAGICK OF
CINDERELLA

I CANNOT REMEMBER WHEN I was first told the tale of the cinder maid whose life is so utterly transformed with the help of her faery godmother. I do remember very clearly, though, when I first became aware of the older, darker versions of the tale, as the self-injury and harm the stepsisters inflicted upon their own feet, attempting to fulfil their mother's relentless quest for status, made my blood run cold. While I didn't include this aspect of the tale, I wanted to reinforce that the stepsisters are not physically ugly. Rather, it is their unkindness, thoughtlessness, and selfishness that makes them unattractive. They even take Ellorah's name from her ... for a time, at least.

History of this Tale

THE TERM "A CINDERELLA STORY" HAS TAKEN on a life of its own over the last two hundred years. But this tale is much, much older than that, with some scholars believing the roots of *Cinderella* can be found in *Rhopsodis*, an ancient Greek tale by Herodotas about a young Greek girl sold into slavery in Egypt. *Rhopsodis* follows the heroine's humiliations and eventual triumph, as she shakes off servitude and rises to become an Egyptian princess.

There are Chinese counterparts, Native American versions, and a Jewish take on the story, which has become, I believe, an archetype, a tale that has such resonance we recognise its theme deep in our souls.

In 1697, the most influential version of *Cinderella* was written by Charles Perrault, and her name was Cendrillon – *Little Ashes*. Perrault is credited with the creation of the pumpkin, the faery godmother, and the iconic glass – or, in my imagination, crystal – slippers.

In 1812, the Brothers Grimm adapted Perrault's tale, adding their own macabre elements, and *Little Ashes* became *Aschenpuutal* or *The Fool of Ashes*. In this version, Aschenpuutal's tears cause magickal trees to flourish, and her sisters take so long to squeeze their feet into the tiny glass slippers that they cut off, respectively, a toe and a heel – and of course, ravens peck out the sisters' eyes, just to add to their punishment.

The version you read here has been influenced by both versions, of course – how could it not be? But I loved the idea of transforming the slippers from glass to crystal, of making the faery godmother an emissary and dear friend of Cinderella's loving mother, and of our heroine shaking off the passivity of Perrault's version (in which she does little but sob and wait to be saved). I hope this young woman comes across as I intended – decisive, full of compassion and fire, with a deep connection to nature, and a rich, independent internal life.

THE MAGICK OF NAMES

CINDERELLA IS NOT OUR HEROINE'S NAME. IT is a taunt that is the stepsisters' way of diminishing Ellorah to subservience and of elevating themselves far above her. A person should never call you names or disrespect you. Although, through her renaming and her stepfamily's treatment, Ellorah comes perilously close to forgetting who she truly is, she transforms her travails into her destiny, aided by the protection of the beech, the strength of the birch, and the magick of her faery godmother. Then, right at the end, when the prince asks for her name, she speaks her own true name – not the name of the role she plays in her step-household. Thus, she reclaims herself and the respect and consideration we are all due.

True names are magickal when they somehow capture the essence of who we are. In times of magick, our names were closer to our soul's vibration – our truest self – than they are today. You may wish to wonder what the name of your true self could be. Perhaps it is the name you were given at birth. Or, perhaps it is there, waiting for you, beneath the names others call you.

When we work magick, one way in which we can offer blessings is to chant a person's name. When we say our name to ourselves, or have others say it to us, perhaps by chanting it or singing it in circle, our name sheds the criticisms and the harsh ways in which it may have been pronounced previously – and who has not heard their name said with disdain? But when our name is said with love, with respect, and with dignity, its magickal qualities return and will be reinforced every time we hear it spoken, write it on a page, or tell another what we are called.

THE WISDOM OF TREES:
COPPER BEECH AND SILVER BIRCH

WHEN PEOPLE PASS, SOMETIMES WE MIGHT plant a tree over their grave. This is a very old tradition. The tree most usually planted in graveyards is the yew. However, beech trees have been planted around the passage grave of Wayland's Smithy and the great stone circles of Avebury. Some of these trees have absorbed the ancestral energies beneath the earth, and have become a repository of the consciousness of those who have passed.

The beech tree's Gaelic name is *Phagos*, which in some translations means "book". To me, the beech is the library of the ancestors. Beech trees are also sometimes called the mother of the forest, and I wanted Cinderella to have a tree that

could offer her mother's comfort to her. Beech is a tree of wisdom, of memory, of knowledge and tradition, so although Ellorah becomes an orphan, she can maintain her connection with her mother through the beech. So, when Cinderella speaks with the copper beech tree, she is effectively speaking with her mother in her new form, reading her maternal wisdom, and coming to know her empathy and kindness in another way. And why a copper beech? I love the idea of the tree being a redhead, because that is the colour I imagined Ellorah's mother's hair to be.

In addition, beech trees are said to contain medicine that heals mental rigidity and protects us from unkind critics, bigotry, arrogance, and attack. The copper beech does all this and more, in this magickal tale.

The silver birch, the tree associated in the story with Ellorah's father, is a straight tree. Tall, slender, it is able to see above and beyond the present and into the future. In the Ogham, it is called *Beith*, and it governs discipline and internal strength. Although this tree is quite often associated with feminine qualities, I loved the idea of Ellorah's father becoming identified with the birch – an unseen source of strength and direction, fortitude and endurance, the kind of qualities that can help our heroine overcome her challenges. And, I thought that, by the time he left home for the last time, the father's hair may have silvered with the grief of losing his most beloved first wife and the disappointment of realising his second marriage could never hope to be one of contentment.

Birch is also associated with the fae, which is where our faery godmother comes in. And it is the wood that witches' brooms are made of. Its bark can be burned to purify a home after

sadness. Thus, birch is often used to clear out negativity. Although Ellorah's father passes away, his presence, in the form of the silver birch, offers his daughter the fortitude to hold on to her true self, to endure, and, finally, to drive out sadness, cruelty, and loneliness – and find in their stead, joy, support, and love.

Since birch can also symbolise new beginnings, it can be seen here as marking both the loss of Ellorah's father and the beginning of her new life, one in which she both reclaims her name and assumes a new identity, at least in the external world. Until that time, however, the combined energies of her parents – as copper beech and silver birch – provide the support and strength she needs to make it through the hard times.

On Faeries and Transformations

Faeries are wise, ancient beings who are the caretakers of the elements and the natural world. They are often assumed to be little, with tiny wings and mischievous personalities. While they may indeed appear like that, many faeries are deep and old and wise – and this is the kind of faery we meet in *Cinderella*. Despite her name, the faery godmother has little to do with any notion of "god". Instead, I prefer to think of her as a faery, who, like many faeries, is connected to the earth and the waters that flow from deep within it and, in particular, to one special place upon the planet. She may have cared for her special place, the spring that is the

source of the well, for many hundreds of years. And since she emerges from beneath the ground, perhaps she has needed an extended period of rest and slumber before arising in time to help Cinderella.

At times, faeries can be very close to humans, particularly those who take the time to speak with them and care for the earth and for nature. Since Ellorah's mother was just such a human, the faery godmother both knew and loved her, and was watching over Ellorah on the girl's mother's behalf – perhaps even at her request.

Like this faery godmother, there are faeries who offer us great blessings when we need healing. Some can help with heartbreak and sorrow, and others with personal transformation. The earth is the element that can transform one thing into another, through transmutation and the slow process of change. The faery godmother has absorbed this ability and is able to transform beings with a kind of earth magick that is channelled through her magickal wand. Wands are often used to direct energy – and they can hold great energy, too. When a magickal wand is in the possession of a wise old faery, they wield great power, as evidenced by the transformative enchantments acted upon the mice, the lizard, and the rat – all of whom volunteered for their impermanent conversions.

ANIMAL MAGICK

MICE ARE INDUSTRIOUS, ALERT, GENTLE, AND quiet. Their energy belongs to those who are often underestimated, as is Cinderella. Although these beings are quiet, they are also very communicative. Cinderella tunes into the mice and values their company and sweet conversation. Rats are highly intelligent, extremely sensitive and alert, and plan for the future. By tuning into their energy, Cinderella can begin to open up to the possibilities that there is a future beyond her servitude. Lizards transform and can regenerate limbs. Cold-blooded, they absorb the warmth about them. They speak to us of the ancient, primal, instinctual part of ourselves that cannot be denied if we are to be whole. When she connects with them in this tale, she begins to grow warm and alive, and to understand that this ball is the prelude to her own rebirth and regeneration.

BY KNOT OF ONE, THE SPELL'S BEGUN

HAIR IS SENSITIVE, LIKE ANTENNAE. IT contains memory and energy and is almost like another organ, which senses everything about you, seen and unseen. We can incorporate some ancient faery magick into the everyday by braiding the hair of our loved ones, our creatures, or ourselves. Braiding hair is a form of knot

magick. When we place energies into the braid, the knot or twist of the braid holds the energy in place. Thus, while the songbirds (representing truth, voice, and freedom) are braiding Ellorah's hair, her faery godmother is pouring magick into the knots with her chant, "Kind, brave, beloved. Kind, brave, beloved."

MAGICKAL DRESSES, ENCHANTED SLIPPERS

CLOTHING CAN PLAY A VERY POWERFUL part in traditional magick. There are tales of enchanted cloaks that make the wearer invisible, shoes that never stop dancing, jewels that hold spirits within them, and robes that are only worn for spells and rituals. When Ellorah finds her mother's dress in the attic, she is restoring a part of her mother's legacy. The dress is imbued with the energy of happier times, and Ellorah's mother may have even worn this dress while courting before passing it on to her daughter. It has seen dances and heard laughter, and into its every thread a precious fragment of those lovely memories is woven.

Blue is the colour of harmony, truth, and communication. At first, the hue of the dress is faded, just as Ellorah's happiness is faded. But when Ellorah first puts on her mother's blue dress, she is remembering that she has the potential to experience great love and happiness. Then, when the dress is torn apart by her stepmother, Ellorah's hopes for just a single night of happiness are ripped away with the fabric. But with the transformational magick of her faery godmother's wand, the dress is not only restored, but becomes a true reflection of herself – flowing and harmonious, sparkling and lovely.

Cinderella's glass slippers may actually have been of pale green obsidian – transparent volcanic glass imbued with properties of protection and the breaking of curses. The slippers' transparency echoes Ellorah's own honesty and vulnerability and shows how willing she is to be "seen" as her true self. I like the emphasis on glass, as that is often such a fragile material, and can shatter unless you are sensitive and graceful – two qualities Cinderella has in abundance. The slippers also "know" the steps to the dances Ellorah once danced, but has forgotten, and they help her reclaim the joyful movement and ecstatic bliss of music and love. They help her to remember who she was – and to become who she is meant to be.

MAKING MAGICK:
CINDERELLA ROSEMARY REMEMBRANCE HAIR POTION

ROSEMARY IS A HERB THAT HAS LONG BEEN associated with memory and the honouring of those who have passed. An aromatic herb, when rosemary is rubbed upon the temples, it increases blood flow to the surface of the skin. A rosemary hair rinse can increase curl and shine, make your hair smell divine, and make you unforgettable! When Cinderella/Ellorah pours the rosemary rinse through her hair, it ignites subtle but special powers: the memory of being loved, the recollection of her true self, and a return of her ancestral knowledge and power.

To prepare your own Cinderella Rosemary Remembrance Hair Potion, you will need:
• A cauldron (a saucepan will do!)
• A French press or a charming teapot
• Nine hand-length sprigs of rosemary
• Three large cups of fresh spring or rain water

Gather your water and spend a few moments visualising healthy, long, lustrous hair, like that of a faerytale maiden. Whisper a blessing to the water. As water retains energy, your rinse will have even more power when you bless it in this way. Pour your blessed water into the saucepan or cauldron and bring it to the boil.

Pour the boiling water into the French press or tea pot and add the rosemary sprigs. Leave it steep for about thirty minutes, or until the water is cool. If you are using a French press, press it down to bring out as much oil as possible. Strain your potion into your container and seal.

Before an important event, or anytime you feel the need to refresh yourself or remember how beautiful you truly are, wash and condition your hair as usual. Then, as a final step, pour the Rosemary Remembrance Hair Potion through your hair, being careful to keep your eyes gently closed. There is no need to rinse it out.

Rosemary can deepen the tone of your hair, but it won't change its colour. You will love your hair's lustre and shine, the natural spirals that form in wavy hair, and how aromatic your hair will be. On an emotional level, you will be soothed, comforted, and self-assured!

THE WISDOM OF CINDERELLA

WE WILL FALL, AND WE WILL RISE. IN MAGIC-kal paths and modern-day paganism, we look to nature, and to the seasons, to reassure us that just as we have summer and growth, we will have winter and loss. We will experience hardship in life, but we can also take comfort from the thought that there is a personal resurrection that will be available for us all.

While Cinderella is most often seen as a story of a mistreated, lonely girl's life being magickally transformed, I think there is a deeper energy within it, one that includes the wisdom of memory, which forms a kind of well, a repository of emotional truth and comfort and teachings. For if we have been loved and encouraged, we can draw upon that well, drink from it, and grow strong again. If we have that sense that we are worthwhile, even if others are treating us as if we are despicable, we will draw from the well, and when we do, we shall rise above the temporary nature of circumstance and be reborn within our own life.

It is often said in spiritual circles that we have soul contracts, and that we have agreed to everything that takes place in our life before our birth. I have a different view, and I think Cinderella illustrates this. We do not have to die to change that contract, if it truly does exist. Like Ellorah, we can be reborn within the life we have. We can change our name, or take back our old one, or choose something new that truly expresses who we are. If we are kind to all, and respectful of creatures great and small, the Universe will bring back to us some of those blessings in sublime and unexpected ways.

So, whisper into wells. Plant trees. Be kind to little creatures. And who knows what magick will flow back to you, for there is more in this world than what humans choose to believe in.

THE
SLEEPING
BEAUTY

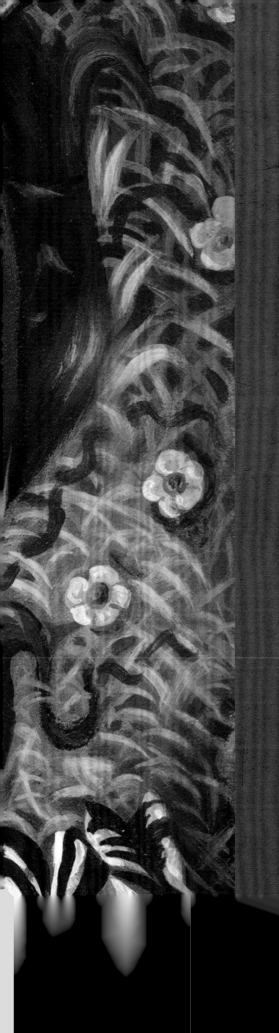

YOU WILL KNOW, OF COURSE YOU WILL, that there are realms somewhere between the land of human and Faerie. In one such place, long ago, two good people had become queen and king. There were faeries and elves and magickal beings of all kinds sharing this realm, for it lived on the very borders of Magick, itself. The queen and the king were deeply in love, and believed in their full and grateful hearts that, one day, this love must give them a child. But they waited, and they waited, and they waited, ever, oh.

And who knows what they did to be sure to have a child?

They were said to have visited the holy wells and drunk of the waters of the goddess. They climbed an ancient mountain and made offerings to a wise one in a crystal cave. They gave the cream of their white cow and the honey from their bees to the land. They leapt the fires at Beltane – and they did all they could to be good friends to the magickal creatures about them.

They offered more, prayed more, wept more, and wished more than any faery could recall any other humans ever doing – but even so, still there was no child for them.

And so, the queen and her king became sad. Their sadness did not make them bitter, though. Their lack made them all the more generous with their blessings, because they understood truly what it was to be without what the heart most longs for.

Finally, this good royal couple heard whispers that there was a waterfall blessed by the most ancient of faeries deep within an ancient wood, and so there they went, on foot, and humbly, as all pilgrims must. When they reached this sparkling, moss-green place, they found it filled with rainbows and mist, and saw water pouring through the perfect circle made of a hole through the rocks. It was so enchanting, they held hands and walked into the waters of the sacred pool. The royal ones were so moved, they shed tears together, and their tears joined the falling waters, and all their despair melted amidst such beauty. And magick touched them that day, for when they returned to the castle, a blessed wee babe was growing within the womb of the queen at last.

Nine times the moon grew bright in the night sky; nine times that same moon turned to darkness, leaving only stars. And by the time the moon was about to grow into silver fullness once again, on a night warm with flowers and soft with spring, the queen gathered all her strength and courage and brought forth into the world a beautiful babe. The tiny girl was delicate and fair, with a face like a wildflower framed with locks like rays of the rising sun. She seemed the start of the couple's lives, and so they named her Aurora, for the goddess who watches over mornings and all true new beginnings.

The king and queen were quite filled with awe and bliss at the health and the sweetness of their girl child, the princess Aurora. Their hearts filled with a strange and new savage love, and after a time spent enjoying the simplicity of their trinity, they knew they must share the joy of this birth and their hope for the future with the realm. So, they issued invitations to a feast for all – highborn and good country folk alike, for faery and for unicorn. And there were, as well, nine special invitations to send, for the blessing faeries were to be called forth.

Blessing fae are very special. They arrive one moon after the birth of children to offer them gifts – and to receive gifts as well. And so, the king and queen asked their finest artisans to craft plates of gold and goblets of crystal to be given to each of the nine faeries who had watched over the little one as she grew within the queen.

The day of the feast was a glorious one, bright and hot and clear – and all day long, preparations were made, and that night, as the sun fell, the feast began. The human people and the faery folk shared tables, and laughed, and danced, and flirted, and the very air was sweet with enchantment. All night long they feasted and rejoiced, until, as the morning light began to whisper the night away, they grew quiet, not for lack of sleep, but in anticipation of the arrival of the blessing faeries. These nine fair folk flew in on dawn's rays, and one by one, they gathered about the king and the queen, who held her babe within her arms. Then one by one, each of the faeries came forward and, reaching out for the infant, took her and cradled her. And one by one, each whispered a blessing to the little princess.

The first wished for Aurora's grace; the second, for her courage. The third blessed the child with wisdom; the fourth, with beauty. The fifth blessing faery conferred upon the princess intuition; the sixth, music. The seventh gifted the little one with health; and the eighth, compassion. Then, just as it was time for the ninth blessing faery to step forward, there was a pause, for that faery, feeling a gathering, a thickening in the energy all about her, held herself back.

As she did so, the people wondered at how the sky, so fair a moment ago, was now darkening about them, and the way the wind had suddenly awakened, so early in the day – and as they became restless, and tense, and utterly uneasy, the queen frowned and gathered her baby closer to her. She glanced at the king, whose jaw was set as if he was about to lead his army into war – and then she glanced at the ninth faery, who put her finger to her lips and stepped back into the gathering shadows.

The doors of the feasting hall flew open

with a fearful crack, and a tenth faery spun into the hall. She was a nightmare, with dank feathers upon her body, her wings all torn and ragged, and the smell of something rotten following her. Her breath came in burning gasps, and she glared all about her, her eyes burning coals, her hands twisted into claws. She was feather, and faery, and fury – and all about stepped back at the force of her presence: piteous, majestic, ferocious.

"You did not invite me, Queen," the dark faery said, shuddering in the air.

"We did not know you," said the queen, handing her baby to the king, and stepping forward to meet the faery.

"You did not *try* to know me," the faery answered. "You only sought *their* offerings – but what of *my* gifts? What of that tenth moon? What of my gift that your Aurora could treasure? Does that not exist? Do I not exist?"

The queen wanted nothing more than to defy this being, to send her away, but she could feel the threat lurking behind the tenth faery's words. So, she reined in her own protective anger and said carefully, "We meant no offence. You are welcome, now, to our feast."

The sinister faery smiled, and for a moment the queen felt all might be well, that she was wrong about the brooding sense that disaster was visiting.

"I accept with thanks, Queen," said the fae one, in a voice soft and laced with subtle menace. "And now, let me hold the child."

Not knowing what else to do, the queen, trembling, turned to the king and nodded to him to hand their daughter to the raven faery.

And when he had done so, Aurora began to cry.

But the dark faery ignored the infant's sobs, and said, "My gift is this ... she shall have a charmed life, indeed. Beloved and loving, the honey of the land shall be hers, the skies so blue and gentle the breezes. All this, so very blessed, and with all your gifts ..." she said, turning her gaze to the nine blessing faeries. "With all your gifts," she repeated, slowly, "so very lucky ... and so Aurora must not be greedy."

And then, to the queen, she said, "Hasn't she already more than most, Highness? Yes, it is more than most, indeed. Therefore, she shall not want too long a life. So, on her sixteenth birthday, this princess shall prick her finger upon a spinning wheel ... and with that, shall come the end of her days."

The queen began to shake as the raven faery passed Aurora back to her. She sank to the ground, holding her child close, stilling her daughter's cries.

"Why do you cry, Queen?" asked this faery, cruel as a storm cloud. "You shall have sixteen years of bliss with this child. It is more than many know. You see, now you will understand what fortunate, blessed folk you are. That is my gift."

And as she began to laugh, a frenzied, fearful sound, tears of blood fell from this faery's eyes. She seemed almost piteous in her bitter joy, born of madness. She laughed and cried and her garments turned to feathers, until all that remained was a great raven, made of utter darkness, which flapped away from the feasting hall, leaving those behind shocked and weeping, too stunned to move.

Then, from the shadows, stepped the ninth blessing faery. Her face was a picture of concentration, her focus steady and true. She gazed upon the queen – who was white with shock, her lips bitten with anguish – and she held out her long, white arms for the babe.

"I cannot lift this awful gift," the ninth faery said, her voice ringing like a bell through the hall so still and hushed. "But I can take from it the sting." She smiled into the flowery face of the little princess. "You shall live a beautiful life," she said, and one pale green tear fell from her moss-coloured eyes onto the babe, who startled, then gurgled with delight.

The last blessing faery smiled. "And on your sixteenth birthday, you shall prick your finger, just as that broken one said, upon that wheel that spins the thread of all of our lives. For faery and human alike, we are all caught upon that spinning wheel of fate. But you shall not die ... not you, not then, sweet princess. No. You shall only sleep, and only for one hundred years. It is just a little time. And you will be awakened by one as noble as you, and who loves you, truly and always. And I will watch over you, and be glad when that day dawns."

She smiled softly at the queen. "That is all I can do," she said, her voice so still and sweet.

"Thank you," whispered the queen, relief and shock and sadness all tangled up within her.

"Farewell, now, little princess," said the ninth blessing faery. "We will meet again."

At that, a great babble of voices rose up and broke the stillness. Amidst the clamour and confusion, no-one saw the blessing faeries depart – they only knew that they were gone from the great hall, leaving behind them the bereft king, and queen, and all the beings of the realm.

And, together, they began to weep.

***

LONG YEARS PASSED. A LITTLE PEACE WAS gone forever from the realm. The king and queen were changed, marked, scarred a bit. A little ripple of fear ran across their faces whenever they saw their daughter playing in the sun, or dancing with a moonbeam, or talking to the wise women who came to visit – for the princess was learning all she could about the use of herbs, although it seemed to her parents that she was preparing for a life that would never have the chance to fully bloom. And so, they did their best to protect her and to give her the most varied and learned and delightful childhood possible.

The king, as so many men do, strode out in defiance of his fear and made a law forbidding spinning, and all the wheels of the kingdom were brought to the courtyard of the castle, and there they were burned and the needles were buried, and all the spinners were told to work the wool on their hands, as had been done in the old days.

And Aurora grew, and was all her parents could have hoped her to be. As the nine blessing faeries had promised, she moved as gracefully as a dancer, and her courage was shown when she stood between a master and the boy he was beating. She was sage and clever, and could often be found sitting very, very still, watching the wise women with their herbs and asking them of all they knew – for she was wise enough to know we must learn, princesses especially so.

She was so lovely to gaze upon that all the boys grew quiet and red in her presence. She could read the language of movements, and often knew what the animals about her were feeling just by laying a hand upon them. She adored music and song, and her soul soared when she sang. She grew sad at times, for she knew how much others suffered, while her own life seemed so blessed.

She was so hale and well, that her cheeks stayed red and her eyes sparkled, even when the castle was full of sniffles and coughs! At those times, she hastened to help those who could not

leave their bed, and the castle and its residents came to feel that they had been given some extraordinary blessing, to have such a princess, who cared so much for them all.

She was spirited and full of life, and the king and the queen loved to hear her laugh, and they held each other tight, whenever the fear of her loss came to them.

The king began in time to wonder if the raven faery had been a dream. "How could this happen?" he would protest when he saw the sadness in his wife's great brown eyes. His daughter was safe. There were no wheels upon which she could spin. No spindles upon which she could prick a finger. So said the king.

But the queen, who would often see a raven swooping about the castle, knew the truth. And she began to prepare.

She forced herself to imagine a world without Aurora, and wondered what she would do if she had the choice. Should she sleep alongside her daughter? Or should she remain awake, and continue on, mourning her loss? She knew that, whatever she chose, Aurora's fate was coming closer with every beautiful day – and she knew there could be no hiding from it, only choices to be made once the moment of the curse arrived.

When Aurora reached her sixteenth birthday, the celebration was as fair and sweet as her blessing day had been. To her surprise, the great hall was filled with all the people of the land – and, of course, her friends the wise women were there, and the faeries, and the most wonderful musicians. And she danced with everyone, from puppies to the stable master to the kitchen maids, and even with a handsome young faery prince, around whom she admitted – just to herself – that she felt a bit strange. His name was Gwynn, and he was only part faery, but he was as royal as

she. And though he looked a young man, he was already three hundred years old.

Gwynn and Aurora danced and laughed, and swirled, and the kingdom was happy. Her fateful day had come, and she was still here. No-one spoke of the raven faery's curse – although they thought of it – and everyone began to believe there might be hope, yet.

Amidst the party were the nine blessing faeries, each watching with happiness as Aurora danced. But on one of the turrets above there landed a raven. And the queen, who watched, knew the end of this jubilant time was coming.

And so, it was that, finally breathless and wanting just a moment to gaze out at the setting sun, Aurora climbed to the very top of the castle. She gazed out a window at the rays of scarlet and gold, and listened with joy as the bells announcing sundown pealed out across the darkening sky.

And as she walked back down the great stairs, she saw a light shimmering from under a door she'd always thought belonged to a servant. The princess had explored so much of the castle, but had never entered that room. And what, she wondered, was that flickering light?

Aurora gave the door a nudge, and it swung wide open. Within the room was a twisted old woman, dressed in a cloak of black feathers, bent over a gleaming wheel of gold. A magickal wheel, no earthly wheel; a wheel with a steely point on its spindle. Aurora walked into the little room, captivated as she always was by old wise women and the knowledge they held, and asked, "Dear wise one, what is it you are doing?"

"Why, my dear, I am spinning this thread? However did you think your fine garments were made? I spin and I spin, and I make up the threads of our fates. Here," the old one said, holding out a thin golden thread in her cracked palm, clawed and crooked. "This thread is your own."

"Oh ...," breathed Aurora, puzzled and intrigued. Then, her amber eyes moved from the golden thread to the silver needle that shone in the sun's last light.

"Teach me," urged Aurora, and reached towards the spindle. And then it was that the princess caught her finger upon the spindle's point.

"Ah ...," she said softly, and put her finger to her mouth to stop the blood. As she did so, she began to feel an overwhelming urge to sleep. And she sank to the floor, curled up like a babe, and lost herself entirely, as the deepest dreamers do.

The old woman smiled and stood and turned three times widdershins, and in her place a great raven appeared, and she flew heavenwards, away to her mountain home.

Hours upon hours later, the princess was found by the queen, who gathered her into her arms again, just as she had done when her daughter was a child. She wept a little, then she called to the ninth blessing faery, whom she could see in the shadows, waiting.

"What shall I do?" she asked the fair one.

"She will sleep for one hundred years, Majesty," replied the faery. "But now you must decide. Do you sleep with her? For otherwise, she will awaken all alone. And there is no saying what could happen if you or your king passes while she sleeps. Another king, another queen, would they care for her in this slumber?"

"You're saying we should sleep, too? I have long thought on it," said the queen. "Let it be done. But first, let us put her to bed."

And so, the queen and the faery gathered Aurora and placed her upon the bed which stood in the room that housed the magickal wheel. They washed her, brushed her sunlit hair, and dressed her in the softest garments the colours of dawn.

Then the queen called the king to her, and together they spoke to the people of the castle, who all agreed that they, too, would slumber while their sweet princess dreamed.

And so, the blessing faery's magick began to work. First, the king and the queen fell fast asleep in each other's arms in their chamber. Then the maids softly slumped to cushions they'd piled on the floors, while stable boys snuggled into beds of hay. The horses, too, grew quiet and still, and even the mice in the kitchen fell asleep, just as they'd stolen some cheese. The herbalists fell asleep amidst the lavender – and the lawmakers and the knights and the librarians and the healers and the bards and the dancers and the musicians, all, utterly, suddenly, and simply, were no longer awake.

And then all was very, very quiet, for even the songbirds were at their rest. And slowly, around that great castle and that radiant princess, so luminous in her sleep, there grew a forest. It was green and wild and fresh, at first, but then as the years gathered together, it became thicker and darker and more and more tangled.

The hawthorn trees entwined with the oak, whose branches grew into the ash, and the roses, huge and thorned, like the spindles of so many spinning wheels, bloomed lushly. And so, a protective shield of green was woven around this sleeping world, ensuring none within could be harmed. It was another place, set in another time, and only those who had magick and courage within their hearts could ever hope to enter.

***

LONG YEARS PASSED, AND AS THE VINES crawled over the turrets of the castle, its enchanted inhabitants faded from the memory of those who lived outside its green walls. And while the otherworldly wood in which the castle slept was quiet and still, everything about it turned and changed, like the great Wheel upon which we all spin.

And in this way, those long years wound themselves out until they reached one hundred years – and on the day of the tenth moon of that hundredth year, a young prince stood before the enchanted forest. He had waited one hundred years for this moment, for he had returned to find the one with whom he had danced so many years ago.

And so, he strode into the brambles and the roses and the thorns as long as his hand. And he frowned. Something lay beyond this wall of woods. He could feel it. Like a silver thread on a spinning wheel, he was being spun into the circle of magick that lay within the woods.

He took out his bright sword, as thin as a needle, and began to slice his way through the woods. But some parts of the forest fought back, and mightily. A thorny branch sprang out and came perilously close to piercing his eye. Ducking, he was tripped by a thick tree root that slithered and curled about his ankle, pulling itself tight and holding him back, until he slashed himself free with his sword – only to be struck by a falling branch the size of six men, which knocked him to the ground, where he lay, dazed and wandering between the worlds, until a sliver of moonlight shivered open his eyes, pulling him back to consciousness.

During a seemingly endless night, Gwynn fought the forest in darkness. But with every setback, his determination grew, becoming stronger every time he brought his sword down – as he slashed again and again and again, until he had cut a bright, moonlit path through that enchantment. And as he created that path, the silver light began to fall upon that enchanted earth for the first time in one hundred years.

Finally, he saw that with each new stroke something strange was happening – the woods were retreating a little, as if they had no more resistance to give him. And while it was harsh work, and he tripped, and fell, and thorns tore his hands, he was as strong and brave and wise as he was fair to look upon. And he persisted.

Finally, in the darkness of the early hours, he entered the strangely still courtyard, where he found people in odd, faded clothing. The men had wild beards and the women's hair lay about them, as long and tangled as the woods, while the dogs rested in the dust of ages. He saw all were still breathing, when he approached them as close as he dared. Certainly, this place was under the deepest form of enchantment.

"Baleful magick is indeed about," he whispered, and was enthralled and excited, for he was a prince of faery blood and he relished a chance to meet ill-wrought magick with something true and good. He wondered if there would be ghosts ahead. Or witches. Or other faeries not inclined to let him enter.

This prince, he was good of heart and had longed as a child, four hundred years ago, to do the very best of deeds within the kingdom, for human and faery alike. Fired by his desire to do such noble things, he longed for a partner who shared the same dreams.

One hundred years ago, he had attended a ball, where he discovered a young woman as wise as she was fair. He had danced with her as often as he could, and between their dances, he spoke to those at the ball, and had learned of Princess Aurora's many blessings.

After the first dance, he had learned from her tutor that this princess could read the old runes and speak the old languages. After the second, the maid pouring his wine shared how the princess had insisted upon fairness, when the maid was falsely accused of stealing a goblet. After the fourth, the pageboy told him of her willingness to stand between a servant boy and the whip.

Everyone had a story – she had climbed a tree to rescue a kitten, and she'd nursed back to health a fallen bird; she knew the right herbs to heal a cough, but never seemed to become ill herself; she could sing all day, and knew the words to the loveliest songs – each of which drew this prince of the old blood more and more under the princess's spell.

And so, he gazed at her as she spun, and when they danced for the ninth time, and he heard her laugh and saw her eyes like honey by firelight, the spark that was her spirit lit the flame of his heart's desire.

He had left the ball without knowing her fate, and his mind, for the hundred years since that night, had been filled with the memory of a twirling, amber-eyed girl filled with grace. But when he learned of her long sleep, he grew sad and vowed never to dance again, unless it could be with her. Now, he was ready to find her and dance with his princess once again.

As night prepared to give way to the dawn, Prince Gwynn went to the tallest tower and stood before it. That edifice seemed dark and sombre and stranger even than the courtyard with its sleeping hounds. He entered the great feasting hall, which felt as though it was waiting. Not one of the men or women or animals about him so much as stirred as he mounted the same staircase the princess had climbed on the way to meet her destiny – and he came at last to a room lit gently by dawn's first light, where a soft breeze was blowing the thick cobwebs like drifting clouds.

There, he saw a bed, and upon it the same young woman he had danced with so long ago. And he saw her beauty, and the sweet smile she wore in sleep, and the gold and silver threads of her garments, and the pallor of her skin, through which the veins ran blue. He stopped breathing altogether, caught in the spell of her stillness, her repose, her dreaming contentment. Nothing about her seemed anything other than beautiful. Asleep, and shining, and still, forever.

Finally, caught in the strangeness of it all, the faery prince began to shake, and on trembling legs, he made his way towards the bed, where he sank to his knees and gazed at the princess Aurora.

At that moment, the tenth moon of the hundredth year reached its fullness, and finally set, and Aurora sighed in that sleep, and broke the spell that seemed to have taken hold of the prince.

"Will you awaken, Aurora?" he whispered, taking her hand "You've slept long enough, my love."

As eyes shadowed by dark red lashes moved hidden beneath still lids, he realised he wanted nothing more than to see their strange colour once again. Would they be as he remembered?

And slowly, she opened her eyes.

And she looked into the eyes of this prince.

"Still just like the harvest moon," he said, quite spellbound.

"What?" she said, beginning to smile.

"Your eyes. They're … like darkest honey."

"Is it you, dear prince?" she said. "You have been long in coming!"

Charmed by these words, and especially by the manner in which they were said, the prince scarcely knew how to express his delight and gratification. He declared that he loved her better than he loved himself. His words were faltering, but they pleased her all the more for that. And she began to laugh, a sound like bells pealing, and as this laughter softly danced through the castle, the enchantment began to fade, and slowly, one by one, the folk of the castle awoke from their hundred-year dream.

Stretching and yawning, one carriage master cried, "I must shave!"

Rubbing her back, a wise woman moaned with delight at seeing the dawn once again.

The dogs began to sniff and stretch, and horses whinnied and nickered, softly, and then the queen and the king were at the princess's door.

"Aurora," cried her mother. "You have come back to us!" She rushed to the window, and her heart soared as she saw the castle returning to life. "We are here," she called to her child, quite overcome. "We are all still here."

Then the queen gazed at the young man near her daughter's bed. "And you, young man?"

The faery prince stood stiffly, and bowed to hide his blush. It was not often he was discovered in a sleeping beauty's bedchamber.

"Prince Gwynn, my Queen," he said, and bowed. "We met, long ago."

"Your coming has awakened my daughter. Awakened us all. Thank you," said the queen. "Thank you, Prince Gwynn."

***

THE PRINCESS NEVER MUCH LIKED SLEEPING after that—and, strangely, no-one else within the castle seemed to need to sleep very much at all,

from that time forth. This, however, gave Aurora even more hours in her busy days to learn about the herbs, and to make arrangements for the land, and to help everyone who had slept a hundred years with her to recover.

And you will know, of course you will, that Prince Gwynn stayed, for he had fallen completely under Aurora's spell, which had nothing to do with anything except the magick of love. And because the sleeping spell had been broken, the raven faery was now powerless, as anger and time and loneliness had withered the power of her magick. So, the king and the queen, the princess and her prince, and all the residents of the castle – two-legged and four-legged and winged and scaled – were safe. And they sent to the raven faery what help and assistance they could offer – the shiny things she liked, and the mirrors and sweet cakes, seemed to take a little of the sting out of her.

And then, after some time, and a handfasting, the nine blessing faeries were called again.

For the princess had given birth to a son. And he, too, hardly ever slept.

THE LAST blessing faery smiled. "And on your sixteenth birthday, you shall prick your finger, just as that broken one said, upon that wheel that spins the thread of all of our lives. But you shall not die. You shall only sleep for one hundred years."

Discover the
Magick of
The Sleeping
Beauty

I'VE ALWAYS BEEN A WEE BIT nervous around sharp things. Knives and needles and other things that can slice you, poke a hole in you, or draw your blood have always made me shudder just a little. (The same with sharp words, come to think of it!)

And I've never really been a good sleeper. My mother told me I never truly slept, even as a babe. So, since deep, long sleep seems both an unattainable luxury and a biological impossibility – people like me, insomniacs, may feel like they need to sleep for a hundred years, at times!

There is another aspect of this tale which made me shiver – that of being cursed by someone whom you have unintentionally offended. I certainly have felt the sting when people seem to take a dislike to me, and although as an adult I have found ways to mind less, when I was young, it really bothered me to be actively disliked.

So, this tale – with its focus on needles and sharp things, people who dislike you for no fault of your own, and a hundred-year-long sleep – had all the ingredients necessary to make me fall, like Aurora's prince, under its peculiar spell. I hope I've teased out the old magick that lay within the traditional story of *The Sleeping Beauty* – and I've also made a few changes to that tradition. I hope you enjoy the deeper enchantments of this wonder-tale.

HISTORY OF THIS TALE

THIS IS A STORY THAT I FEEL HAS TRULY ancient roots. The association between sleep and death must have seemed extraordinary close to our ancestors, and a sleep that was lengthy – be it simple unconsciousness or the long absence of a coma – must have seemed a breathing death, indeed, and many tales have been told that feature such sleep.

In the Icelandic Völsunga saga, you can encounter the Valkyrie Brunhilde, who is punished by Odin to an everlasting sleep on earth, within an enchanted ring of fire, a curse which is finally broken when the hero, Siegfried, crosses the threshold of flame and awakens Brunhilde with an ardent kiss.

The French chivalric tale *Perceforest*, from the 1500s, revolves around a princess in an enchanted sleep and a prince who wishes to win her. In the tale, the heroine is passed from father to husband, thus capturing some of what is both the best and the worst of the Middle Ages.

There are also two Italian folktales from the 1600s that foreshadow *The Sleeping Beauty*, and one in particular, *Sun, Moon, and Talia*, maintains its influence within the story we read today.

Charles Perrault wrote the classic version of *The Sleeping Beauty*, 'La Belle au bois dormant', which was published in French in 1697. The Brothers Grimm were told the French story and changed it up so that it became more their own. Their version was republished as *Briar Rose* (I love that name!), and their take on the sleeping beauty in the wood was first published in 1812.

WORLDS BETWEEN THE WORLDS

THIS PARTICULAR RETELLING OF *The Sleeping Beauty* is set in a mysterious realm that lies on the borderlands between the human world and the Faerielands – and some of the beings we encounter are similarly a blend of human and faery. There have always been such places. We know them when we encounter them, as they feel different – they can be marked by a certain presence, a difference in weather, time, or atmosphere that is undeniable. When we spy faery rings – circles of mushrooms, flowers, moss, or stone – we know we are somewhere special. There also remain forests in the world that are home to ancient trees, and I truly feel such places are vestiges of a time when we shared our lives more openly with the fae – we saw them, spoke with them, shared with them ... and, just like Aurora, we danced with them, too!

ST NECTAN'S GLEN AND SACRED FAERY PLACES

IN MANY CULTURES, THERE ARE SACRED PLACES where people go when they wish to conceive. The one within this tale is based on St Nectan's Glen, a beguiling waterfall found near Tintagel, in Cornwall. While the original story does mention that the king and queen go on pilgrimages in their quest to conceive, I wanted to enhance this aspect of the tale. When I discovered that two lovely people I know had gone to St Nectans and then did conceive a child shortly after that visit – after many years of yearning – this dreamlike place wove its way into this tale! It is one of the most magickal places I have ever been, and I hope you can sense its power and its unique presence!

NINE MOONS OR TEN, FOR PREGNANCY?

IT'S A COMMONLY HELD BELIEF THAT HUMAN women are pregnant for nine months. But when I was pregnant, I was surprised to learn that for some woman – myself included – it is more like ten months! So, if the king and queen invite nine faeries to offer a blessing for each moon of the pregnancy but there were actually ten gestation moons, what happens? Well, once we've read the tale, we know!

The outcome aligns with my decision to include nine faeries, rather than the traditional

seven, and it gives our "evil" faery a place to enter the story – the right to feel at least a little of her grudge! Perhaps she was just tired of her contributions being so overlooked. She didn't have to make her point quite so harshly, of course, but perhaps, after a few thousand years of oversight, she had just had enough!

THE GODDESS AURORA

THE LONGED-FOR DAUGHTER WITHIN THIS tale is named for the Roman goddess of the dawn, Aurora, who is associated with morning and rebirth, hope and possibilities. A powerful goddess, she is sister to both the sun god Helios and the moon goddess Selene. So while she is often considered to be beautiful, and gentle, she is also a being who brings us out of the "death" that is sleep and night and into a rebirth, which is morning. Aurora, of course, will have the longest night, the deepest sleep perhaps ever known – and when she awakens, morning comes not only to her life, but to the lives of the people who slept with her, sharing the enchantment, ensuring she would not wake up alone, or an orphan. (I would love to see, in a parallel story, what would happen if Aurora was to awake in a totally new time, with her family's descendants, and learn how she navigates this new world!)

THE GIFTS OF THE BLESSING FAERIES

IN SERBIAN FOLKLORE, YOU CAN FIND A VERY special kind of faery being called the "Oosood", who is said to appear to a newborn to offer blessings for their life and to share the child's destiny with the mother. I wanted to take this idea, that we all have a faery who looks after us, which is common to many cultures, and develop it more fully in *The Sleeping Beauty*. So, within this tale, there are nine blessing faeries, who offer gifts and share the fate of the child with the parents.

But there is one special difference – an uninvited faery, having been offended, turns her blessing into a deep and enduring curse, with profound ramifications for the entire community. The cruelty of the curse is softened by the clever ninth blessing faery, who withholds her gift until after the curse is delivered, so she can use her powers to change death into a lifetime-long sleep.

A measure of the intended cruelty remains, however, for Aurora might well have died while she slept. Or, if her community had not agreed to share her hundred-year fate, she could have been left to awaken in a strange and unknown world. I liked the idea of the whole castle going into sleep with her in a kind of bewitched solidarity. Faeries, being naturally long-lived, did not have quite the same concerns!

GWYNN, OUR FAERY PRINCE

OUR PRINCE IN THIS VERSION OF THE TALE IS called Gwynn. This is a very deliberate reference on my part to a wonderful and rather famous faery king named Gwynn ap Neath, who is Welsh in origin, but whose court is said to be located directly beneath Glastonbury Tor, in England. A Welsh saint, Collem, even went to Glastonbury Tor and attempted to drive out Gwynn with an exorcism – and there are thousands of testimonials from visitors to the Tor who have encountered this fae king, and even been taken beneath the Tor to his great feasting halls for balls, where humans dance and dance, and even partake of faery food!

"Gwynn ap Neath", or "Nudd", in the Welsh, means pure, bright, white, and sacred, which made the name seem fitting for such a fine prince as the one we meet in this telling of *The Sleeping Beauty*. Also, I wanted to support the idea that this indeed is a prince who is part faery and part human – perhaps even a son of Gwynn ap Neath himself!

SPINNING WHEELS, FATE, AND BLOOD MAGICK

THE BURNING OF THE SPINNING WHEELS THAT have been gathered together by the king cannot prevent the fate of the princess Aurora. She will come across that spindle, she will prick her finger, and she will fall into a death-like sleep. The king

and the queen do their very best to avoid the curse of the malignant blessing faery – but what is fated will take place. This is a very Roman concept, and is based upon the idea of Lady Fortuna, a goddess spinning her wheel, upon which all humans are placed. At times, our fortunes are fair; at other times, foul. But all the while, Fortuna's wheel still spins.

There is also an allusion, here, to another goddess, one whose name is Arianrhod, known as the Lady of the Silver Wheel. While this Welsh goddess's wheel is the moon, she too governs the fortunes and curses and challenges that come to us, called in the Celtic philosophy, *geis*. And it is indeed a challenging fate, or geis, that Aurora has been given. The moon is an important symbol within this story – so perhaps Arianrhod herself is watching over Aurora while she sleeps, ensuring she meets her fate, yet eludes the death curse visited upon her by one whose true calling is to bestow blessings. For the blessing faery who offered a curse surely is misusing her own power.

And then there are the Norns, the three sisters who dwell beneath the mighty world tree, Yggdrasil, in Norse mythology. These three sisters are charged with guarding the well of wisdom – and with weaving the destiny of individual

humans and gods. While the Norns are not always depicted with a spinning wheel (often they are hand-looming our destiny), they are often enough depicted sitting around a great spinning wheel to have subtly woven their way into this marvellous tale.

Also, I think it is very telling that not only does the wheel spin Aurora to her fate, but the princess must prick her finger upon the spindle, too, thus creating a kind of blood magick within the tale. Without her blood, the spell would not begin to be spun. Those sacred drops of blood provide the energy and life force propelling the spinning of fortune's wheel and sending the princess to her unavoidable destiny.

MAGICKAL DIRECTIONS: WIDDERSHINS AND DEOSIL

IN THIS VERSION OF THE SLEEPING BEAUTY, our very angry faery turns widdershins three times before turning into a raven. What is widdershins? Well, in magickal work, there are two ways to cast a circle, or two ways to work with energy using directions. One is for increase and development, for gathering and sending the energy; the other is for banishing and depleting, for closing and diminishing the energy.

Widdershins, then, is Old Anglo-Saxon for "against the sun", and it is the direction used to close magickal circles, to diminish or banish energies – or, for those who use it for a more sinister purpose, to curse. In the northern hemisphere, widdershins is anti-clockwise, and in

the southern hemisphere, it is clockwise – as the sun rises in the east, moves to the south, and sets in the west within the northern hemisphere, but rises in the east, moves to the north, and sets in the west in the southern hemisphere.

Deosil, on the other hand, means "with the sun", and it is the direction which magickally – and naturally – increases energy. It is clockwise in the northern hemisphere and anti-clockwise in the southern hemisphere.

Want proof that there are these natural differences? Check out the difference in the direction in which cyclones whirl in each hemisphere!

HANDFASTING: A YEAR AND A DAY OF BLISS!

IN MODERN MAGICKAL PRACTICE, HAND-fastings are becoming more and more popular, while pagan elements of this traditional Celtic practice are also finding their way into mainstream wedding celebrations.

Traditionally, handfastings took place at or around Beltane (April 30th/May 1st in the northern hemisphere) and were said to last for a year and day. Handfasting lovers drank from the loving cup, leapt bright fires hand in hand, and stepped lightly over broomsticks, pledging their troth – but only for those sacred thirteen moons! After that time, the lovers could decide whether to stay together. Or, if they chose to part, it was to be without bitterness or animosity, and they could go forth the following Beltane, free to choose new partners when the fires of fertility burned high across the land.

The term "handfasting" comes from the part of the ceremony where the hands of the lovers are literally bound together. These bonds actually once held for a whole moon cycle, during which time mead and sweets were brought to the lovers, so they need not leave each other's side – thus, the term "honeymoon"!

Today, there are many types of bindings or handfasting ribbons that can be used. The choice of colour, number, and makeup of the bindings are symbolically – and energetically – very important. Who knows what bound the hands of Aurora and Gwynn? Perhaps refracted rays of light formed a ribbon of rainbow to bind them, or vines from a faery forest garlanded their wrists as they pledged themselves, one to the other, soul to soul.

MAKING MAGICK: SLEEPING BEAUTY'S SMUDGE STICK

I CAN ALMOST IMAGINE OUR SLEEPING BEAUTY, post-awakening, wielding about a mighty smudge stick to ensure a sweet sleeping space for herself and her faery prince! We are most vulnerable to psychic attack and unwanted energies when we are asleep, so you may want to make a smudge

stick that will help create a very safe and soothing sleeping space for you.

You will need:
• One long-ish stemmed rose (Keep the thorns, as they work to drive off unwanted energies; however, remove the thorns from the end of the stem, if you can, or simply be sure to place the rose in the centre of the smudge stick so you can hold it safely.)
• A long stem of leafy lavender flower
• A sprig of rosemary (Which can be beautiful if flowering, but just the stems with their glossy dark green needles are perfect, too.)
• And if you are blessed to have mugwort, one length would be perfect
• Cotton thread, twine (I like to work with thread the colour of sunrise for this smudge stick – a violet colour for that incredible first light, no-that's-not-quite-pink, not-quite-blue, but somewhere-in-between.)
• Fireproof dish
• Matches

Layer the rose, the stem of lavender, the rosemary sprig, and the stem of mugwort so that the flowering parts are all at the same end – that will be the "top". (Try and keep the stems similar lengths, so your bundle has a lovely shape to it. I sometimes remove a few leaves here and there to create the right feel.) Now, snip off a piece of thread or twine that's about three times the length of the smudge stick itself. Place the thread beneath the top of the bundle, so there are even lengths on each side, and tie one good, tight knot at the top. Then weave your way down, criss-crossing the thread. Make it nice and snug, and tuck in any loose flowers and leaves along the way. (I wrap the end of the stick good and tight, circling round and

round, which helps with the "hold." That part will not get burned!)

Let it hang for a few days, upside-down, to cure, before burning. Then, with a fireproof dish to hold beneath the smudge stick to catch any falling ash or embers, light the top, let it burn for a moment, then lightly blow out the flame, so it is smouldering.

Hold the stick and wave it gently through the air, letting the smoke do its clearing, healing work. You may wish to say:

I clear this space and make it true,
Bring in dreams and wishes, too.
Make my sleep be sound and long,
Awaken me with day's bright song.
By the power of three by three,
As I do will, so mote it be.

When you feel the energy has shifted, gently put out your smudge stick by pushing its lit end into the fireproof dish until it is completely out.

Use whenever you feel your space needs that refresh, or your sleep is troubled to restore the beautiful energy we all need to slumber well.

The Wisdom of The Sleeping Beauty

There are many powerful lessons within this tale. One is the idea that some of our fate is inevitable – there are certain difficulties within our lives that cannot be avoided. Another important thought here is that we may all, sometimes, "go to sleep" during a portion of our own sacred and precious lives, not really being as aware and as powerful as we could be, essentially sleepwalking through our days.

I think another strong concept illustrated here by the raven faery's attitude toward the royal family is that, in life, some people may take a strong, seemingly unfounded dislike to you, and may even try to cause you harm. But even if they do, and even if you cannot avert the harm, if you try, you can resurrect yourself and come back to a new life.

Most of all, though, this tale is about awakening. It provides a reminder that we will all come through our dark nights and experience new dawns, new days within our lives. We can take from *The Sleeping Beauty* the reminder that the possibility of comebacks in our lives endures – that there is always hope that we will literally wake up to ourselves and realise just how many blessings we have.

The Ninth Wave

An Original Faerytale by
Lucy Cavendish

THERE ONCE WAS A YOUNG GIRL WHOSE name was Morwenna. She lived in a crooked stone cottage just beyond the end of a little village that grew like moss along the rocks that edged the dark blue sea, meeting it where the cliffs were high and the sky was cold.

Morwenna was moonlight pale, with a long streak of silvery hair and skin that glowed white as the cuckoo flowers that sprang up about the small cottage she shared with Ciabhan, her father – a lean and tight-lipped fisherman, who'd seen happier days – and the sea was the place she knew best in all the world.

Every day, she spent the frosty early hours before the dawn knitting together the flax nets in which she and her father would capture the fish each night. Though the rough strands pricked her hands till they bled, she did not complain. And she always made sure to make the holes large enough that the young fish could escape and be saved for another season. She twisted cockle-shell charms for the prow of the curragh to protect it from storms, and tied the four winds into old rope to carry on board so she and her father would have fair sailing, whatever the weather. When all that was finished, she helped her father patch their curragh.

"Sleep now, Morwenna," her father would say when she had done enough, and she would curl upon her bed of moss and rest until the sun was close to the end of its journey in the sky.

Then, every evening at twilight, she and her father would push the curragh into the cold shallows, leap into its narrow interior, and raise the tattered sail, helping the wind along by rowing, their oars dipping quietly in the silky waters. In that way, they would go in stealth, as humans do, to the places the fish would run. When they arrived at the very best place for that night, Morwenna would take a tallow light, bind it to one of the rowan branch oars, and hold it high over the edge of the boat so the fish swimming deep below would be drawn to the top of the water and into those nets she'd spent the hours before dawn mending.

Since she and her father fished so often, and always at night, Morwenna almost forgot what the world of day, the world of most men, was like. Instead, she was present for every scarlet sunset, for every golden sunrise, and for every phase and flow of the moon and its light in between – and so night-lived was her life that she would spend the church day, when she would go to market, blinking in the unfamiliar light.

Morwenna knew no people at all, not really, not to share her thoughts with. She had never played or laughed or skipped with a soul of her own age. The other children of the town lived in the world of day, the streets, the earth, and the cobblestones. She was the night, the sea, and the foam flying from the wind-licked waves.

They spoke the old words, this girl of the moon and the sea and her fisherman father, a language forgotten in the towns. She felt the power in those old words, and would practice saying them over and over, strange rolling words, like rough song in her mouth. With these words, she could charm the bees and take out the sweet honeycomb from the great oak, where they hid their queen in her castle, the hive. She could whisper up the dolphins and share secrets with the seals. But there were other things she did not know, and she had no-one to tell her. She asked the bees and the dolphins, the seals and the silver fish, but none seemed to know what she needed.

So, hidden away inside her, questions tumbled ... What colour were her mother's eyes? Why was she no longer with Morwenna and her father? But what the girl longed most to know was simply her mother's name.

Her father hardly spoke at all, not even

in the old tongue, and she could not remember him laughing since her mother, her lovely mother, had gone. When she would ask of her, he would say she'd been taken by the sea, and so Morwenna thought her mother must have drowned one night while fishing, or perhaps she was stolen by a storm. But there was something about the way her father would stare at night, from the curragh into the lamp-lit waters, that made her feel he was looking for someone – perhaps her mother, whose name he had never spoken, the sound of which his daughter longed to hear, so she too could say it, like the strange old words she murmured.

Her mother's name, she felt, held power, and if she knew it, she could call to her, just as she called to the dolphins and the seals. They would come close, hearing their old secret names, and she would feed them the fish she saved, just for them. If she knew her mother's name, she could call her close, too, she thought, and so she would whisper the old names to the sea creatures, waiting for one of them to tell her the name of her mother.

On a church day, she would take the fish to the markets at the dock in the little town, and when travellers would come from the hill villages inland, she would do her best to speak the new words with them. She smiled as they haggled, and knew just when to strike the bargain, and she always made sure she had a fair price.

But, other than that, she kept herself quiet, and listened to their talk, hungry for clues to life beyond the boat, and the cottage, and the fish in her basket. She paid careful attention as mothers told their children stories of the sea god Macnannán mac Lir and of the Blessed Isles. And she watched closely as the children played their games, games in which they were a prince, or a voyager, or a member of the Tuatha de Danaan, the old ones who were here before the humans.

And she noticed, too, how they spoke of all of these things in whispers, with little, quick glances about them, so careful were they, the mothers and children, both, never to mention such things in earshot of the man of the new god, the priest.

***

One market day, Morwenna found herself watching as a boy and his young sister enacted a strange game. The older boy darted in and out of the adults' legs, picking up pebbles and counting out loud, until he had nine stones in his hand. Then, clambering over the rocks, he plucked off a handful of moss and put the stones in one pocket, the moss in another.

His sister was sitting on the cobblestones, hunched over, muttering and rocking, speaking in an old and creaky voice.

The boy bowed before her, his movements quick and light as a wren. "Sea Mother, let me in!" he cried. "I wish to ask a favour of you."

The girl gestured imperiously with her small white hands for him to be seated, and he sank down before her, only half-feigning to be nervous.

Morwenna could not take her eyes from them. Without knowing she had done so, she moved a little closer to the children, feeling as though she was on the verge of an important discovery.

"Have you brought me your offering?" the little girl asked.

"Yes, Sea Mother. Here is my honey," he said, laying his handful of moss before her.

"Humph," spat the girl, obviously unimpressed. "Now, your payment," she said, her voice harsh.

"Nine gold coins," he said proudly, dropping each pebble before her. "Just the right number."

"It will do, I suppose. What is it you wish to know?"

Morwenna had heard of the Sea Mother before. The town folk often spoke of her – in whispers, in groups that broke apart when the priest emerged from the church to wander through the crowds, offering his blessing. And she knew where the woman's cave was, as she had walked the cliffs so often.

They said there had always been a wise woman in that cave – nobody knew for how long, but it seemed to most people that she had always been there. And even when the priest from the town had come to drive her out, splashing her with holy water, the woman had laughed, her teeth like lonely stones in her mouth. "She stood, and her eyes flashed lightning and demons," said the priest, "to drive me out."

This was the tale he told the villagers upon his return. Then, he set about spreading awful rumours before he prepared to leave the town.

"A sickness is coming," he said, "and she is the source. The devil is with you, and that old woman in the cave is his mistress, and every soul in your cliff-struck village is going straight to hell!"

But the wind had snatched away his catechism, and the villagers only nodded, but turned away when he was gone – headed east, "Where the people are land-bound," he said, "and seem to be more God-fearing" – and they went back to the sea witch's cave, that temple by the sea, the only church they'd ever known to have answered their prayers. There, as those who made the pilgrimage knew, the Sea Mother slept in the bones of a great whale, its ribcage her guardian, pelican feathers her garments.

A kinder priest came in time, and he

welcomed those who came to the church, dismissing the Old Ways and the woman in the cave. And in this way, people began to gather in the church, feeling they were good and righteous and, somehow, more civilised. But the Sea Mother remained, and they still visited her from time to time, in secret, when there was no help to be found within the walls of the church.

And so the Sea Mother grew older and older, until she alone knew the ancient ways of the ocean and of the people who lived from her bounty. Until she alone held the keys to holding the great waves back that came when winter was at her most furious.

***

MORWENNA HAD NEVER BEFORE UNDERSTOOD how it was that one requested a boon from the Sea Mother. But now, after watching the boy and girl at play, she frowned … wondering … feeling an idea stirring within her, ready to be born.

The children's mother called to them, and the two leapt up and ran to her, and the spell was broken – and suddenly, Morwenna became aware of a small group standing near her, murmuring together, huddled in their dark garments, glancing over to her every few words, picking over their gossip like crows over a corpse. She was used to that. Never had she gone to church. Never had she been blessed, or baptised. She was just the fisherman's daughter, and people often wondered about her, and grew so used to her quiet presence they would speak of her as if she was not able to understand a word they said.

But this time, the boy broke free from his mother's hand and ran back to where she stood. Morwenna was only a little older than the boy, but he was well-dressed and clean, and she was

conscious, suddenly, of the smell of kelp in her hair and her briny hands, with their half-healed cuts from the flax and nettles, and the dark lines beneath each fingernail.

The little boy gazed up into her face, fear and wonder in his eyes.

"Is it true?" he whispered, his eyes staring into hers.

"Is what true?" she asked slowly, trying hard to make the new words sound the way they ought to.

"They say your mother went to the Sea Mother – and she was sea-taken, claimed by Macnannán mac Lir, himself," he blurted, stumbling over the old name, just as she stumbled over the new words.

Morwenna could see the child meant no harm, though his words cut through her so that the hidden pain rose up from deep within.

"Perhaps she was," she said, cautiously, fearful of the pain his words could cause her if he spoke again of her mother, yet hoping he would say more, and so reveal a part of the answer to her questions.

"So, the sea god claimed your mother?" he breathed, eyes widening with fear and awe.

It was all the boy could manage to get out before his mother strode over, swept him up, and snatched him away, tossing some coins to the ground at Morwenna's feet, a slight blush of shame upon her cheeks.

"Hush," she scolded her son, her voice low but fierce. "We're sorry for your troubles," she said to Morwenna. "No child should grow up without a mother," she whispered, before scurrying off, her son's white collar grasped firmly in her clean hands.

***

Morwenna was glad of the coins, but she winced as she heard the laughter of the others, the small group of mothers and children, as they bustled away. She stared after them, wondering if they could tell her more, but was too proud – and too used to having her questions go unanswered – to try to catch them. *They won't help me*, she thought.

The gulf between her and the people of the town seemed wider than ever. She didn't feel the same as them at all, in their dark clothes and their church ways and their glances like cuts from little knives. She sighed. If what the boy had said was right, maybe she wasn't like them. Perhaps children with sea-claimed mothers were not meant to fit in, or be a part of anything at all like church, or school, or brothers and sisters, and dinner tables, and friends.

But maybe, like her mother – whose name her father kept such a secret – she was sea-claimed, too. Chosen, even, by the sea god, himself!

She stooped down and picked up the coins and put them in her pocket, well away from the money she'd been given in exchange for the fish. *These coins are mine*, she thought. *I don't need to tell him. For as he has his secrets, I will have mine, too.*

Then Morwenna took the fish no-one had chosen from the upended basket that served as her market table, popped them into its wicker depths, slung the basket over her shoulder, and began the long walk home.

On her way, she wondered how she could learn more about herself, how to find for certain if she was sea-claimed, like her mother. She could ask her father – he would know. But would he tell her? He kept such knowledge locked tight inside. While he would teach her of the tides and the fish, of the friendship of the dolphins and the songs of the seals, he would not share what her heart needed to know.

But perhaps there was someone who could tell her more – who would do so for the price of nine coins and a handful of honey ...

When Morwenna got home, she found her father chopping wood. He paused in his work, wiped his curling hair back from his brow, and held one hand up in greeting.

She smiled at him and stepped forward, words spilling from her lips before she could catch them. "I sold plenty, Father," she said, although this was not what her heart, which longed to know much deeper truths, wished to say. "But there is a little left for our supper."

He nodded and picked up another log to split, and Morwenna, seeing their conversation was over, went into the cottage. She put the basket to one side, its unwanted catch destined for a stargazy pie, with its fishheads staring up to the sky like they still searched for her lamp at sea. Then, she placed the coins she'd been given in a small seashell box, counting them carefully, smiling over her newfound wealth.

If I can gather nine, she thought, *I can go to the sea witch and ask her my questions.* Dreaming of the coins and their promise of possibilities, she lay down on her bed of moss, which was covered with cloth her mother had woven, and settled in to sleep for the hours of the growing day, till it came time to take out the little curragh with her father again.

***

While Morwenna slept, she dreamt, as she so often did, that she could hear her mother was calling to her, so faintly, from beyond the ninth wave – which was the farthest that one could travel out from the land and yet hope to return, the place where the great sea god Macnannán mac Lir lived, far away from humans like those in the town. Beyond the ninth wave there would be peace and life eternal – no grief, no sorrow, no memory of stinging hands and sorrowful fathers who never spoke a girl's mother's name.

Stirring between her dreams, awakened by her father coming in to rest, Morwenna turned over, nestling deeper into her little bed to keep herself warm and safe. She smiled, as she stared into the darkness of the cottage. *I could go to the shore*, she thought, *and whisper my wish to the ninth wave, and then I could receive the invitation, the echtrae, and see the wonders of the Blessed Isles.*

She stayed awake a little longer, imagining how she would explore the Isle of Joy and venture all the way to Hy Breasil, the best island of them all. There she could drink from the cup of truth and learn all she longed to know. *And if I dared*, she told herself, *I could go to Tir fo Thonn, the land beneath the waves.* But what she did *not* dare was to say, even to herself, that it was in that deep and enchanted place that she felt her mother, the sea-claimed one, must dwell.

Unable to resist the waves of drowsiness pulling her under, she drifted off to sleep again, and this time she dreamed not just of hearing her mother's faint voice calling, but of seeing her mother, her hair spread all about her beneath the waves, a halo of red-gold fire.

Then, Morwenna saw her mother rise up, up out of the deep, calling to her, now, in a voice clear and strong, her arms stretched out long and pale, her flesh honey-toned, her voice the long wail of those who have left their children behind. She spoke a word Morwenna did not know, spoke it as if it was important, somehow, and the girl woke, startled and panicked, the dream of her mother's

wail blending with the howl of the wind.

Sitting up, she rubbed her eyes and tried to say the word she'd heard her mother say.

Her father glanced over and, seeing she was awake, gestured towards the door, signalling that the evening's duties called. Morwenna cleared her throat, sticky from sleep, and fixed her turquoise gaze on her father's slate-grey eyes.

"I dreamed of her again," she said.

He grunted in sympathy, and reached over and patted her hand, a clumsy kindness, but, still, he was unwilling to speak and open his old wounds again.

Her father dreamed of the girl's mother, too, most nights. He did not know where she had gone, or if she lived, or if she was captured in some in-between place. He simply knew the only light left in his life was the lamp held high by the child, and he struggled each day against the dark clouds of misery that suffocated him. He preferred the pain, though, to the great endless numbness that forgetting her could bring. His misery was a comfort, for in it, he recalled her: her bright hair, tangled and falling like copper through his hands, her sea-coloured eyes, her long neck, white as a swan's, her voice, a high, piercing sweetness, which called the dolphins, who would circle about as she made little clicks and spoke to them in their old words, the oldest tongue, the one which all beings understood.

The tongue her daughter knew, too.

"Time to go, Morwenna," he said firmly, his voice's soft harshness making everything suddenly more real than either of their dreams.

***

Daily, Morwenna swallowed down her questions, knowing from long experience that asking them of her father would bring no answer. Soon, though, she thought, she would go see the old sea witch, out in her cave beneath the cliff – the one who lived, as the town folk said, amidst the crabs and the curlews and the creatures of the tides, the one who all went to for their healing and the knowledge of what would come or of what had gone before.

Weeks passed, and finally the day came that the girl – who had haggled harder at the church-day market than was her habit – had saved the nine coins she needed. While her father slept, she left the cottage and set out over the cliffs, barely stopping to gaze at the wildflowers bending in the breeze that caressed the coastal path. Her feet flew, and she sang a little sea-song, high and sweet, as she moved towards the place she would find out about her mother.

Maid-of-the-Wave, oh! list to our singing;
The white moon is winging its way o'er the sea.
Maid-of-the-Wave, the white moon is shining,
And we are all pining, sweet sister, for thee.
Maid-of-the-Wave, would thou wert near us!
Come now to cheer us – Oh, hear us! Oh, hear us!

The sky was streaked with silver and charcoal, and a soft rain fell, as she slipped down the path that led down the cliff, the path so many feet had carved out over the years.

Morwenna had peeked within the cave on her walks, but never had she dared pass its threshold. This time, she paused at the entrance, her knees trembling, and she felt a strange power, like an invisible wave come to test her balance, a change in the way the world was made. She climbed in, stepping lightly over slick rocks, and blinked, her eyes adjusting to this different darkness.

The night that Morwenna knew had cold white stars and a seal-silver moon, but this cave was a night set alight by fire. It glowed with flickering candles, its walls were lined with sealskin, a driftwood fire lit its centre, and shell after shell was jammed amidst rock and moss, forming strange shapes, a language only the sea gods could read.

Morwenna crept and stood, trembling just a bit, her eyes growing wide at the strange home of the sea witch. The darkness of the cave made the dull day outside seem like high summer, and she could smell the sharpness of all the creatures who had lived here before. This scent was fresh and keen, but savage as a storm at sea.

Finally, she made out the Sea Mother, herself, a tiny tangle of limbs and hair and feathers and shells, sitting cross-legged on her driftwood floor. She was stirring a small pot that had three dark legs. About her were herbs drying, and around her child-like shoulders she wore a great cloak of feathers.

Morwenna crept closer, head down, barely daring to look. Her hand was cramped with clutching her coins and her gifts. She now knew the rules. The first thing to do was make an offering. A handful of honey.

She unfurled the fingers of one cold hand, and the sweet smell of beeswax rose up out of her palm, as she revealed the pot filled with the honey she'd plundered from the bee-trees one day when sleep seemed less important than learning the source of her dreams. That day, a great golden mist of bees had risen up before her, but not one had stung her, as her hand dived again and again into their hive within the old oak.

The Sea Mother turned and looked at

Morwenna, her eyes so dark they seemed little more than openings that sucked in all the light. Then she smiled, showing her mossy teeth, and raised one long hand, which was traced with the pathways of her years upon the earth, and touched the face of the girl.

"Morwenna," she said, her voice younger than seemed possible for a face that could have been made when the old stones were rolled into their circles on the moor, thought the girl.

"You know my name?"

The old woman ignored the question, gathered up the small clay honey pot Morwenna had made to add the honey, and she snuffled and licked and gave little moans of ecstasy at its sweetness.

Morwenna felt pleased, and breathed out in relief. *She likes my offering – surely she will help me now!*

"So," said the sea witch at last, her lips glazed with honey. "Tell me what it is you want." Her voice was not kind, but nor was it cruel.

Morwenna opened her mouth. The moment was here.

"My mother," she began. "I want to know what happened to her."

"Are you sure, Morwenna?" asked the old woman. "You could go on, holding the light for your father, until one day he falls into the ocean in search of her, and leaves you alone with the boat and the cottage. You could find a fisherman to wed," she said, nodding to herself. "No dreams would greet you then. You'd be bearing your own girl, and your mother would be a pale memory in a year …"

Her voice drifted off, her eyes widened with what could be.

"Why not let her go, child?"

"I want to know," Morwenna replied, a

flinty edge to that soft voice.

"How will you pay? What could you have?"

"I have coin," Morwenna said, a little pride in her young voice, as she stretched out her other hand and let the nine coins fall on the moss before the old woman. The Sea Mother swept them up, bit down upon one, and laughed. "Your father would stripe your legs for this."

"I didn't steal," Morwenna said slowly, her voice like iron, in the dark.

"I didn't mean that," snapped the old woman. She sat for a moment in silence, as if thinking things through. Then she turned those lightless eyes on the girl.

"What is it you want, child? Not to know what happened, not that alone, surely?"

I want to see her again, the girl thought in a rush, her heart tight within her chest. *Not just in my dreams. I want her to hold me, to sing to me once more, and tell me what I need to do, where to go. How to live.*

Her unspoken words were a waterfall. One hand moved softly over her mouth, fearful she'd spoken out loud.

"To see her again," the old woman finally said, her voice like a knife. "To receive the invitation – the echtrae. That alone will allow you to venture into the realm of Macnannán mac Lir."

Morwenna nodded, fear nibbling at her edges.

"There's another price to pay," the sea witch said.

Morwenna felt the blood pounding at her temples. She stared into the pale face of the old woman. "I'll pay it."

"Are you sure, my child?" The old woman sounded sorry.

"I'm sure."

The sea witch shook her head, as if the stupidity of humans was still capable of surprising her, and she pushed herself upright and shuffled to a driftwood shelf. There, she rummaged, rejecting one item after another, until she found a small, kelp-brown bottle, with something inside it that stirred and whirled and danced through its murky darkness, like the bottom of the sea itself.

Returning to the girl, she handed her the bottle. "This one is yours."

Morwenna took it with a little nod of her head to say thank you.

"Go home," the Sea Mother said. "Next sunrise, go to the ocean, and drink this after you see the ninth wave after sun up. The ninth," she repeated.

Morwenna nodded again, this time with a great smile. "Thank you," she whispered, aloud this time, clutching her echtrae, her invitation in the bottle, close to her heart.

"Don't thank me, child. It's as close to a sin as I've ever come." And she kissed Morwenna, who, puzzled, held the potion as tight as could be in her left hand, shook her head a little to clear the clouds from it, and bid the wise woman farewell before leaving the cave and climbing to the top of the cliff, back to the path that led home.

Standing for a moment, she breathed in the misty air and let the quiet rain wash her face and mingle with the tears that began to fall. She hardly ever cried, but when she did, she cried in the rain, for her father could not tell, then, that she wept. Now, her tears tasted like salt, and the rain was freshwater, and they ran together for a time, like they were the same river, heading for the ocean.

***

Morwenna made herself as small and quiet as she could, when she arrived back at the cottage. She crept about the side and peeked in the window – and, seeing her father asleep, opened the door as carefully as she could, holding her breath as it creaked open. She tiptoed across the earthen floor to where her father lay, deep in the ocean of dreams, and stared at his face, his bleak features softened in sleep, his eyelids flickering as he dreamed – and she touched his cheek softly, filled with tenderness for him and his endless sorrow. Then she slid into her own bed and drifted off, lulled into her own dreams by her father's soft breathing.

She awoke only an hour or two later, her father gently shaking her shoulder.

Morwenna opened her bleary eyes and smiled so brightly into his face that his grey eyes seemed happy, just for a moment.

He cleared his throat and looked away for a second or two, and when he turned back, his eyes seemed to sparkle with heavy, unshed tears. "Here," he said simply, handing her a bowl full of creamy, warm milk and patting her shoulder.

Morwenna sipped at the creamy milk, thinking over what was to come. Her heart felt bright and full of hope, and her only sorrow was that she would leave this sad man behind.

"Let's go, Morwenna," he said firmly, and they readied themselves for the work ahead.

The night was good to them both – for the father, the ocean was generous, their catch plentiful, and his daughter quiet, and as happy as he'd ever seen her. For Morwenna, she enjoyed the man's company, appreciating the peace of his silence, and the depth of his unspoken love. Their nets were rich with bream and flounder, silver whiting and pink-tinged cuttlefish. She weeded through the nets for any ill-caught fishlings, cast them back beneath the waves, and enjoyed the quiet moonlight over the inky waters.

Her father did not smile once, but Morwenna caught a strange expression cross his stony features as she leaned over the waters, whispering old charms to the deep. In the black waters, she could see her own face changing with the silky movements of the current, and she touched her pocket, where her bottle lay quietly, its secret invitation awaiting its awakening at dawn.

She stared into the water until her father's voice broke the spell, calling her back to hold the light a little higher, though it was hardly needed, the moon was so near full.

They pulled the curragh back over the mud before their cottage, well before the new day was to dawn, and she and her father sorted the catch into what would be kept, what would go to market, and what to share with the sea creatures she loved. She smiled at him, his back bent over the nets, a kind of ill-won satisfaction in his stance. He was always just the same, she thought, and she was on the very edge of everything changing.

She looked up. A familiar shift in the light on the faraway horizon told her it was time.

"Father, I'm going to see to the stones," she said softly. "They didn't seem in place when we pulled the coracle up."

He nodded, knowing, as every fisherman does, that the little labyrinth before their home protected them from ill winds and unkind spirits. He went into the cottage and came back, handing Morwenna a piece of the hevva pie she'd baked, its crust criss-crossed like the nets she wove. She swallowed it down, grateful for its warmth, then kissed her father gently, surprising him, pleasing him, she could see. She hoped it would soften the blow she would bring him in the days to come.

Leaving her father at the cottage, Morwenna went down to the labyrinth. She straightened the stones and checked the knots that released the winds. And then she went to the edge of the sea and waited for the moment the sun would come. And when its glorious light split the sky, she began to count the waves ...

***

MORWENNA AWOKE MUCH LATER, HEARING her father roaring into the wind for her to get to her feet. She cracked open her eyes and smiled at him. Then she reached up her arms, for her legs would not move, not in the usual way. It was as they were boneless. Was this the price the Sea Mother had spoken of?

He lifted her up and carried her back to the cottage. "You saw that old witch," he said, his voice wracked with anguish. "Like her. Like Cliodna."

That's my mother's name, she thought. *It's already worth it. I know her name.* And Morwenna fell back into a dreamless sleep.

She slept all day, and awoke after the sun had set. Her father was not there, and she knew he had taken out the curragh without her. She pulled herself from the bed, shoved open the heavy door, and began dragging herself through the mud and the sand and the stones along the shore to the very edge of the sea. She could see him out there, and she called to him. But he kept rowing.

She stared at the sea awhile, unwilling to go inside after her efforts. She calmed herself by speaking some of the old words, but what she said most was her mother's name, murmuring it over and over: "*Cliodna ... Kleeee ... unnnnn ... yahhhhhh,*" over and over, like an incantation, till the word became a wish, and the wish became a prayer, and the yearning overtook every cell within her.

Her father found her there when he came back from the sea, and he carried her inside, again, closing the door behind her.

He tried to lock Morwenna in after that, fearful she would take to the waters. When he returned home from fishing each morning, he would find her just inside the door to the cottage, begging to be returned to the sea, entreating him to let her go out with him again in the little boat.

But he said not a word, and Morwenna would stare down at her legs that would not walk and wonder what she could do to get down to the sea again.

One night, though, her father went out in the boat, and perhaps he forgot, or perhaps he knew he could not keep her locked away forever, but that night he did not turn the key in the lock – and Morwenna, seeing this, dragged herself to the door and managed to open it. She pulled herself down the little slope towards the sea, and she pushed herself through the stone labyrinth that was no longer in its right order, and she went down to the waters and called out to her mother.

After calling and calling, she heard something... a voice, but not in a dream, this time. It came across the waters, from beyond the ninth wave, she was sure.

Morwenna did not hesitate. She pulled herself into the water with her strong, white arms. Then farther and farther she crawled, her body beginning to tingle with the icy waters, her cold hands pulling her deeper and deeper, until at last her silver head disappeared beneath that moonlit sea.

When Morwenna's eyes opened beneath the waves, she stared into the face of her mother, Cliodna, whose hair swam all about her, whose body was pale and beautiful as a woman, above, and softly green and scaled like a fish, below.

As Morwenna opened her mouth to smile, the water rushed in, and she lost all sense of the world.

She awoke an age later to her mother's crooning.

Maid-of-the-Wave, oh! List to our singing;
The white moon is winging its way o'er the sea.
Maid-of-the-Wave, the white moon is shining,
And we are all pining, sweet sister, for thee.
Maid-of-the-Wave, would thou wert near us!
Come now to cheer us – Oh, hear us! Oh, hear us!

And Cliodna smiled into Morwenna's eyes, and her child looked down and saw that, instead of legs, insensate and dull, from her own narrow white hips grew a pearlescent tail, all the myriad colours of light upon the ocean. It shone, and moved with power and grace, serpentine and scaled like armour. And with a flip of that powerful tail, Morwenna rose through the waves, and swam beside her mother, and sang with her.

And to the lands of Promise they swam, for there she was to dwell with her mother, beyond the ninth wave, and within the domain of her sea father, Macnannán mac Lir.

***

When it became clear that Morwenna was gone, her land-father held onto the girl's clothes for an age, and he would sit, opening and closing the little seashell box that he had made for his wife, Cliodna, until, finally, he raged, and wept – then calmed, just as the sea does.

And he made his way to the old oak tree, where the honeybees had their hive, and thrust

his hand in, quieting the bees with the old words, drawing out the golden sweetness of their queen. He walked the path home for the last time, threw the contents of his last catch to the creatures of the sea, gathered up nine coins, and left the nets and coracle by the cottage he had lived in since he was a boy – the same cottage he had dwelled in when Cliodna had first come to him, at full moon, cold and shivering, with her hair of copper, holding a little silver girl-child, like moonlight in her arms. Cliodna of the sea, and her little maid of the waves.

He left the house of all his days and strode along the sea-path, his broken voice humming the old song she'd taught him, gold in his pockets, honeycomb in his hands.

Maid-of-the-Wave, oh! list to our singing;
The white moon is winging its way o'er the sea.
Maid-of-the-Wave, the white moon is shining,
And we are all pining, sweet sister, for thee.
Maid-of-the-Wave, would thou wert near us!
Come now to cheer us – Oh, hear us! Oh, hear us!

Climbing down beneath the great cliff, he entered the cave.

"What is it you want?" asked the Sea Mother.

And with more words than he'd spoken in an age, Ciabhan of the Curling Locks, land-husband of Cliodna of the Ninth Wave, father of the Maiden of the Sea, fisherman, lost soul, abandoned one, began to tell her of his need.

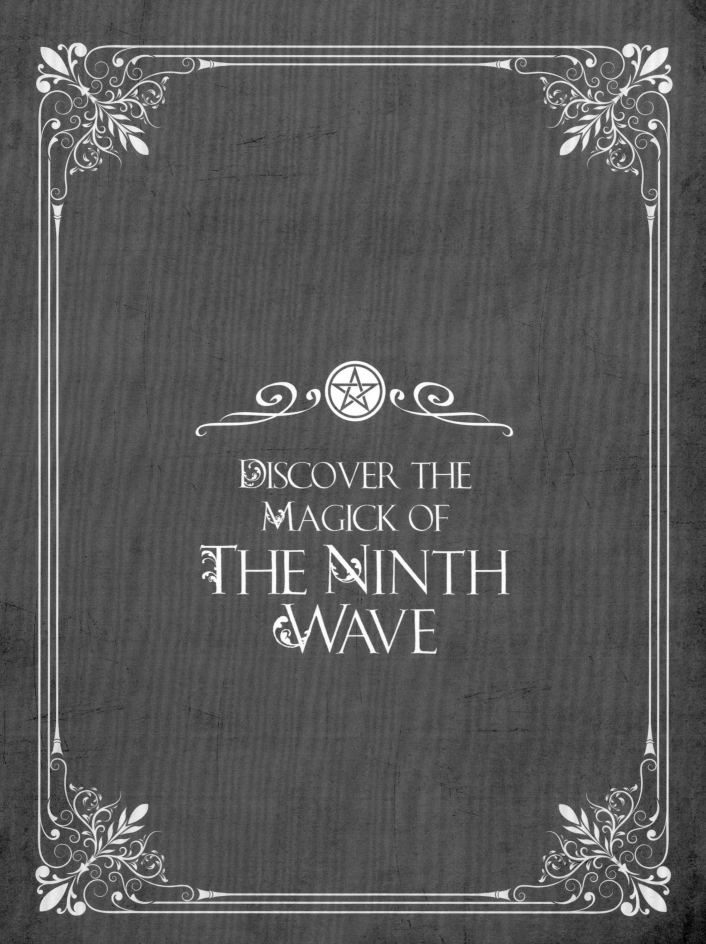

Discover the
Magick of
The Ninth
Wave

MORWENNA had never played or laughed or skipped with a soul of her own age. The other children of the town lived in the world of day, the streets, the earth, and the cobblestones. She was the night, the sea, and the foam flying from the wind-licked waves.

WHEN I WAS YOUNG, ALL I wanted to be was a mermaid, to be able to breathe underwater and stay in that weightless bliss, the warmth of the magickal currents.

I loved so many aspects of the Hans Christian Anderson story *The Little Mermaid*, but it left me cold in many other ways – cold, and hurt, and betrayed. How could he make her endure so much pain? The descriptions of the pain she felt, due to her becoming a human, horrified me. Anderson describes her every footstep causing her to feel as if a knife is shooting through her feet. Why was she so ready to give up the beauty of being a mermaid – to me the most amazing possibility – simply to win the love of a prince, a prince she, herself, had rescued? And why, when he did not return her horrible, sacrificing love, was she turned to sea-foam? Could it be true that she had no soul, as it says in the story? That seemed to me wrong, somehow – magickal creatures, earthly creatures, human creatures all have souls, I believed (and believe to this day!)

It is a beautiful, dreadful fairytale – about losing your voice, abandoning yourself, inviting terrible pain in the desire for love. Anderson masks it as a quest for a soul, but to me, *The Little Mermaid* resonates as a cautionary tale for people who cut off parts of themselves, or become something else, in order to please someone they love, in the hope that that person will love them back.

On the other hand, I remember as a child crying out, defiant and angry, at all the parts of the original story left out and rewritten in the Disney version, which presents *The Little Mermaid* as a happy story. But of course, it is not.

So, I wrote *The Ninth Wave* as a kind of antidote, I suppose, to these versions of *The Little Mermaid*, asking myself, *What if a girl wanted to become a mermaid, as I did, when I was a child? What if a girl had that opportunity – to leave the land and to enter the world of the sea? What else could her story be?*

HISTORY OF THIS TALE

THE NINTH WAVE IS MY OWN TALE, AN original, so while it is, in some ways, my "reply" to *The Little Mermaid*, it is *not* the same story. It does owe much to my travels in Cornwall and Ireland, and so it is set in a very Celtic land – somewhere in between, somewhere slightly out of time, when there was conflict between the old and the new, both in terms of language and of faith, and perhaps even between the land and the sea. Certainly, there is some conflict between the mother and the father for the child, and of course, between the village and the cliffs, those pagan places.

If you wish to find where it is located, you can see her for yourself. Just look out from the cliffs, step into the ocean, and see her, in all her silver glory, under the moonlight.

THE NAME MORWENNA

"MORWENNA" IS AN OLD, OLD CORNISH NAME that has been claimed, some say, by the Welsh, now. It means "waves of the sea", and "sea maiden", and so of course I loved that the girl in this story was named for a part of her own enchantment. *Mor* means sea, and within her name is a reference to the Morgens – the ancient sea priestesses, who have come to be associated with Avalon in particular. Morwenna is also the name of a mysterious Cornish saint, said to have been trained in Ireland, worked in Wales, and finally settled in a hermitage by the sea in Cornwall. Our Morwenna is no saint, but she is most certainly a maid of the sea, and she and the waves have a very special relationship indeed.

WILDFLOWERS AND
CUCKOO CHILDREN

WHEN I HAVE VISITED CORNWALL AND Ireland and walked the cliffs by the sea, I have seen a breathtaking abundance of wildflowers of all kinds. They are so delightful, their velvet delicacy adorning harsh cliff paths, free and lovely, and their heads bowed in the wild winds that blow up those ancient coastlines.

The cuckoo flowers in particular hint that Morwenna's parentage may not be straightforward. Also, symbolically, these flowers were said to never be brought inside for fear of offending the nature spirits. Morwenna, herself, is not someone who thrives inside – and when she is locked away, she must find a way to escape.

CURRAGHS AND COCKLE SHELLS

A *CURRAGH*, OR *CURRACH*, IS AN ANCIENT FORM of boat in the Celtic lands that is still in existence today. In earlier times, animal hides were often stretched across curraghs' wood frames, but today canvas is most often used. The curragh is particularly associated with Ireland, where great wonder-voyages, called *imrams* or *imrammas*, were undertaken through nine sacred, or blessed, islands.

For Morwenna and her father, who fish for their survival, their curragh is first of all a practical thing. But this vessel also hints at their going on a great mystic voyage together – just as the Druids did, just as the priestesses did, as mystics in search of something *beyond*.

As to the cockle shells a-hanging on the bow of the boat, I have seen many of these kinds of charms in other lands. From Cornwall to the sacred Okinawa Islands in Japan, simple strings of shells are attached to something that leads us forward – whether that is a door, or a boat's bow, or the front of a car – to ensure that we proceed with good magick before us, so we may follow in

its protective wake.

Cockle shells, themselves, have many associations. To me, as they are a bivalve – two-shelled – they speak of the need to be together as one. Sometimes two souls cannot bear to be apart – and sometimes three cannot bear to be separated, as in this tale. Without her really knowing it, Morwenna is working an enchantment, sending a message to the sea – to her sea father – that she wishes to be reunited with her mother and with the great, soulful essence of the ocean.

Cockle shells also offer sustenance, protection, love, and help in finding the people we are meant to be with – not the twin flame of modern spirituality, a concept I find greatly destructive, but with our *anam-cara*, as our soul-friend is called in Celtic mysticism.

The Old Words, the Old Language

FOR A VERY LONG TIME, CORNISH WAS SPOKE in Cornwall, Gaelic in Scotland and Ireland, Breton in Brittany, and Welsh in Wales. Today, these languages are being revived after nearly losing their lives. In the village of this story, people have stopped speaking in the old tongue, and they have forgotten the power and magick

of the old words. They are disconnected in ways that Morwenna is not. For all that Morwenna struggles with the new words (which I imagine is an early form of English), she can still speak to the elements, to the animals, and to the sea gods, themselves.

The Sea Father: The Mysterious Macnannán mac Lir

I ADORE THE TALES OF MACNANNÁN MAC LIR, the ancient primordial Irish god of the sea. He has a version of himself in Wales, too, called Manawyn fab Llyr. I have been under the spell of the story of his love for Aoife, a human woman, and the origins of the crane bag – a kind of Irish medicine bag – for a long time. But in this tale, it is his presence as the father of mermaids that is important. He is a great, potent, masculine life force, as wild and unpredictable as the sea, as tender and loving and giving as the ocean.

In many of his legends, he has daughters, and one of them is called Cliodna. Yet, in other versions of the story, Cliodna is his wife. In County Cork, on the west coast of Ireland, the tide, to this day, is called Cliodna's wave – which reflects that part of the legend that tells us that Cliodna was permitted to go to the land and live with a human, and even have a child. But in time, she was re-taken by the sea in a great wave. In some versions, she drowns. In others, she turns into a mermaid.

In a way, *The Ninth Wave* is a very brief retelling of that tale, and of what happened to that

daughter, left alone on the land with a father of her heart, but not of her blood and soul.

What is the Ninth Wave?

To the Celts, all that lay beyond the ninth wave was the Otherworld, a place of indeterminable magick, a force that could emerge in the human world through faery rings and forests, or through bubbling wells and waterfalls. The ocean, itself, was the very edge of the Otherworld, the domain of the gods of the sea. The ninth wave in a group of waves was considered to be the largest and most powerful of that group and to have special qualities, depending on the time of year and where you were. When the ninth wave would roll in, it was seen to be crashing its otherworldly magic upon the shore!

Beyond the ninth wave was said to lie the Blessed Isles, where none grew old, or sad, or bitter, and where there was no death, not as it is known in the human realms. The Blessed Isles – sometimes said to be nine in number, sometimes more – were thought to have particular qualities, and to visit them all, as a human, would bring great blessings and beauty not only to the individual who braved the imramma to reach them, but to their people, as well.

Water gathered from beyond the ninth wave is believed, in Celtic sea magick, to have healing and magickal properties – even the property of helping us change our shape. I suspect the sea witch has made a part of Morwenna's potion – or *echtrae*, her invitation – with that touch from the Blessed Isles and the sea realms of Macnannán mac Lir

Morwenna's mother may even have come from beyond the ninth wave. She is named for Cliodna, the daughter, or lover (it depends on the tale), of Macnannán mac Lir. Cliodna of the Fair Hair is considered one of the Tuatha de Dannan, the magickal original inhabitants of Ireland. She is a deity of waves – the ninth being hers in particular, of course! – and she rules the lands of Promise, one of the Blessed Isles, where there is no death, no separation, no violence, and no ill health.

There is a legend of a Cliodna – the deity, or the faery, or perhaps a woman simply named for her – who was the daughter of one of the last Druids of Ireland. Cliodna is said to be able to take human form for a time, and to have human lovers – so perhaps Morwenna's mother is the sea goddess, herself. The men of the sea who fall in love with Cliodna cannot bear parting from her, and they often are said to drown themselves in their quest to be with her again. I hope this did not happen to Morwenna's lovely, sad father, Ciabhan. I hope he was able to strike a strange bargain with the sea witch, so he could join his family once again, far beyond the ninth wave.

There is also a legend of Cliodna and Ciabhan of the Curling Locks and their ill-fated love that found its way into this tale. Cliodna banished herself from the Otherworld of the sea – almost like the Little Mermaid – but one day, she fell asleep on the shore, and wave after great wave came, and with the ninth, she was taken from her life on the land and returned to the sea. In some of the legends, a great old witch creates this spell with the water. In others, it is the sea god himself, insisting upon Cliodna's return.

To me, Cliodna represents the raw desire

of women to return to their wildest self. She is like the selkie who rejects her life on the land, and even her children, to take back her skin and dive beneath the waves. She is the mermaid who may fall in love, but who cannot abandon her true home – the great and endless seas, from which we all emerged, from that cauldron of the Mother.

Making Magick: The Ninth Wave Blessed Waters Spell

To journey beyond the ninth wave is to enter a magickal realm of healing and freedom. Water blessed with the magick of the ninth wave will be filled with that energy, helping us to heal from past hurts and abandonments. This spell will refresh and cleanse us, and remind us of the magick that lies at the heart of who we are.

(Just a note on location! If you do not live near an ocean, there is still a way for you to work with this magick. You could toss a stone into a pond and collect the water of the ninth set of ripples. Or collect nine drops of rainwater.)

If you work this spell at the ninth hour of the day (or night, if this is safe for you) it will add to its healing power.

You will need a bottle used specifically for magickal purposes. Cleanse your bottle thoroughly and place it on your altar for a night or two, or out under the moonlight, to charge it magickally.

Then, go to the beach and wade out into the water. Count each wave as it begins. There will always be a lull, and then waves will strengthen again. Simply count each one, and when the ninth of that set approaches, let it wash over you and then fill your bottle, saying:

> *By the power of three by three,*
> *The ninth wave heals and strengthens me.*
> *And by the power of three by three,*
> *As I do will, so mote it be!*

As you dry yourself off, feel the cleansing powers of the crystalline waters have left on your skin. Cap your bottle and let it charge upon your altar. Add nine drops to your bath water or to your cooking water, for healing, prosperity, and growth. I also like to charge spring water by adding nine drops of ninth-wave water, along with three drops each of three of my favourite oil blends – for example, three drops of frankincense, three drops of orange sweet, and three drops of lavender. Then I spray this about me for a simple auric refresh, and I spray it around my home to uplift and connect me to the otherworlds that lie beyond the ninth wave!

Of Labyrinths and Ligature

The sea can be a cruel mistress for those who make their living from her. She is as hazardous as she is intoxicating, capricious and beautiful beyond measure. Many specific forms of magick grew out of the seafaring cultures of Western Europe, and I've borrowed an old northern tradition regarding labyrinths for this tale.

Labyrinths are very different to mazes, for a labyrinth has one distinct path to follow, and once we step into a labyrinth, we are weaving energy; reborn when we connect with the centre; and when we emerge, we are different. I was fascinated to learn that in the Scandinavias, in ancient times, sailors would build intricate labyrinths in the path from their boat to the sea to capture ill winds or wishes and keep them busy while the sailors headed out into the vast and freezing waters.

There are still these stone labyrinths in sea villages like Landsort, in Sweden, and others in Finland and Norway. Swedish historian J. A. Udde says these labyrinths are built into the cold northern seas islands to calm strong winds. Said fisherman Anders Öhman to Udde, "If one walked the proper way through the labyrinth, all would go well. But if one walked the wrong way, things would go badly."

In a similar way, magickal knots were tied into rope in a form of sea magick called ligature. Different knots had different effects. Certain knots could keep hearts true while your love was at sea. Others could literally hold the fair winds within them, and these were often carried within the boats – and if you needed the wind to change, a knot would be untied. These knots had to be made by one who knew what she was doing. This is something that Cliodna may have taught Morwenna, as a mysterious sea-being with only a temporarily human form, she would know the deepest sea magicks of all.

There are some wonderful examples of ligature in the Museum of Witchcraft at Boscastle, in Cornwall, a fascinating and authentic treasure trove of magick and folk traditions with a very Cornish flavour. You can almost feel the breeze crying to be free still held fast within the knots untied to this day.

Mermaids, Selkies, and the Absent Mother

Indirectly, there is something of the selkie legend within this tale. *Selkie* means "seal" in old Gaelic, and people to this day in the islands of the northern edges of the British Isles believe there are selkie ancestors within their families.

Although Morwenna's mother's other

form is not that of a seal, there is about her mysterious return to the ocean an echo of the tales of the selkies – seals who become women under full moons, women who return to their seal-form when their dancing upon the moonlit shore has finished. Sometimes, while dancing, these selkies' skins are stolen, and then the selkie must live as a human woman for years with a fisherman, bearing his children, only remembering who she truly is when she finds her skin and slips back to the sea.

Like the selkie who left her child, Cliodna is an absent mother, but one who is still calling to her daughter from her heart's choice, the sea. Cliodna's abandonment of her husband, and the girl who may or may not be his child, has created a void that has only enhanced their aching sense of her loss.

Her absence, too, reminds me of the first priest in the tale. He, in turn, feels under the influence of Saint Patrick. The legends of Saint Patrick include one story of how he turned pagan women into mermaids. But I do not think the priest has this power. Although I am sure he would claim he turned Morwenna's mother into a mermaid, he cannot, for that is purely the domain of the ninth wave, the Blessed Isles, and the old magicks of the sea witch, whose cave is full of ancient enchantments.

FOLK SONGS, CHANTS, AND MAGICKAL DOORWAYS

THE SONG THAT MORWENNA SINGS IS AN OLD, old Scottish folk song. I've never heard it sung, I've only known its lyrics. I'll keep searching to hear it, and one day, I may finally know the melody of this magickal song of the sea. To me, there is something about it that conveys a wish, a wish that opens up a kind of door into the magick of transformation. Song can literally be a "key" that opens us up to the Otherworlds – and mermaids have long been associated with song.

Maid-of-the-Wave, oh! list to our singing;
The white moon is winging its way o'er the sea.
Maid-of-the-Wave, the white moon is shining,
And we are all pining, sweet sister, for thee.
Maid-of-the-Wave, would thou wert near us!
Come now to cheer us – Oh, hear us! Oh, hear us!

THE WISDOM OF THE NINTH WAVE

WHAT COULD THIS TALE'S MEANING BE? IT IS hard for me to say, but when I think deeply about it, I feel that it is about how inseparable we are from the elements, how part of us always longs to be within nature, whether in the form of the forest, or the lake, or the ocean. We will sacrifice our comfort and our reputation to get closer to the source of energy and cycles and to become part of something truer than man-made religions and rules.

The story is also about abandonment, and the yearning for knowledge of the truth about our families, and the guilt that accompanies the one who leaves – especially, I think, the mother who leaves.

The Ninth Wave shows us that the longing for that return, and for the freedom and sensuality of the ocean, is deeper than our urge to be safe, and dry, and fed. Sometimes, we sacrifice all we could be to stay within a prison – not so bad a prison, perhaps, but a place of confinement that lacks the unknowable mysteries of the wilderness. When Morwenna changes her shape, she takes back a lost part of her own self and chooses a life. Not to be a fisherman's wife. Not to live with her father's grief and his desire to keep her away from the depths. But to learn the women's mysteries, to belong completely to a stranger world, and to dive deeper into her own being than she could ever dreamt of if she had stayed within the certainty of the shore.

ABOUT THE AUTHOR

LUCY CAVENDISH is an internationally acclaimed spiritual author. She exhibited strong extra-sensory abilities as a child, and with no answers from school or mainstream religion, Lucy set out on a personal quest to understand and develop her magickal gifts. Lucy grew up in Sydney, Australia, and has lived in Paris, London and the United States. When she's not writing or speaking, you'll find Lucy surfing in the ocean, wandering deep within a faery forest, or dancing with the spirits in an ancient stone circle.

Today Lucy is an exciting, enchanting voice in the field of inspiration, noted for her breadth and depth of knowledge on sacred rites and sites, magickal history, folklore, alternative spiritual practices and intuitive traditions. Lucy shares her knowledge and gifts to inspire people to break through their conditioning, be open to their potential, discover their personal genius and dare to live brave, bright lives. Lucy is about spirited self-development and her work embraces both our shadows and our light. Her remarkable vision, compassion, wisdom, and insight has struck a chord with contemporary seekers ready to create lives of courage, spiritual adventure and enriching magick.

Lucy lectures and teaches around the world. Her books and oracle card decks are available in many languages.

Visit Lucy's website at:
www.lucycavendish.com.au

Enjoy more from Lucy Cavendish

BOOKS & JOURNALS

The Lost Lands
Book of Shadows and Light
Faery: A journal of enchantment
Hidden Worlds Journal
The Mermaid's Mirror
Wisdom of the Shapeshifters
Wisdom of the Vampires
Wisdom of Shadows and Light

ORACLE DECKS

Alice: The Wonderland Oracle
Blessed Be Oracle
Faery Forest Oracle
Faerytale Oracle
Foxfire: The Kitsune Oracle
Magickal Spellcards
Oracle of Shadows and Light
Oracle of the Dragonfae
Oracle of the Hidden Worlds
Oracle of the Mermaids
Oracle of the Shapeshifters
Wild Wisdom of the Faery Oracle
Les Vampires
Faery Blessing Cards
Oracle fo the Hidden Worlds

ABOUT THE ARTIST

JASMINE BECKET-GRIFFITH is a world-renowned fantasy artist. Born in 1979, she has spent all of her adult life working as a fine artist, painting traditionally by hand with acrylic paints, combining elements of realism with fantasy and the surreal. Historical and spiritual references are intertwined with fairy tales and the beauty of nature. Her trademark liquid-eyed maidens evoke a wide range of emotions and responses to the surrounding imagery.

Her artwork can be found in private collections and public displays throughout the world. Jasmine's paintings blend realism with wide-eyed wonder – exploring gothic themes, with elements of classical literature, the occult, nature and fantasy – and of course, faeries!

Jasmine's paintings appear in countless books (notably *The World of Faery* with Alan Lee, *The Art of Faery* with Brian Froud, *Spectrum 21, Spectrum 24, Gothic Art Now, Big Eye Art: Resurrected and Transformed,* and her solo art books *Strangeling: The Art of Jasmine Becket-Griffith, Fairy: The Art of Jasmine Becket-Griffith* and *Jasmine Becket-Griffith: Portfolio Volume I* and *Portfolio Volume II,* as well as *Forever Strange: The Big-Eyed Art of Jasmine Becket-Griffith.*

Collaborating with Lucy Cavendish, Jasmine has illustrated five oracle card sets: *Oracle of Shadows and Light, Oracle of the Shapeshifters, Les Vampires, The Faerytale Oracle* and *Alice: The Wonderland Oracle.* Also available are three coloring books, *Jasmine Becket-Griffith Coloring Book, Jasmine Becket-Griffith Halloween Coloring Book* and *Mermaids Coloring Book,* and another oracle card set, *Myths & Mermaids: Oracle of the Water,* co-created with Jasmine's two sisters Amber Logan and Kachina Mickeletto.

Her work also graces many television shows and movies, magazines and advertisements, tattoo parlours, theme parks, and of course her range of hundreds of different licensed merchandise products (distributed at Walt Disney World and in Disneyland theme parks and galleries) as well as lines of collectables through the Bradford Exchange and Hamilton Collection.

Jasmine lives in Celebration, Florida with her husband Matt and their cats, and also divides her time between her secondary studios in Kansas and in London, England.

Jasmine's official website and online gallery can be seen at: **www.strangeling.com**